W9-BYY-436

THE SCIENTIFIC INTELLECTUAL

THE SCIENTIFIC INTELLECTUAL

The Psychological & Sociological Origins of Modern Science

LEWIS S. FEUER

BASIC BOOKS, INC., PUBLISHERS
NEW YORK
LONDON

© 1963 by Basic Books Publishing Co., Inc.

Library of Congress Catalog Card Number: 63–12845

Printed in the United States of America

DESIGNED BY GUY FLEMING

Q
125
.F43

~~501~~
F434

To ANNA
and PHILIP DESIND

Preface

THIS BOOK IS NOT A HISTORY OF SCIENCE. IT DOES NOT AIM TO set forth the development of scientific theory and experiment. Rather, it seeks to trace the evolution of the scientific intellectual as a human type, to see what ethic inspired him and the underlying emotions that created him. My interest is in science as a human activity, and in the conditions that have made for the rationality of men.

This study was originally motivated by my discontent with the prevailing view, which makes the modern scientific spirit into an offspring of Protestant asceticism. This view seemed to me wholly at odds with what we knew of the psychological conditions making for human curiosity about the world we live in, and its expression in the observation of nature with our senses and experiments upon it with our hands. I therefore undertook to re-examine the alleged evidence for this generalization. As my study continued, a general conclusion emerged: that wherever a scientific movement has begun, it has been based on emotions that issue in what might be called a hedonist-libertarian ethic. The scientific intellectual was neither a Protestant ascetic, as Robert K. Merton would have it, nor a "sleepwalker," as Arthur Koestler would tell us. Rather, he was a person for whom science was a "new philosophy," a third force rising above religious and political hatreds, seeking the world of nature with liberated vision and intending to use and enjoy its knowledge.

To validate this conclusion, I studied the scientific intellectual in a variety of places and times—in the Copernican revolution, among the medieval nominalists, eighteenth-century Scots, nineteenth-century Jews, the scientists of Napoleonic France. I have inquired into the failure of the scientific intellectual to appear in Asian civilizations. I am not a historical specialist in any of these periods. My purpose, however, has not been to adduce some hitherto unknown facts but, rather, by making use of biographical annals and the labors of historians of science, to develop a generalization concerning the scientific intellectual that will be valid for all societies. Such an inquiry naturally involves considerable risk. The person who ventures to follow his problem where it leads, regardless of the boundaries set by specialties, may well stumble in unfamiliar terrain. If our social-scientific studies, however, are to lead to a significant conception of man, more scholars must undertake this kind of risk.

There were once scholars who denied that the same physical laws could hold for heavenly objects as for earthly ones; the celestial and the terrestrial systems, they said, must have different laws. Similarly, there are those who will object on principle to the effort to find a socio-psychological generalization that will apply to diverse peoples and societies. Many sociologists are so concerned with "social systems" and their differences that they tend to forget the basic human nature, the common psychological laws that define the human beings who make up *all* societies. The conditions that promoted or frustrated the emergence of a scientific movement were, in my view, basically the same in Western Europe, Protestant England, Catholic Venice, Confucian China, and Moslem Mesopotamia.

For the most part, the methods I have used are those of historical sociology. Occasionally, however, I have ventured to make use of what I take to be psychoanalytical insights, as in my discussions of the medieval realists, the Asian "masochist mode of perception," and such figures as Kepler, Vesalius, and Newton. I propose these analyses in a tentative spirit, well aware of the large—if unspecifiable—margin of error in such an effort. I believe, however, that this method, when enriched as a result of experience with living scientists, will make more intelligible to us the groping history of human knowledge-seeking.

A word concerning my use of the term "scientific intellectual." I see him as a person who is no mere technician, looking at science as just a job to be done, but one for whom the scientific standpoint is a philosophy in its fullest sense. An intellectual generally, we might say, has come to mean a person whose consciousness determines his existence, who does not suffer the world passively but seeks a mode of existence more in accord with his philosophy, his ideas, and his feelings. In this sense, the seventeenth-century scientist who was fired with a vision of the "new philosophy" as superseding religious and ideological orthodoxies can be legitimately described as a scientific intellectual, though the noun "intellectual" did not come into use until much later.

Mr. Warren Hagstrom kindly read through the entire manuscript, and gave me much helpful criticism. I am grateful to Patricia Montee and Carolyn James, who prepared most of the typescript, and to Charles J. McCracken and James Petras for their careful reading of the copy. This book would not have been written without the encouragement of my friend and editor, Mr. Irving Kristol.

Contents

THE SCIENTIFIC INTELLECTUAL

I

The Psychological Revolution: The Emotional Source of the Scientific Movement

THE RISE OF SCIENCE IS THE GREAT DISTINCTIVE INTELLECTUAL phenomenon of modern times. The scientific movement that emerged in the seventeenth century brought a promise of progress and of the realization of man's deepest hopes. It proposed not only to liberate men from ignorance but also to free them from superstition, religious hatred, irksome toil, and war. For science was then not the pursuit of technicians; it was the "new philosophy," as Francis Bacon called it, the "active science," the first genuine alternative that had been contrived to dogma, myth, and taboo.[1] The world of medieval gloom that denigrated the powers of man gave way to an optimistic faith in his capacities. The scientist of the seventeenth century was a philosophical optimist; delight and joy in man's status pervaded his theory of knowledge and of the universe. And it was this revolution in man's emotions which was the basis for the change in his ideas.

Behind the history of ideas lies the history of emotions. Every major intellectual movement is preceded by the advent of new kinds of feelings that shape the new mode in which reality is to be intellectually apprehended. Emotions determine the perspective, the framework, for the explanation of the perceived world. Whatever the social and economic forces that are operative in the background of people's lives, they impinge on men's ideas through the intervening channel of feeling and emotion. The categories and forms of explanation that characterize the thinking of any given era are thus intimately connected with its underlying emotional structure.

That the birth of modern science was linked to the rise in Western Europe of a new sensibility—what I would call an ethics of freedom—was candidly avowed by philosophers, historians, and scientists in the eighteenth and nineteenth centuries. The Victorian era, in which men such as W. E. H. Lecky and Thomas Henry Huxley lived, saw the promise of the seventeenth century being fulfilled in its own time—in such great generalizations as the law of conservation of energy and the theory of natural selection, and in the discoveries in electrodynamics which opened prospects for human use even more imposing than the mechanical forces that the seventeenth century had released. The telegraph, the wireless, the dynamo were regarded as only beginnings, and it was serenely assumed that they would be followed by a series of inventions and scientific advances which would be the instruments of man's progress.

The youthful optimism of the seventeenth century and the mature confidence of the nineteenth have, however, in the twentieth century given place to philosophies of torment and despair. As science in practical purport becomes more destructive, the scientist and philosopher speak all the more of the theoretical "impotence principles" of modern physics. Einstein, with his belief in the possibility of a determinate complete system of physical theory, has come to be regarded as essentially a classical, Victorian personality. As the scientist's work, moreover, has become more of a job in an institutionalized and bureaucratized setting, he has surrendered the optimistic self-dedication which characterized his predecessors. The contemporary scientist usually advocates no "new" philosophy; instead he shares the prevalent ideology and values.

The twentieth century has likewise produced a new sociology of science, which aims to discard the union of liberal values with science. The optimistic standpoint of the nineteenth-century spokesman of science is generally regarded today as naïve. The contemporary sociology of science stresses especially the irrational sources of scientific inquiry; it tends to regard the rise of science as a by-product of man's neurotic striving. When the erudite German sociologist, Max Weber, affirmed half a century ago that "the empiricism of the seventeenth century was the means for asceticism to seek God in nature," he was in effect challenging the whole notion, affirmed throughout the previous three centuries, that the spirit of scientific research was born of hedonist-libertarian values. Empirical science, as the outcome of ascetic repression, was conceived instead as rooted in human self-aggression. Thus began an imposing body of sociological and psychological thinking concerning the origins of science which has culminated in the bold picture that Arthur Koestler gives of the scientist as a "sleepwalker." Where Andrew D. White in the last century spoke of a warfare between science and theology, Koestler emphasizes that both Newton and Kepler were "crank theologians." The myths that were the scientist's theology were said to have made him fecund and fertile with ideas. Mystical, Pythagorean convictions as to an underlying order in the universe were the source of the new science; the scientist, according to Koestler, was a theologian with measuring instruments.[2]

Weber's impressive sociological theory was largely conceived as a reply and alternative to the historical materialism of Karl Marx. Weber denied that material and technical interests were the motive forces in the origin of science; the primary causal factor was Protestant asceticism, combined with the belief that "the knowledge of God and His designs can only be attained through a knowledge of His works. . . ." The scientific investigation of Nature is held to have been the way that ascetic Protestants sought to find God. This standpoint has found especial support in the influential writings of the American sociologist Robert K. Merton, and has become a familiar proposition in contemporary social science. Merton enunciated what has been the dominant view for a generation: When the evidence is examined, he wrote, "Puritanism and ascetic Protestantism generally, emerge as an emotionally consistent system of beliefs, sentiments, and action which played no small part in arousing a sustained interest in science." [3] Contemporary psychoanalytical theory seemed likewise to support the notion that Protestant asceticism was the mainspring of modern science. According to Freud, man's achievements in the arts and sciences are the product of a repression and sublimation of energies; scientific curiosity is sexual curiosity altered by a repressive agent. It was thus consistent with psychoanalytical theory to maintain that Protestant sexual repression had caused a redirection of human energies into scientific research. According to both Weber and Freud, science was born of man's inner unhappiness.

Marxist sociologists, on the other hand, trying to provide a historical materialist explanation for the rise of science in the seventeenth century, have not really dissented from the thesis of Protestant asceticism. They have emphasized, to be sure, the primary importance of technological needs, but have not disputed the relevant role of Protestant asceticism as the ideology of the bourgeoisie, and hence, of the rise of science. Technological factors, however, as the driving force in the history of science have been their dominant concern. "The history of sciences," wrote Friedrich Engels, cannot be written "as if they had fallen from the skies." "If society has a technical need," he said, "that helps science forward more than ten universities. The whole of hydrostatics (Torricelli, etc.) was called forth by the necessity for regulating the mountain streams of Italy in the sixteenth and seventeenth centuries. We have only known anything reasonable about electricity since its technical applicability was discovered." And Marx attributed "the greatest importance" to the "sporadic use of machinery in the seventeenth century . . . because it supplied the greatest mathematicians of that time with a practical basis and stimulant to the creation of the science of mechanics." [4] A whole area of research in the sociology of science was opened when this standpoint was presented in 1931 by a Soviet delegate at the International Congress of the History of Science and Technology. In a pathfinding paper, "The Social and Economic Roots of Newton's *Principia*," Professor B. Hessen argued that the technological needs of the seventeenth century defined the theoretical problems for Newton's analysis. Behind Newton's quest for a system of the world were, according to Hessen, such problems of navigation as the accurate determination of longitude, while his laws of motion were seen as the theoretical outcome of tasks that arose in the course of the development of heavy artillery. According to Soviet pragmatism in its extreme form, every scientific theory was an instrument for the solving of some technological problem in the given time.[5]

The history of science, however, is not reducible to technological pragmatism. The driving force in Galileo's study of projectiles, A. R. Hall argued cogently, was in large part the desire to correct the received Aristotelian doctrine rather than the improvement of weaponry. Although there was a strong movement to draw science "closer to the field, the forge, and the workshop," the deepest motive for scientific research remained the love of truth.[6] Whatever its ultimate psychological source, curiosity, the desire to know the why, how, and wherefore of things, was the basic motive power of science. Curiosity was, however, regarded by Weber's school as a by-product of Protestant asceticism, as a sublimated seeking of God in His works.

There has been a basic agreement, indeed, between the leading sociological schools, the Marxist and the Weberian, as to the significant role of Protestant asceticism. Both schools asserted that there was a functional linkage between the Protestant ethic and the scientific activity of the new bourgeois civilization. While Weber, on the one hand, held that the Protestant ethic was a precondition for the rise of European capitalism and science, Marx said it was, rather, the concurrent consequence of this rise.[7] Yet Marxists and Weberians alike shared the view that the Protestant ascetic ethic somehow made it likely that its adherents would become more effective seekers after scientific truth.

Has this concentration on the Protestant ethic, however, radically misperceived the origins of modern science? Misgivings have persisted. Pitirim Sorokin, in a bypath to his studies of cyclical fluctuations in human history, noted that the scientific contribution of Catholic Italians during the first half of the seventeenth century was higher than that of any other country. This fact alone, he held, would refute the notion that there was a direct causal relationship between the Protestant ethic and the emergence of modern science.[8] Even those who acknowledged that Protestant England had led European science at the end of the seventeenth century were uncertain as to what exactly the alleged connection between Puritanism and science had been. "The influence of Protestantism on natural science," wrote Richard S. Westfall, "is nebulous and difficult to determine." S. Lilley accepted the documentation by Robert Merton and Dorothy Stimson, which purported to prove that Puritan beliefs had been a driving force in the origins of modern science, but both he and James W. Carroll wondered whether "Protestant" and "Puritan" were being used so loosely as to conceal under their rubric rationalistic, empirical, skeptical, and even atheistic tendencies.[9] Was it possible that two disparate contemporary phenomena were being assigned a relatedness that had never obtained in actuality?

That the scientific revolution was the outcome of a liberation of curiosity all would agree. The question, however, remains unsettled: What was the emotional revolution in seventeenth-century thinkers which turned them into men of science? What was the psychological revolution upon which the scientific revolution was founded? Modern science, writes Lynn White, Jr., as it first appeared in the later Middle Ages, "was one result of a deep-seated mutation in the general attitude toward nature." The new science, he continues, was an aspect "of an unprecedented yearning for immediate experience of concrete facts which appears to have been characteristic of the waxing third estate." [10] What, then, was the character of this deep-seated emotional mutation? What changes in attitude and feeling toward human thought, sensation, and knowledge made possible the emergence of scientific intellectuals?

Certainly there are strong antecedent grounds for doubting that Protestant asceticism would have nurtured the spirit of science. The Calvinist doctrine of original sin was plainly hostile to the pretension of ordinary human beings to understand the world. For the Fall of Adam and Eve, according to the Calvinist, so corrupted their descendants' faculties and senses as to destroy their natural powers for knowing the world. It was a consequence of the ascetic Protestant standpoint, as Paul H. Kocher writes, that "all science was false, and would continue to be so, except as God rescued it by giving to chosen individuals at chosen times a special grace to discover the truth." [11] Perhaps one might certify Protestant scientists as having been elected to know the truth, but there was always the difficulty of what to do with Catholic and Mohammedan ones. It was altogether implausible to regard them, from the Calvinist standpoint, as having received a grace that rescued their senses from corruption. The eminent Elizabethan surgeon William Clowes could not, as he wrote in his *Treatise for the Artificiall Cure of Struma*, in 1602, be troubled by the question whether grace had rescued infidel physicians:

> . . . if I finde (eyther by reason or experience) any thing that may be to the good of the Patients, and better increase of my

knowledge and skil in the Arte of Chirurgery, be it eyther in Galen or Paracelsus; yea, Turke, Jewe, or any other Infidell: I will not refuse it, but be thankefull to God for the same. How be it, I will in no wise meddle with their Infidelity, though I embrace their knowledge and skill in human verityes and inventions. . . .[12]

Luther and Calvin were naturally reluctant to derive consequences from the doctrine of original sin which would have committed them to a flagrant assault on the cosmopolitan, scientific sense of reality. They decided by way of compromise that while original sin had totally depraved man's knowledge of God, it had only partially depraved his understanding of the physical world. Such partial depravity of the senses and understanding may have been a satisfactory escape clause for theologians seeking under duress to come to terms with a scientific knowledge they disliked. It was scarcely, however, a doctrine that could inspire scientists in their search for truths about the world in which they lived.

Meanwhile the scientists of Elizabethan England were going their own happy way, enjoying an independence from their clergy, and trusting simply and optimistically that the perceptions of a healthy human being gave him trustworthy information concerning the external world. "God did not put us here on earth under a life sentence of illusion" very well describes their cheerful, untroubled attitude, which was anything but the pessimist metaphysic of Protestant asceticism.[13]

Myth and fantasy can infiltrate the perception of even great social scientists, and the consistent scheme of Weber's hypothesis may also consistently misrepresent the origins of science.

In this study, I shall try to show that the scientific intellectual was born from the hedonist-libertarian spirit which, spreading through Europe in the sixteenth and seventeenth centuries, directly nurtured the liberation of human curiosity. Not asceticism, but satisfaction; not guilt, but joy in the human status; not self-abnegation, but self-affirmation; not original sin, but original merit and worth; not gloom, but merriment; not contempt for one's body and one's senses, but delight in one's physical being; not the exaltation of pain, but the hymn to pleasure—this was the emotional basis of the scientific movement of the seventeenth century. Herbert Butterfield has spoken of "a certain dynamic quality" which entered into Europe's "secularization of thought" in the seventeenth century.[14] What I shall try to show is how the hedonist-libertarian ethic provided the momentum for the scientific revolution, and was in fact the creed of the emerging movements of scientific intellectuals everywhere.

Varieties of Hedonistic and Ascetic Ethics

What do we mean by the "hedonistic ethic"? What likewise is meant by the phrase "ascetic ethic," or "Protestant ethic" in Weber's sense? Basically, an ethic is hedonist when it is free from a sense of primal guilt; a hedonist outlook is characterized by an absence of internalized self-aggression. "Good" can then be defined in terms of the person's spontaneous likings and desires. The Calvinist ethic, in which the asceticism of the sixteenth and seventeenth centuries was expressed, was founded by contrast on an assertion of the primacy of guilt. When Thomas Hobbes explained the power of the Presbyterian preachers at the beginning of the English civil war, he emphasized that they could make young people feel guilty about their impulses:

> They brought young men into desperation and to think themselves damned, because they could not (which no man can, and is contrary to the constitution of nature) behold a delightful object without delight. And by this means they became confessors to such as were troubled in conscience, and were obeyed by them as their spiritual doctors in all cases of conscience. . . .[15]

The Calvinist philosophy was a metaphysics of guilt; it held that man is a creature born in original sin, pervaded by sin, maimed by sin; with St. Augustine, Calvin declares that "the naturall giftes were corrupted in man by sinne." [16] Repentance was man's primary virtue; his salvation could come only through God's grace. The Calvinist ethic was permeated with hatred of the body, hatred of the senses and pleasure. Man's desire for pleasure had brought his fall; austerity, frugality, self-denial were good because they mortified the fount of man's sin.

Now, there are various types of asceticism, as there are different kinds of hedonism. Asceticism has taken different forms under different historical conditions. By and large, however, we can distinguish two principal varieties of asceticism, the first of which we may call "utilitarian asceticism" and the second "masochistic asceticism." [17]

The utilitarian ascetic is a person who forgoes an immediate pleasure in order to have a greater one in the future. The pioneers who endured the hardships of the American frontier were utilitarian ascetics; they looked forward to the enjoyments of the future, when their houses would be built, when their fields would be under cultivation, and they would know the blessings of peace and prosperity. Pains, deprivations, frustrations were undergone not for their own sake but because they would make possible more of pleasures, life's goods, in the future. The masochistic ascetic, however, has come to value pain for its own sake. He is punishing himself. From the domain of his unconscious, a harsh, cruel tyrant condemns any spontaneous desire he may have for pleasurable experience. The masochistic ascetic acquiesces to the will of the unconscious authority, his superego. His self-punitive asceticism is the outcome of an identification with or submission to the absolute superego, and this internalized self-aggression issues in self-reproach, in spiritual groveling, in humility, in torments of anxiety and guilt. Within the unconscious, the longing for joy persists; on the level of overt action, however, the masochistic ascetic has become a seeker after pain. The psychological revolution which made possible the birth of modern science consisted precisely in the overcoming by an intellectual elite in Western Europe of masochistic asceticism.

It is also useful to distinguish between the asceticism which is mother-centered and that which is father-centered. The Roman Catholic ascetics were typically mother-centered; from St. Augustine on, they were dominated by loyalty to their mother—which they combined with a rejection of other women. The mother, in the symbolic person of the Virgin Mary, was progressively purified of any sexual impurity; the father was allowed to recede into the background, and the ascetic fulfilled a son's loyalty to the mother. "The amount of attention and significance given the Virgin Mary, the mother of Christ," writes W. Lloyd Warner, "is a crucial test of what it means to be a Catholic or a Protestant. . . . The role of the pure virgin and the saintly mother, combined in the figure of one woman, creates a symbol of ideal simplicity to arouse and evoke the deep oedipus love of all males. . . . The love for their own mother is contained and bound by the worship of virginity." [18]

The Protestant ascetic, on the other hand, is father-centered and dominated by a strong superego figure. The father frowns on the terminology of love; he prefers the language of fear, and prizes the "God-fearing man." William Jennings Bryan, an exemplar of American fundamentalism, was an ideal type of Protestant ascetic in his upbringing and in his attitude to science. Bryan's father, a Baptist, would often stop work at noon to hear his son read him a chapter from the Bible; then they would discuss it. His virtues were always those his father had taught. Religious uncertainties crossed through Bryan's mind in his adolescence, but he surmounted them by identification with his father and teachers. He was always grateful, he wrote, to his Christian instructors, under whose guidance "the doubts aroused by my studies were resolved by putting them beside a powerful and loving God." [19] Parental authority in Bryan was strengthened at this critical time against the threat of scientific method, and he went on to become the doughty champion of American ascetic Protestantism against modern science.

Both the mother-centered and father-centered varieties of asceticism, with different emphases, are hostile to the scientific spirit. It does not follow, however, that every form of hedonism is cordial to it. Confucius, for instance, approved of pleasure-seeking through listening to music, being with one's friends, and discussing moral excellence. He was an empiricist; he rejected any claim to innate knowledge, and refused to discuss questions concerning the supernatural. But his hedonism was authoritarian rather than libertarian, and, as such, was constrained within a demarcated domain. Reverence for antiquity, for the received opinion, dominated his thinking; his was an empiricism of the status quo. "The Master said: I am not one who has innate knowledge, but one who, loving antiquity, is diligent in seeking it therein." The cult of ancestor worship inhibited the questioning spirit which is essential to scientific activity. Confucius's authoritarian hedonism placed an inordinate emphasis on filial piety, on "not being disobedient," morally and intellectually, to parental injunctions.[20] Authoritarian hedonism, with its limited friendliness toward the senses, does not espouse the self-hatred of the body. But it discourages originality in hypothesis or experiment. The fear of one's elders which it inculcates makes always for a component of pain both in the unconscious and in consciousness. As such, its hedonism is always partial, incomplete. Authoritarian hedonism, by instilling a powerful, cultural superego, undermines an essential component of the scientific spirit.

The hedonist-libertarian ethic, on the other hand, includes that ingredient which makes for what Francis Galton simply called "independence of character." In his classical study on the sociology of English scientists in the nineteenth century, Galton observed, "The home atmosphere which the scientific men breathed in their youth was generally saturated with the spirit of independence." The autobiographical comments of many scientists indicated the measure of their independence in conflict with society:

> "Left, aet. 12, a school where I had received injustice from the master."
>
> "Opinions in almost all respects opposed to those in which I was educated."
>
> "I have always taken my own independent line. My heresy prevented my advancement." [21]

The menace of a stern religious or authoritarian superego was strikingly absent among the English scientists. As far as their religious beliefs were concerned, wrote Galton, "they seem singularly careless of dogma, and exempt from mysterious terror." Piety, the "dependent frame of mind," as Galton called it, was not a trait of the scientists' characters. He noted, furthermore, that "few of the sons of clergymen" were to be found on his list of scientists, a remarkable fact when we remember to what a large extent the universities of England in the nineteenth century were devoted to training young men in divinity.

This freedom from an authoritarian superego, so typical among Victorian men of science, was likewise an essential constituent in the hedonist ethic which nourished the childhood of modern science. The hedonist-libertarian ethic thus involves an individualistic emphasis, in the sense that the individual does not feel himself enthralled by some cultural censor. This new scientific individualism was abhorred by those who, like Martin Luther, regarded with affright the prospect of a continuous revision of received opinions by successive generations of independent thinkers. "Whoever wants to be clever," wrote Luther sardonically against the scientific individualists, "must needs produce something of his own, which is bound to be the best since *he* has produced it."

The greatest original scientific thinkers, we might say, are persons whose thought has remained incompletely "socialized." Einstein once described himself vividly:

> I have never belonged wholeheartedly to any country or state, to my circle of friends, or even to my own family. . . . Such isolation is sometimes bitter, but I do not regret being cut off from the understanding and sympathy of other men. I lose something by it, to be sure, but I am compensated for it in being rendered independent of the customs, opinions, and prejudices of others. . . .[22]

This libertarian trait was shared by such thinkers as Newton, Freud, and Darwin. The sociological theory of knowledge has usually failed to do justice to this asocial element in creative thought. Sociologists have justly documented the social roots of scientific activity, for often the materials for scientific problems are socially provided and socially determined. But in original thinking the particular combination or form that is given to intellectual elements breaks with the traditional ways of solving problems, disrupts the traditional categories, and has a quality of the subversive. This component differentiates the influence of the hedonist-libertarian ethic from authoritarian hedonism. The libertarian has either been spared the necessity for the intellectual "parricide" which many people must enact to achieve independence of insight, or he has somehow accomplished that parricide in such a way as not to have his psyche's energies consumed in self-reproach.

There were four ways in which the makers of the scientific revolution adhered to a standpoint more hedonistic, more expressive of their underlying human desires.

First, the new scientists found a direct joy and pleasure in scientific activity itself. The source of scientific creativity has always been a spirit of play, not of work. In play, the free imagination leaps out of customary channels, delighting in novelty, so that it is filled with an exhilaration, an excitement. When Einstein described the inwardness of his thinking, he said it was a kind of "combinatory play," an "associative play" with images.[23] Such was likewise the spirit of Kepler when he wrote that science was play, akin to God's play, like a child's play, purposeless, but with a simple delight in configuration and form: "As God the Creator played, so He also taught nature, as His image, to play the very game which He played before her." [24] This direct joy in scientific activity, characteristic of the childhood and youth of science, we shall call *immediate* or *expressive hedonism.* It is a quality of experience lacking in an era of institutionalized, bureaucratized scientific research, but it pervaded the scientific revolutionaries. In Kepler, it reached the extreme form of a *cosmological hedonism,* in which joy was projected as the essence of all things. The cosmos was a spiritual harmony, said Kepler, "which pure spirits and in a certain way even God sense with no less enjoyment and pleasure than man experiences when listening to musical chords." [25]

"The sense of beauty is the moving power," says Jacques Hadamard in describing the psychological drive of the mathematician. The feeling of beauty, whatever its ultimate source, rests on the direct enjoyment of the perceived forms and qualities of things. Scientific creativity is heightened by the pleasure taken in the vivid imagery of underlying physical forces and scientific laws. Poincaré, looking back on a sleepless night that opened great discoveries, recalled, "Ideas rose in crowds; I felt them collide until pairs interlocked, so to speak, making a stable combination." [26] Scientists often "sleep" on their problems, and allow a kind of incubation to take place in their unconscious. Perhaps one function of this incubation is to outmaneuver the cultural superego, to allow the free play of imagery to burst through the resistances of some commanding authority, and to breach the restraints of tradition with the liberated energies of originality. An ascetic ethic, however, is hostile to the direct sense of beauty, and deprives the thinker of the idle richness of imagery. The ascetic ethic, besides being sense-mistrustful, is image-destroying; the fear of the Eternal Father—and the image of the Father castigating the lowly human for his sinfulness—is a totalitarian one, co-ordinating and pervading the ascetic consciousness, and banishing idle, enjoyable images into the undisciplined turmoil of the unconscious.

The scientists of the seventeenth century, in addition to being expressive hedonists, were also *utilitarian hedonists.* They claimed that the pursuit of science would alleviate men's toil, rescue them from the curse of drudgery, and ensure to them a more pleasant, civilized existence. Descartes and Leibniz foretold that science opened the prospect of an immense technological advancement for mankind. We can "render ourselves the masters and possessors of nature," wrote Descartes, if in place of the schoolmen's philosophy, we learn the forces and actions of physical bodies "as distinctly as we know the different crafts of our artisans."

> This is not merely to be desired with a view to the invention of an infinity of arts which enable us to enjoy without any trouble the fruits of the earth and all the good things which are to be found there but also, and principally, because it brings about the preservation of health, which is without doubt the chief blessing and the foundation of all other blessings in this life.

"In mathematics," he said, "there are the subtlest discoveries and inventions which may accomplish much, both in satisfying the curious and in furthering all the arts, and in diminishing man's labor." [27] Leibniz was from his youth dedicated to projects for the foundation of academies and societies that would stimulate the application of science to manufacture, and would revive the industrial prosperity and scientific leadership that the Thirty Years' War had destroyed in Germany. But it was Francis Bacon who was the outstanding prophet of the utilitarian contribution of science; the Royal Society venerated Bacon, and promised Englishmen in the age of the Merry Monarch, Charles II, that scientific research would make for an even merrier England. If "man is a God to man," wrote Bacon, it is because of his achievements in the arts; advancement in technology raised "the most civilized province of Europe" over "the wildest and most barbarous districts of New India." Three recent inventions especially, said Bacon, had changed the whole face of the world—printing, gunpowder, and the magnet; "these mechanical discoveries" had influenced human affairs more profoundly than any political changes. Bacon called on men to redirect their aggressions from against each other toward the conquest of the physical world, "to establish and extend the power and dominion of the human race itself over the universe." The sciences were the necessary instruments for the human conquest of the environment; "the empire of man over things depends wholly on the arts and sciences." [28]

The Baconian conception of science is predominantly that of the utilitarian hedonist; the pursuit of science, apart from its joy in itself, is an instrument for the improvement of the lot of mankind. Insofar as it has an element of direct pleasure, this derives in part from its satisfaction of aggressive drives directed against the environment. The liberation of human energies which it advocated was to be attained by rechanneling internalized self-aggressive energies into externalized aggressive energies. The human race was not to war against itself either in individual asceticism or group destruction; it was to conquer nature. Bacon, moreover, as Francis R. Johnson has noted, was the spokesman for a creed shared by the English scientific workers of his time, a creed compounded of the spirit of revolt against ancient authority, a faith in the experimental method and the greater earthly happiness it would bring man, and the belief in human progress.[29]

Though the scientific intellectuals, an emerging community, cooperated on behalf of a common ideal and aim, they were as individuals often intensely competitive. In addition to being expressive and utilitarian, theirs was an *individualistic* hedonism. They abandoned any abnegation of self; they longed to see their own names linked to discoveries; they came to value a this-worldly immortality. So far from regarding it a sin, the scientific intellectuals took frank delight in pride. Henry Oldenburg, the first editor of the *Philosophical Transactions of the Royal Society*, assured Robert Boyle that his journal would carefully record priorities in scientific discovery:

> I acknowledge that that jealousy about the first authors of experiments which you speak of, is not groundless; and therefore offer myself to register all those you, or any person, shall please to communicate as new, with that fidelity, which both the honor of my relation to the Royal Society (which is highly concerned in such experiments) and my own inclinations, do strongly oblige me to.[30]

Scientists posed problems as challenges for their fellow-scientists, and the competition was keen, sometimes envious. Jacques Bernoulli of Basel, in 1696, challenged the mathematicians of Europe to solve the problem of isoperimetrical figures. He even offered a reward to the solver. Many sought for the solution. Jean Bernoulli, Jacques's brother, claiming erroneously to have the solution, quarreled bitterly with Jacques; then he published Jacques's solution as his own after his brother died—yet Jean was the gifted discoverer of the exponential calculus! Competitive strife over the priority in the discovery of the calculus separated with suspicion and malevolence the greatest of the mathematicians, Newton and Leibniz. A competitive individualism was part, however, of the pride in selfhood which the psychological revolution endorsed.[31]

Lastly, the makers of the scientific revolution found themselves seeking a conception of the universe in which man would be less fear-ridden, less anxiety-surrounded, less open to the terrors of bewildering supernatural agents. What gave wings to Kepler, says Caspar, was his "refreshing optimism" about the capabilities of the human understanding.[32] In our time, there has been a reluctance to acknowledge that the scientific standpoint brought to the seventeenth-century thinkers a greater self-confidence and sense of assuredness as to their place in the universe. The scientific standpoint, says Charles Gillispie, for example, alienated man from nature; it created a tension, he writes, between science and humanity's aspiration to participate morally in the cosmic process. With Galileo, he says, began the Fatal Estrangement "which has left us in a world in which we have no peace"; "after Galileo science could no longer be humane. . . ."[33] The achievement of impersonal objectivity, it is maintained, involved men's renunciation of their wishes; the journey from the pleasure principle to the reality principle was presumably one in which the travelers had to repress wish-fulfillment as the basis for asserting matters of fact. But in actuality there was no such feeling of renunciation or alienation on the part of the scientists of the seventeenth century. Their feeling was of delight that they could understand the world. Whereas God's laws had once been held to transcend the human understanding, now mathematics, as Spinoza said, had furnished "a standard of verity" which would enable us to discern the truths of the universe.[34]

Those historians who read the pessimism of the scientists and philosophers of the twentieth century into the emotions of those of the seventeenth are engaged in retrojective activity. Thus the scholarly Edwin A. Burtt has depicted a crushing of optimism and a darkening of the world's variegated brightness as the work of the seventeenth century:

> The gloriously romantic universe of Dante and Milton . . . had now been swept away. The world that people had thought themselves living in—a world rich with color and sound, redolent with fragrance, filled with gladness, love and beauty, speaking everywhere of purposive harmony and creative ideals—was crowded now into minute corners in the brains of scattered organic beings. The really important world outside was a world hard, cold, colorless, silent, and dead; a world of quantity, a world of mathematically computable motions in mechanical regularity.[35]

The cosmology of the seventeenth century is thus portrayed as the ascetic's projective Universe, whose "reality" is one deprived of color and vitality; it is desexualized, castrated. The science of the seventeenth century, writes Norman O. Brown, was dominated by a drive toward death in life, expressing itself in the distinction between the objective, primary qualities of matter and the subjective, secondary qualities of human perception. Mass, length, and shape were taken as primary qualities, inherent in physical objects themselves, whereas their colors, smells, and tastes were regarded as psychological effects dependent on human organisms, and not qualities of the external objects themselves. To Brown, this dualistic distinction, this "bifurcation of nature" (in Whitehead's phrase), is the hallmark of the ascetic's projective metaphysics. Brown calls with Whitehead for a science that will restore the glorious colors to a decolorized world; he calls for a new science that will be based on a restored "erotic sense of reality." [36]

This is the retrojective myth. The truth is, rather: The scientists of the seventeenth century swept away the miserable universe of death, famine, and the torture of human beings in the name of God. They took a world that had been peopled with demons and devils, and that superstition had thronged with unseen terror at every side. They cleansed it with clear words and plain experiment. They found an ethic that advised people to renounce their desires, and to cultivate in a hostile universe the humility which befitted their impotence, and they taught men instead to take pride in their human status, and to dare to change the world into one which would answer more fully to their desires. Descartes, drawing up his program of inventions to be made, listed an inventory of man's hopes, not a catalogue of his sins and despairs. The prospectus of optical instruments, labor-saving machines, new medicines, flying machines, the means to bring sight to the blind and wisdom to the ignorant, and even the extravagent hope, which Constantijn Huygens wrote to Descartes, that "*cette fâcheuse coutume de mourir prendra fin un jour*" ("this disagreeable custom of dying will have an end someday"), were the harbinger of a new mood in which man was presented with a universe which was malleable in great measure to his wishes, if he would reinforce those wishes with scientific understanding.[37] The world became a place in which men might find happiness, a stage on which no cosmic dramatist had preassigned their lines but on which they could create their own. And the primary qualities of the mechanical universe were precisely those which they could handle literally with their own hands, to alter the shapes and sizes of things, so that the world of human experience would be more laden with joys.

The classical expression of the hedonist-libertarian ethic in the seventeenth century came in Spinoza's philosophy. "The two archenemies of the human race," Spinoza said, are "Hatred and Remorse." [38] Neither repentance nor humility was a virtue in the ethics of the free man, as Spinoza conceived it. "A free man thinks of death least of all things; and his wisdom is a meditation not of death but of life." The anxiety of salvation, the fear that he might not be predestined for the elect, was alien to Spinoza's free man. There was no preordained aristocracy of the elect: "The highest good of those who follow virtue is common to all, and therefore all can equally rejoice therein." And "good" for Spinoza had a simple biological significance. A thing is good, he said, "because we desire it"; "in no case do we strive for, wish for, long for or desire anything because we deem it to be good, but on the other hand, we deem a thing to be good, because we strive for it, wish for it, long for it, or desire it." The free man was no ascetic, brooding, dwelling in loneliness, fear, and trembling. On the contrary, wrote Spinoza:

> I say it is the part of a wise man to refresh and recreate himself with moderate and pleasant food and drink and also with perfumes, with the soft beauty of growing plants, with dress, with music, with many sports, with theatres, and the like such as every man may make use of without any injury to his neighbor.[39]

The scientific movement in the seventeenth century was not the by-product of an increase of repression or asceticism. It was the outcome of a liberation of energies; it derived from a lightening of the burden of guilt. With the growing awareness that happiness and joy are his aims, man could take frank pleasure in the world around him. Libidinal interests in external objects could develop unthwarted; the world was found interesting to live in—an unending stage for fresh experience. Energies were no longer consumed in inner conflicts. With an awakened respect for his own biological nature, self-hatred was cast off. Empiricism was the expression of a confidence in one's senses; the eyes and ears were no longer evidences of human corruption but trusted avenues to a knowledge of nature. The body was not the tainted seat of ignorance, but the source of pleasures and the means for knowledge. Human energies, hitherto turned against themselves, could reach out beyond concern for exclusive self.

NOTES

1. Francis Bacon, *The Great Instauration,* in *The Philosophical Works of Francis Bacon,* ed. James Spedding (London, 1861), Vol. I, Translations, p. 22. Cf. Charles Monroe Coffin, *John Donne and the New Philosophy* (New York, 1958), pp. 65 ff.

2. "The history of cosmic theories, in particular," says Koestler, "may without exaggeration be called a theory of collective obsessions and controlled schizophrenias." Arthur Koestler, *The Sleepwalkers* (London, 1959), p. 15.

3. Robert K. Merton, "Science, Technology, and Society in Seventeenth Century England," *Osiris,* IV (1938), Pt. 2, pp. 494-5. Max Weber, *The Protestant Ethic and the Spirit of Capitalism,* trans. Talcott Parsons (New York, 1958), p. 249. Weber, however, did not always hold that asceticism was a creative stimulus to science. In another work, he states: ". . . the ascetic sects of Protestantism have also been disposed to have nothing to do with science, except in a situation where material requirements of everyday life were involved." Cf. Max Weber, *General Economic History,* trans. Frank H. Knight (London, 1927), p. 368. The two standpoints are plainly at odds.

4. Karl Marx and Friedrich Engels, *Correspondence: 1846-1895,* trans. Dona Torr (New York, 1935), p. 517. Karl Marx, *Capital: A Critique of Political Economy,* trans. Samuel Moore and Edward Aveling (Chicago, 1906), pp. 382-3.

5. B. Hessen, "The Social and Economic Roots of Newton's 'Principia,'" *Science at the Cross Roads* (London, 1931), pp. 174-5. Lewis S. Feuer, "Dialectical Materialism and Soviet Science," *Philosophy of Science*, XVI (1949), 105-24.

6. A. R. Hall, *Ballistics in the Seventeenth Century* (Cambridge, England), 1952, pp. 4, 160-3. G. N. Clark, *Science and Social Welfare in the Age of Newton* (Oxford, 1937), p. 89.

7. Karl Marx, *Capital: A Critique of Political Economy*, trans. Samuel Moore and Edward Aveling (Modern Library, New York), pp. 91, 150, 303, 645, 650. Frederick Engels, *Socialism: Utopian and Scientific*, trans. Edward Aveling (Chicago, 1908), pp. 26-7.

8. Pitirim A. Sorokin, *Social and Cultural Dynamics*, Vol. II; *Fluctuations of Systems of Truth, Ethics, and Law* (New York, 1937), p. 152.

9. Richard S. Westfall, *Science and Religion in Seventeenth Century England* (New Haven, 1958), p. 7. S. Lilley, "Social Aspects of the History of Science," *Archives Internationales d'Histoire des Sciences*, XXVIII (1949), pp. 432-4. James W. Carroll, "Merton's Thesis on English Science," *American Journal of Economics and Sociology*, XIII (1954), 427-32.

10. Lynn White, Jr., "Natural Science and Naturalistic Art in the Middles Ages," *American Historical Review*, LII (1947), 435.

11. Paul H. Kocher, *Science and Religion in Elizabethan England* (San Marino, 1953), p. 32.

12. Quoted in Paul H. Kocher, *op. cit.*, p. 254.

13. *Ibid.*, p. 30.

14. H. Butterfield, *The Origins of Modern Science, 1300-1800* (London, 1951), pp. 162-3.

15. Thomas Hobbes, *Behemoth: The History of the Causes of the Civil Wars of England*, in *The English Works of Thomas Hobbes*, ed. Sir William Molesworth (London, 1840), p. 196. Cf. Sandford Fleming, *Children and Puritanism: The Place of Children in the Life and Thought of the New England Churches, 1620-1847* (New Haven, 1933), pp. 153 ff.

16. Paul H. Kocher, *op. cit.*, p. 34, quoted from John Calvin, *A Commentarie upon Galatians*, 1581.

17. This terminology is derived from John Carl Flügel, *Man, Morals and Society* (New York, 1945), pp. 87-94.

18. W. Lloyd Warner, *The Living and the Dead: A Study of the Symbolic Life of Americans* (New Haven, 1959), pp. 380, 386. *The Vanishing Irish*, ed. John A. O'Brien (New York, 1953), pp. 29, 35, 56-8, 95, 121, 172, 211, 220.

19. William J. and Mary Baird Bryan, *The Memoirs of William*

Jennings Bryan (Chicago, 1925), pp. 44-51. Sandford Fleming, *op. cit.*, p. 188.

20. *The Analects of Confucius,* trans. William Edward Soothill (World's Classics, Oxford, 1951), pp. 9, 10, 13, 65, 82, 180.

21. Francis Galton, *English Men of Science: Their Nature and Nurture* (London, 1874), pp. 122, 129, 135.

22. Philipp Frank, *Einstein: His Life and Times,* trans. George Rosen (New York, 1947), pp. 49-50.

23. Jacques Hadamard, *An Essay on the Psychology of Invention in the Mathematical Field* (Princeton, 1945), pp. 142-3.

24. Max Caspar, *Kepler,* trans. C. Doris Hellman (New York, 1959), p. 185. W. Pauli, *The Influence of Archetypal Ideas on the Scientific Theories of Kepler,* trans. Priscilla Silz, in C. G. Jung and W. Pauli, *The Interpretation of Nature and the Psyche* (New York, 1955), pp. 171-2.

25. Max Caspar, *op. cit.*, p. 95. Cf. Edward W. Strong, *Procedures and Metaphysics: A Study in the Philosophy of Mathematical-Physical Science in the Sixteenth and Seventeenth Centuries* (Berkeley, 1936), p. 173.

26. Jacques Hadamard, *op. cit.*, pp. 14, 18, 39, 127.

27. René Descartes, *A Discourse on Method,* in *The Philosophical Works of Descartes,* trans. Elizabeth S. Haldane and G. R. T. Ross (Cambridge, 1911), Vol. I, pp. 84, 119-20. Cf. Georges Canquilhem, "Descartes et la technique," *Travaux du IXe Congrès International de Philosophie* (Paris, 1937), II, 77-85. John Theodore Merz, *Leibniz* (Edinburgh, 1894), pp. 76-7. Philip P. Wiener, 'Leibniz's Project of a Public Exhibition of Scientific Inventions," *Journal of the History of Ideas,* I (1940), 232-40.

28. Francis Bacon, "Aphorisms Concerning the Interpretation of Nature and the Kingdom of Man," *The Philosophical Works of Francis Bacon,* Vol. I, p. 114.

29. Francis R. Johnson, *Astronomical Thought in Renaissance England: A Study of the English Scientific Writings from 1500 to 1645* (Baltimore, 1937), p. 296.

30. Dorothy Stimson, "Hartlib, Haak and Oldenburg: Intelligencers," *Isis,* XXXI (1940), 321.

31. Moritz Cantor, *Vorlesungen über Geschichte der Mathematik* (Leipzig, 1898), Vol. III, pp. 85-6, 224 ff. Florian Cajori, *A History of Mathematics* (2nd ed., New York, 1919), pp. 220-5.

32. Max Caspar, *op. cit.*, p. 377.

33. Charles Coulston Gillispie, *The Edge of Objectivity: An Essay in the History of Scientific Ideas* (Princeton, 1960), pp. 44, 81.

34. Spinoza, *Ethics,* Pt. I, Appendix: *The Chief Works of Benedict*

de Spinoza, trans. R. H. M. Elwes (2nd ed., London, 1887), Vol. II, p. 77.

35. Edwin Arthur Burtt, *The Metaphysical Foundations of Modern Physical Science* (Revised Ed., Anchor Books, New York, undated), pp. 238-9.

36. Norman O. Brown, *Life Against Death: The Psychoanalytical Meaning of History* (Modern Library, New York, 1959), pp. 314-16. Actually, there were marked traits of the theological ascetic in Whitehead's own emotional perspective. "As a young man," writes his collaborator, Bertrand Russell, "he was all but converted to Roman Catholicism by the influence of Cardinal Newman." "Something of the vicarage atmosphere" always remained in his feeling and thought. Whitehead in later years admired the monasteries as refuges for the "more sensitive and imaginative types of humanity in the Middle Ages." For eight years at Cambridge, his principal extracurricular reading was theology, and he became a don at a time when they could not marry without taking orders. There seems also to have been an admixture of anti-Semitism in his feelings. Whitehead's opposition to Einstein's theory of relativity was scarcely related to any desire for an erotic universe. It is noteworthy that George D. Birkhoff, whose views concerning Jews in science coincided with those of Whitehead, likewise devoted considerable effort to trying to work out an alternative to Einstein's theory of relativity. Cf. Norbert Wiener, *I Am a Mathematician* (New York, 1956), pp. 28, 281. Whitehead's view of the world was essentially that of a Victorian clergyman of the Established Church. Cf. Bertrand Russell, *Portraits from Memory* (London, 1956), pp. 95-6, and Lucien Price, *Dialogues of Alfred North Whitehead* (Boston, 1954), pp. 8-9, 45, 35, 3, 59, 80, 109.

37. In a letter to Descartes on May 28, 1639, Huygens wrote of a Hollander who had expressed this hope in the end of human death. *Œuvres de Descartes*, ed. Charles Adam and Paul Tannery (Paris, 1898), Vol. II, pp. 549-50.

38. *Spinoza's Short Treatise on God, Man, and His Well-Being*, trans. A. Wolf (London, 1910), p. 33.

39. *The Chief Works of Benedict de Spinoza*, trans. R. H. M. Elwes (2nd ed., London, 1887), Vol. II, pp. 223, 232, 219, 137.

II

The Royal Society and the Scientists of England

BY COMMON CONSENT, THE FOUNDING OF THE ROYAL SOCIETY OF England in 1662 is the great landmark in the history of science as a social institution. It marks the emergence of the scientific intellectuals as an organized force in modern history. It therefore provides a crucial test for the hypothesis that the psychological revolution of the sixteenth and seventeenth centuries was the necessary condition for the scientific revolution. The able advocates of Weber's thesis have especially relied on the evidence of the Royal Society to substantiate their claim for the scientific fertility of the Protestant ascetic ethic. We shall therefore study closely the story of the Royal Society.

◆§ The Founders of the Royal Society

THE ROYAL SOCIETY WAS CONCEIVED when a group of jovial coffee-drinkers, who disliked theological hairsplitting and were tired of sectarian disputes, finally left the universities' precincts to set up their own "College" in London. They wanted a free atmosphere, in which they could inquire, enjoy themselves, as well as work for the happiness of England. They had had their fill of religious "enthusiasm." They wished to have done with mortification, predestination, asceticism. They had survived Cromwell, and had more than made their peace with the pleasure-loving Restoration monarchy of Charles II.[1]

The early history of the Royal Society, as set forth first in 1667 by Thomas Sprat, later Bishop of Rochester, makes clear the quest for freedom that animated the Society's founders:

> It was some space after the end of the Civil Wars at Oxford in Dr. Wilkins his lodgings, in Wadham College, which was then the place of resort for virtuous and learned men, that the first meetings were held which laid the foundation of all this that followed. The University had at this time many members of its own who had begun a free way of reasoning; and was also frequented by some gentlemen of philosophical minds, whom the misfortunes of the kingdom, and the security and ease of a retirement among Gownsmen had drawn thither. Their first purpose was no more than only the satisfaction of breathing a freer air, and of conversing in quiet one with another, without being engaged in the passions and madness of that dismal age.

These free-minded men, Sprat continues, hoped to educate a race of young men

> . . . invincibly armed against the enchantments of Enthusiasm. . . . For such a candid and impassionate company as that was, and for such a gloomy season, what would have been a better subject to pitch upon than Natural Philosophy? To have been always tossing about some Theological question would have been to have made that their private diversion the excess of which they themselves disliked in the public.[2]

These scientific pioneers had wandered in the desert of theology, and Bacon was their Moses to light the way to the promised land. They sang the words of Abraham Cowley's ode which Sprat took as his preface:

> From these and all long errors of the way
> In which our wandering predecessors went . . .
> Bacon like Moses led us forth at last . . .
> To fadome the vast depths of Nature's sea.[3]

Bacon's bust quite properly appeared on the frontispiece of Sprat's *History of the Royal Society*.

Who were the original group that grew into the Royal Society? As Sprat tells us,

> . . . the most principal and most constant of them were Doctor Seth Ward, the present Lord Bishop of Exeter, Mr. Boyl, Dr. Wilkins, Sir William Petty, Mr. Matthew Wren, Dr. Goddard, Dr. Willis, Dr. Bathurst, Dr. Christopher Wren, Mr. Rook. . . .

They were joined in London for their meetings at Gresham College by several eminent persons including Lord Viscount Brouncker and John Evelyn. They met "with the concurrence of many Worthy Men, who, to their immortal honour, had followed the King in his banishment, Mr. Erskins, Sir Robert Moray, Sir Gilbert Talbutt. . . ." [4] Anti-Puritan in their political philosophy, the founders of the Royal Society were well-known for their hedonism in ethics. In 1663, there circulated in London a "Ballad of Gresham College" whose author was probably Joseph Glanvill, elected a Fellow of the Royal Society in 1664.[5] The ballad celebrates the knowledge that makes for earthly happiness, and the liberation of the human intellect:

> Thy Colledg, Gresham, shall hereafter
> Be the whole world's Universitie,
> Oxford and Cambridge are our laughter;
> Their learning is but Pedantry.
> Those new colleagues doe assure us,
> Aristotle's an Asse to Epicurus.
>
> The noble learned Corporation
> Not for itselfe is thus combyn'd
> But for the publique good oth' Nation
> And general benefit of Mankynd.
> These are not men of common mould:
> They covet fame but contemn gold.

The "public good" which the new scientists aimed to promote was identified with long lives filled with pleasure:

> O blessed witt that thus contrives
> By new found out but facile Arte
> In pleasure to lengthen out our lives
> To teach us next to perfume ———.

The ballad narrated the "Colledge's" concern with such lowly matters as clothing manufacture, diving bells, the tanning of leather, the growth of oaks, a universal language, and, last, as forerunner of the smog and smaze of latter-day industrialism, with measures against smoke:

> And without fuell or smoake make fire
> Some other Member will aspire.

Man's general welfare was the Society's province. It embraced all men's concerns except theology:

> They'll demonstrate all things but a Dietie.

From its foundation until 1710, with the exception of seven years following the Great Fire of London in 1666, Gresham College gave the Royal Society a meeting place. The College itself was an Elizabethan precursor of the Royal Society. Administered jointly by the Mayor and Aldermen of the City of London, together with the Mercers' Company, it was a venture in the diffusion of science among the rising middle class. Its seven professors took turns during the week in giving lectures in English on divinity, astronomy, music, geometry, law, medicine, and rhetoric. The College, which opened its doors in 1597, and included among its professors some of the ablest scientists in England, had from the first had a practical cast; its professor of astronomy thus taught the use of mariners' instruments and the art of navigation.[6] Gresham College, indeed, was the first institution in England with endowed professorships in astronomy and geometry. The sciences thus found their first home in a college that in its time was an experiment in adult education and technical training outside the halls of the established universities. Gresham became a center to which all persons with scientific interests gravitated. Merchants and mariners, professors, physicists, physicians, public officials, naval officers, and shipwrights found there a common language, a common ethic and purpose. It was the natural meeting place for an informal group of young scientific intellectuals in the year 1645.

The early fellows of the Royal Society were later popularly called "Greshamites" or "Men of Gresham"; they were habitués of this College, which granted no degrees but gave a first lodging place to the lowly sciences. The Greshamites would linger after the lectures, and then repair to the lodgings of the professor to continue their inquiries. They were in 1645 a predominantly youthful group; of the first ten Greshamites, Boyle was only eighteen years old, and five others were between the ages of twenty-eight and thirty-one.[7] "They were not grey-beards spending their days at a club," writes Dorothy Stimson, "but active men of affairs following up a hobby that fascinated them." By 1658, the Greshamites were regularly assembling at the Wednesday and Thursday lectures of Sir Christopher Wren and Mr. Rooke, the professors of astronomy and geometry, and adjourning afterward to their private apartments.

During that year, they were joined by the men of the Oxford circle that had been growing up around John Wilkins at Wadham College. The Royal Society was born out of a union between the Greshamites and this Oxford circle. These "virtuosi" were fortunate in having the warm good will of the restored King, the hedonistic Charles II, who felt an especial kinship with them. "His Majesty is said to profess himself one of these Virtuosi," wrote Samuel Hartlib in 1660 in a letter to a friend about the weekly meetings at Gresham College.

The men of Gresham College and the Royal Society shared a common aversion to Calvinist theology and doctrinal extravagance. As we study the philosophies of the principal founders, the picture emerges of a common philosophy of tolerance, an Epicurean outlook, a turning away from dogmatisms as to religious ultimates.

◆§ Robert Boyle

ROBERT BOYLE WAS, BY GENERAL CONSENT, the moving spirit of the nucleus around which the Royal Society came into being. What was his personal philosophy? Boyle had experienced, at the age of thirteen, a religious crisis; he contemplated suicide, lived for two years in Calvinist Geneva, and then returned to an England torn with civil war. Experience alienated Boyle from religious dogmatism; "he became bitter against a radical Protestantism; for to him the essence of Christianity was peace and charity." He rejected the Calvinist doctrine of election, and wrote:

> Concerning the controversies betwixt the Calvinists and the Remonstrants about predestination . . . I think it not amiss to

> advertise you, that the doctrine of predestination is not necessary to justify the freeness and greatness of God's love.

Boyle was repelled by theological polemics. His earliest biographer wrote that Boyle had

> . . . an amiable view of Christianity . . . he was much troubled at the disputes and divisions . . . and as he did not shut himself with a party, so neither did he shut any party from him. . . . He had a most particular zeal against all severities and persecution upon the account of religion. . . .

For his understanding of the Bible, he looked to lay liberal scholars rather than the austere clerics. He declared that Christian theology and texts have been better explained by such persons as "the excellent Grotius" and Sir Francis Bacon than by "vulgar expositors, and other divines." [8]

Though no Puritan, Boyle was a religious man, a loyal adherent to the established Anglican Church. He was worried by the fact that "in the age we live in, there are too many persons" who have been estranged from religion by the arguments of the divines themselves. Boyle was among the first to envisage God as a great Clockmaker; the world, he said, is "like a rare Clock, where all things are so skilfully contrived, that the Engine being once set a Moving, all things proceed according to the Artificer's first design. . . ." [9] To promote this benevolent theism, Boyle in 1691 endowed an annual lectureship which was to combat the "fashionable atheism" of Hobbes and Spinoza, and to advocate faith in a benevolent God, "watchful over the public good . . . and careful to administer all things wisely for the good of the particular parts of it. . . ." He was explicit in recognizing the hedonistic value of science, in both its expressive and utilitarian senses. Philosophy "bribes the senses," said Boyle, with its arts of coloring, perfuming, confectionery, and the preparation of cosmetics. A few pieces of wood joined with "the guts of cats," he noted, "when artificially struck, afford the most ravishing pleasure." He urged philosophers to remain no longer "strangers to the shops and practices of tradesmen," and, indeed, to learn "from illiterate mechanics." The trades, he wrote, are "of the more noble and useful parts of natural history; for they shew us nature in motion, and that too when turn'd out of her course by human power." Boyle said that he learned more about stones, for instance, when he talked to masons and stonecutters than he did from reading Pliny and Aristotle. And philosophy, in turn, would make its greatest contribution to the manual trades, "for neither nature, nor human invention, is not so far exhausted" as not to profit greatly from the scientist's search. Philosophy for Boyle was no meditation on guilt, original sin, or the misery of human existence; it was a quest, with God's benign approval, for the greater happiness of mankind, and, in its experimental signification, designed to make man's earthly abode more abundant and joyous.[10]

☙ John Wilkins

A FELLOW-OXONIAN CALLED WILKINS "a notorious complyer." That he may very well have been, for many scholars in those days acquired a remarkable capacity for the flexible adaptation of principles; it was evidently the price of survival. When the visitation of Parliament at Oxford took place in 1647, Wilkins, like all his colleagues, was asked, "Will you submit to the authority of Parliament on this visitation?" Four hundred scholars, perhaps half the university, "made the great refusal." But Wilkins submitted, became Warden of Wadham, and married Cromwell's sister. He used his influence, however, to protect Royalists.[11] Wilkins, indeed, was neither a Calvinist nor a confirmed Puritan. At Oxford, he was known as an Independent, and there was a great difference between the austere Calvinist Presbyterians and the more pleasure-loving Independents. Anthony Wood, his gossipy Oxonian contemporary, compared the two groups:

> The Presbyterians with their disciples seemed to be very severe in their course of life, manners or conversation, and habits or apparell. . . . The other [the Independents] were more free, gay, and with a reserve, frollicsome, of a gay habit. . . . [The Presbyterians] for the most part preached nothing but damnation, the other [the Independents] not, but rather for libertie; yet both joyne together to pluck down and silence the prelattical preachers. . . .[12]

Wilkins early in life had come to the conclusion that one must bend one's aims and connections with the time. He said he got his first hint of "Rising" when "an ingeniose Gentleman of good quality" told him that he would never get "any considerable preferment" by staying in the university, but must betake himself "to some Lord's or great person's House that had good Benefices to conferre." [13] Wilkins followed this advice. After Cromwell's death, Wilkins resigned his Wardenship, but with the Duke of Buckingham's help he became Bishop of Chester in 1668. More notably indeed, Wilkins became a friend of the Merry Monarch, Charles II. Wilkins was a pleasant moderate, as befitted the author of *The Principles and Duties of Natural Religion*, in which it was affirmed that there are no demonstrations in theology. He used all his influence for tolerant reconciliation, and labored to bring back to the Church of England many ministers who had been deprived of their livings for failing to conform to the Act of Uniformity.

To us, Wilkins is best known for his pioneer work, *Essay Towards a Real Character and a Philosophical Language*. This remarkable effort to create a universal language was not in keeping with the Calvinist ethic. For, according to Scripture, men were punished with many languages at Babel because of their sin of pride. That, said Wilkins, was "the curse of the Confusion, with all the unhappy consequences of it," and he added, "It cannot be denied, but that the variety of Letters is an appendix to the Curse of Babel." [14] But Wilkins did not propose to acquiesce in God's decision. He sought "the surest remedy that could be against the Curse of the Confusion." He aimed to circumvent the Eternal Decree by fashioning "a Real universal Character, that should not signifie words, but things and notions, and consequently might be legible by any Nation in their own Tongue." The quest for a universal language began with a thinker who refused to bear the burden of a sense of guilt.

All his life, Wilkins' mind was restless with projects, as had been that of his father, the goldsmith of Oxford, "a very ingeniose man" with a "very Mechanicall head" and "much for Trying of Experiments," especially upon perpetual motion. When Wilkins was dying, he did not approach death with the trepidation of a Calvinist; rather, he remarked on his deathbed that he was "ready for the Great Experiment." His first publication in 1638, when he was but twenty-four years old, the *Discourse on the Discovery of a World in the Moone, or A Discourse Tending to Prove That ('Tis*

Probable) There May Be Another Habitable World in That Planet, was in a speculative vein that was alien to both Calvinist and Catholic, for whom the Earth was the exclusive planet set aside in God's scheme for the suffering trial of living beings. The hypothesis of a plurality of worlds was one of the typical daring speculations of the "new philosophy" in the seventeenth century. Wilkins, in his very first work, called for disengagement from "Aristotle's Principles." "'Twould be much better for the Commonwealth of learning," he wrote, "if we ground our Principles rather upon the frequent experience of our owne, then the bare authority of others." To the Royal Society, Wilkins was later the first to suggest, in 1665, experiments on blood transfusion. In the realm of blood as of language, he refused to accept man's fate as predestined.[15]

☙ Sir William Petty

THE NAME OF SIR WILLIAM PETTY, the founder of "Political Arithmetic," looms high in the roster of the Royal Society's fathers. Son of a clothier, apprenticed as a seaman, merchant, administrator of Irish lands under Cromwell, Petty embodied in his person the traits of the emerging commercial and industrial England. The formative intellectual influence on his life was "Mr. Thomas Hobbes, who loved his company." Petty had assisted Hobbes in the drawings for a book on optics, "for he had a very fine hand in those dayes for draweing." As an inheritor of the Hobbesian mantle, Petty wished to study social and political phenomena with a mathematical method. But there was no trace of Hobbes' authoritarianism in Petty. He rejected all the dogmatisms, religious and political, of his time. Petty was neither Cavalier nor Presbyterian, and he had a vision of a broad church founded on ethical ideas rather than theology. "In theology his views were liberal," writes Fitzmaurice, his biographer, "and his mind was that of a disciple, not of Calvin, but of Bacon." He disliked the Calvinist philosophy, and loved to mimic all the religious parties. "He can be an excellent droll," said Aubrey, "and will preach extempore incomparably, either the Presbyterian way, Independent, Cappucin frier, or Jesuite."

> He would take a text and preach [wrote Evelyn], now like a grave orthodox divine, then falling into the Presbyterian way, then to the phanatical, the quaker, the monk, and frier, the Popish priest, with such admirable action and alteration of voice and tone as it was not possible to abstain from wonder, and one would sweare to heare several persons, or forbear to think he was not in good earnest an enthusiast and almost beside himself.

He ridiculed the ascetic spirit: ". . . to be a Clergy-man then was a kinde of Mortification," wrote Petty, "whereas now (praised be God) 'tis a matter of splendor and magnificence." He satirized the notion "that Religion best flourisheth where the Priests are most mortified," and with consummate irony urged that the supply of ministers be limited to the demand, for otherwise, the excess would start persuading the people that the incumbents "do poison or starve their souls, and misguide them in their way to Heaven: . . ."[16]

Petty was the center of the lively coffeehouse group, which Pepys frequented, where life and literature were discussed, and where world systems and items of gossip were exchanged. Petty had once been perturbed by the rising tide of disbelief, and had planned for a while to write a treatise showing that a First Cause necessarily exists, and thereby to "check the insolent scepticisms, which do now pester the world. . . ." The essay, however, was uncompleted, and when, shortly before he died, Petty drew up a list of men he regarded as great, the names were such as Francis Bacon, Hobbes, Descartes, Molière, and Galileo. He was concerned with the art of human happiness. In 1686, he set forth instructions for the education of his sons, instructions that have all the sagacity of our modern manuals on how to be happy and successful:

> To pursue dancing, fencing, and riding; to fence in public, if you do well, otherwise not.
>
> To pursue the flute and sing justly. . . .
>
> To practice Arithmetick upon real business that shall be given you. . . .
>
> To dress yourself well without help.
>
> To carve at table and treat friends and strangers.
>
> To pitch upon ten good families, whereupon to practice civility and conversations.

To heare 4 or 5 of the most eminent preachers.

To goe to plays and learn the company, and also to the Drawing Room, St. James Park, Hyde Park, and balls. . . .

To know the alliances of all the noble families, with their friends and friendships. . . .

To be acquainted with 3 or 4 that make news their business.

To have a friend in every great office. . . .

To go to Gresham College.

His illegitmiate daughter, who of all Petty's children most resembled him, was an actress, Aubrey tells us, "at the Duke's Playhouse." Petty's "rude assertion of virility was in his case," says E. Strauss, his most recent biographer, "not an attempt to disguise its opposite. . . . On one occasion Petty suggested the possibility of measuring 'Vice and Sin in the nation' by various factors, amongst them 'the number of unmarried persons between fifteen and fifty-five years,' and we may assume that he lived up to his diagnosis during his many years as a bachelor, for he was forty-four years of age at the time of his marriage."

"I was counted as an enemy even to all the Sects and Factions," said Petty. His plan for education is certainly no design for religious dogmatism; it is a document of hedonistic tolerance. Petty once remarked jokingly, early in the Royal Society's history, that it should have chosen as its saint's day not St. Andrew's but St. Thomas's Day, for, like the Doubting Thomas, "he would not believe till he had seen and putt his fingers into the holes, according to the [Society's] motto '*nullius in verba*' ['in nobody's words']." When he built a ship for himself in 1664, he called it "The Experiment." Petty lived and died by the philosophy of experiment. We can well agree with the judgment of Fitzmaurice that "under less favorable circumstances, the fate of Dr. Petty might have been that of his brother physician, Michael Servetus," who fell into Calvin's hands, and was burnt at the stake in Geneva.[17]

☙ Sir Christopher Wren

SIR CHRISTOPHER WREN, DESTINED TO BECOME England's greatest architect, drafted the preamble for the charter of the Royal Society in 1662. He was a prodigy of science. At the age of twenty-five, in 1657, he was Professor of Astronomy at Gresham College, and four years later Savilian Professor at Oxford. He left teaching in 1673 to devote himself fully to architecture. Wren came from a family that was staunchly Cavalier in its political sympathies. Toward nonconformists and advanced Protestants, Wren himself took "the tolerant attitude of a philosophical scientist." He was essentially aloof from all sectarian controversies.

Above all, Wren felt at home in the enlightened atmosphere of the Masonic Lodge. Two obituary notices in newspapers of March, 1723, referred to him as "that worthy Freemason Sir Christopher Wren." He was described as having been "by birth and upbringing a confirmed Erastian." Freemasonry in England at this time was definitely anti-Puritan in its tone. The Masons were suspected by Cromwell's government of plotting with secret emissaries for the restoration of the monarchy, and the order was consequently hampered in its activities. It is no surprise therefore that Charles II's relations with the Masons were excellent. Wren is said to have been elected both in 1685 and 1698 as Grand Master of the Ancient Order of Free and Accepted Masons. Legend has it, moreover, that as Master of St. Paul's Lodge, he presented his brother Masons with the trowel and mallet he had used in laying the first stone of the Cathedral. This man gloried in the splendor of London, the city he was helping to create, and his paean was pagan in its imagery when he gave his inaugural lecture at Gresham:

> . . . for what city in the world so vastly populous, yet doth enjoy so healthy an air, so fertile a soil? Venus hath given it a pleasant situation. . . . Mercury hath nourished it in mechanical arts and trade. . . . Lastly, the moon, the lady of the waters, seems amorously to court this place. . . . And now, since navigators bring with it wealth, splendour, politeness and learning, what greater happiness can I wish to the Londoners, than that they may continually deserve to be deemed as formerly, the great navigators of the world . . . and that London may be even as Alexandria the established residence of the mathematical arts?

Not Calvin's Geneva, but pagan, scientific, commercial Alexandria was the city-ideal to Christopher Wren. He wrote to Sprat in 1663:

> . . . now I look about me, what need have I to go any further? . . . All the world are at present Poets; the poetical bees are all at

work, comedies, tragedies, verses, satires, burlesques; songs buzz every where about our ears. . . .[18]

◆§ Ward, Matthew Wren, Goddard, Bathurst, Rooke, and Willis

AMONG THE FOUNDING CIRCLE of the Royal Society were also Seth Ward, Matthew Wren, Jonathan Goddard, Ralph Bathurst, Laurence Rooke, and Thomas Willis. Only one of them was a partisan of Cromwell, and none of them can be regarded as an adherent of the Puritan ethics.

Seth Ward, a friend of Wilkins, was an obstinate Cavalier. He was ousted, as an uncapitulating Royalist, from his fellowship at Cambridge. The perverse Anthony Wood, however, alleged that the expulsion was "for a good cause," that the ribald verses were accurate:

> For what hee of the tenants receives
> He payes againe unto their wives.

Ward managed, nonetheless, at the cost of an oath of loyalty, to secure the Savilian Professorship of Astronomy at Oxford. His Royalist friends meanwhile promised him that, upon the return of happier days, his loyalty would be rewarded with ecclesiastical preferment. With the Restoration, indeed, Ward was honored with a deanery and two bishoprics. Theology did not oppress him, however, and he was kindly inclined toward Hobbes' materialism. But when that dour figure exceeded good judgment in his assault upon the universities, pronouncing them subversive and backward, Seth Ward took up a polemical cudgel of reply in his *Vindiciae Academiarum* of 1654.

Seth Ward was a staunch anti-Puritan. In 1644, together with several Cambridge colleagues, he published a pamphlet directed against the Puritans, *Certain Disquisitions and Considerations Representing to the Conscience the Unlawfulness of the . . . Solemn League and Covenant.* The Puritan government seized and burned the entire edition. When Ward became Dean of Exeter in 1661, he had his turn for reprisal. He expelled the Presbyterians and Independents from the Cathedral, and expended considerable funds for restoring it to its previous beauty. The beautification of the Cathedral and Palace of Salisbury was again Ward's principal concern when he became its Bishop in 1667. He harried dissenters and nonconformists so much that, in a petition to the Privy Council, they said he was ruining their cloth trade. Burnet sums up Ward's character: "He was a profound statesman, but a very indifferent clergyman." [19]

Matthew Wren, Christopher's nephew, was an ardent Cavalier, unswervingly loyal to his father, a Royalist bishop who was imprisoned for many years because of active adherence to the king's cause. In defense of Royalist principles, Matthew wrote a criticism of Harrington's radical *Commonwealth of Oceana*. Harrington answered with a defense of popular government, whereupon Matthew rebutted in 1659 with a book called *Monarchy Asserted*. During the reign of Charles II, Matthew held a series of political posts, and was finally secretary to the Catholic James, Duke of York.[20] Matthew Wren was certainly no Puritan.

Jonathan Goddard was a ship carpenter's son who rose to be an eminent physician, perhaps because all his cures were done with three or four medicines. He became Cromwell's personal physician, and, according to Anthony Ward, his "great confident." This seems, however, to have been due more to his medical talent than to his Puritan character.

> He loved wine and was most curious in his wines, was hospitable, but dranke not to excess, but it happened that comeing from his club at the Crowne taverne in Bloomesbery, a foote, 11 at night, he fell downe dead. . . .

Goddard, the first Englishman to make telescopes, was known as a skilled experimentalist, so that his associates in the Royal Society "made him their drudge, for when any curious experiment was to be donne they would lay the taske on him." He published in 1670 a work in which he pleaded as a utilitarian hedonist with his fellow-doctors to apply their "study to Natural Philosophy, such as is more real and solid in this Age, by many happy Experimental discoveries in Nature." When he lectured in 1648 at the College of Physicians, his theme was how the wisdom and goodness of God were exhibited in the structure of the human body. Politically, however, Goddard was a partisan of Cromwell's, and he served in both the Little Parliament and the Council of State. Later he is said to have concocted and sold secret remedies to Charles II.[21] One gathers he was more a political physician than a man ruled by the Puritan ethic.

Ralph Bathurst was a king's man in spirit and action. Six of his brothers lost their lives in the service of Charles I. Bathurst himself was compelled to relinquish his clerical career at the outbreak of the civil war. He studied medicine, and became a physician. Although he was a known Royalist, he was employed by the parliamentary government as a physician to the sick and wounded in the Navy. He gave good service, but also participated during that time in dangerous illegal clerical activities. He removed the old painted glass from the Oxford library to save it from the parliamentary committee looking for "new popery." With the Restoration of Charles II, he gave up medical practice, and resumed the clerical profession. Bathurst rose to positions of high distinction —the Presidency of Trinity College, the Vice-Chancellorship of Oxford. He was a close friend of Petty, the unsectarian statistician, and was believed to have written laudatory verses concerning the materialist Hobbes. Together with Wren and Boyle, he studied under the Rosicrucian chemist Peter Sthael. He became Chaplain to King Charles II in 1663, and was the Royal Society's president in 1688.[22] The two writings that Bathurst projected were tracts against Puritanism, one a *History of Ceremonies, Together with Their Usefulness, or Rather Necessity in Divine Worship,* the other a *History and Genuine Notion of Preaching,* designed to reduce "the erroneous and superstitious concert of sermons which obtains so among the vulgar. . . ."

Laurence Rooke was Professor of Astronomy at Gresham College in 1652, and subsequently its Professor of Geometry. His character can be surmised only through his choice of intimate friends. Rooke, who died in 1662 at the age of forty, was the good companion of Seth Ward and Christopher Wren. He made the carefree Ward his heir, but stipulated that the persons bound offer their payments willingly, otherwise there was to be no payment. "For," said Rooke, "as I was never in law, or had any contention with any man in my life, neither would I after my death." The Cavalier Ward "gave a pendulum clock to the Royall Society (which goes a weeke) to perpetuate the memory of his deare and learned friend, Mr. Laurence Rooke." This uncontentious man was also valued by the disagreeable, saturnine Hobbes as one of his familiar friends and acquaintances. Rooke was welcome in the king's entourage. The Marquis of Dorchester used to "bring him every Wednesday in his coach to the royal society." Rooke, "*consuetudo facilis et accomoda*," was a fitting co-worker of the free-minded men who conceived the Royal Society.[23]

Lastly, there was Dr. Thomas Willis, a distinguished physician and, in 1660, the Sedleian Professor of Natural Philosophy. Willis, the son of a farmer, actually fought in the ranks of the king's army against Parliament. When Charles II returned to his throne, Willis was rewarded with a professorship. Toward the end of his life, Willis became a critic of the loose morals at court, but the political choice he made during the Civil War was emphatically Royalist. His good friend was Sir Christopher Wren, whose liberal ethics we have already discussed. Wren did several of the engravings in Willis's book on the anatomy of the brain and nervous system. During his lifetime as an anatomist, he made a transition from the metaphysical to the scientific stage. He regretted his youthful treatises, in which he had set forth "unlikely Hypotheses . . . accrued into a certain System of Art and frame of Doctrine." In his maturity, he wrote:

> I determined with myself seriously to enter presently upon a new course, and to rely on this one thing, not to pin my faith on the received Opinions of others, nor on the suspicions and guesses of my own Mind, but for the future to believe Nature and ocular demonstrations.

The touchstone of "ocular demonstration" was part of the new respect for the senses which was characteristic of the psychological revolution and its hedonist-libertarian ethic.[24]

John Wallis

DR. JOHN WALLIS, WHO WAS also among the original founders' circle, was perhaps the foremost mathematician of his time. It would not do to classify him as either Calvinist or Cavalier, for in truth he appears to have been prepared to use for his own advantage whatever happened to be the prevailing ideological wind. Wallis himself put the matter neatly. He wrote in 1697:

> It hath been my lot to live in a time wherein have been many and great changes and alterations. It hath been my endeavour all along to act by moderate principles, between the extremities on either hand, in a moderate compliance with the powers in being.

"Hereby," he concluded, "I have been able to live easy and useful, though not great." Wallis was a brilliant cryptographer, and his services for the parliamentary army were rewarded with a living and a fellowship at Cambridge. Later he claimed that he had concealed vital information from the Parliamentarians. In 1657 Wallis got himself chosen through intrigue as Custodian of the Oxford Archives; he alleged that the elected candidate "had talked against Oliver." A few years later, after the Restoration, he spoke, however, with different purport. Wallis and Hobbes had become embroiled in their celebrated controversy, probably the most malignant debate in which two English thinkers have ever engaged. Wallis charged that the *Leviathan* was "written in defence of Oliver's title, or whoever, by whatsoever means, can get to be upmost." Wallis was now the king's man, appointed a royal chaplain in 1661, in reward for past services, and a commissioner for the revision of the prayer book. Hobbes taunted Wallis for having been a "decipherer" of captured Royalist correspondence—that is, an Oliverian agent. Wallis replied with gibes concerning Hobbes' lowly social origin and lack of a doctor's degree. Each then accused the other of having excreted his arguments.[25]

Wallis wrote an account of the origin of the Royal Society somewhat variant to that of Bishop Sprat. His enumeration of the founders differed in part from Sprat's, and gave a greater importance in the formation of the Royal Society to the Greshamites; but Wallis acknowledged that the meetings at Oxford might have been "conducing" to the emergence of the Royal Society, and he recognized the pre-eminent role of Wilkins and Petty. Wallis, too, described the circle's prohibition of theological discussion, and their meeting at a tavern. Portions of it are vivid with the venturesome flavor of the time:

> I do acknowledge that some years before . . . His Majesties happy Restoration, such Meetings had been at those Lodgings (though

not at that time, viz. in the year 1659) and that those Meetings might be somewhat conducing to that of the Royal Society which now is: But (without disparagement to Bishop Wilkins) not, that the first Ground and Foundation of the Royal Society was there laid. Which I take to be much earlier than those Meetings there.

I take its first Ground and Foundation to have been in London, about the year 1645 (if not sooner) when the same Dr. Wilkins (the Chaplain to the Prince Elector Palatine, in London), Dr. Jonathan Goddard, Dr. Ent (now Sir George Ent), Dr. Glisson, Dr. Scarbrough, (now Sir Charles Scarbrough), Dr. Merrit, with my self and some others met weekly sometimes at Dr. Goddard's Lodgings, sometimes at the Mitre in Wood Street hard by. . . . Where (to avoid diversion to other discourses, and for some other reasons) we barred all Discourses of Divinity, of State Affairs, and of News . . . confining our selves to Philosophical Inquiries . . . as Physick, Anatomy, Geometry, Astronomy, Navigation, Staticks, Mechanicks, and Natural Experiments.

These meetings were removed soon after, to the Bull-head in Cheapside; and (in Term Time) to Gresham-Colledge. . . .

About the years 1648, 1649 some of our Company were removed to Oxford. . . . Those at London . . . met as before. Those of us at Oxford . . . met weekly (for some years) at Dr. Petty's lodgings. . . .[26]

Four new persons appear in Wallis's list of the progenitors of the Royal Society—Doctors Scarbrough, Ent, Glisson, and Merrit. All four, interestingly enough, were physicians, and furthermore, the evidence indicates that at least three of the four were either Royalists or opposed to the Puritan party.

Barrow and Whiston: Lucasian Professors of Mathematics

Apart from the founders of the Royal Society, the most illustrious English scientists of the seventeenth century with unanimity rejected the Calvinist theology and ethics. Newton, Halley, Hooke, and Flamsteed, in their respective ways, made human happiness central to their philosophies. Their God, when they had one, was benevolent, and He imposed no way of asceticism upon human beings.

The Lucasian Professorship, which Newton held, was indeed steeped in heresy. Isaac Barrow, its first incumbent and Newton's teacher, was driven out of Cambridge in 1655 by the intolerance of the Parliamentary partisans. Thomas Barrow, Isaac's father, was a Royalist, and, indeed, held an appointment at Court as the king's linen draper. Isaac Barrow, too, was steadfast in his Royalist convictions. He returned to Cambridge in 1659, after Cromwell's death.

Appointed in 1662 as Professor of Geometry at Gresham College, London, Barrow in his inaugural oration gave praise to geometry as "the fecund parent of many arts . . . the perennial spring of benefits to human commerce," the means whereby "we delight our eyes with fine pictures and our ears with harmonious sounds." Barrow paid tribute to God the Geometer—"O Lord, how great a Geometer art Thou!"—but he went on not to denigrate the human mathematical achievement, but to declare that "the human brain has succeeded here in achieving something—nay, something vast and wonderful—nothing more wonderful. . . . For this, then, I rejoice to love Thee." Barrow's anti-Calvinism was almost as pronounced as his anti-Catholicism. In his theological works, he denounced "the bold and blind Bayards who, usually out of self-conceit, are so exceedingly confident of their election and salvation," and attacked Calvin's "notion" as "very uncomfortable" because it rejected "every man from the company of believers who is either ignorant or doubtful" concerning "his final state." Puritans disliked not only what Barrow said but how he said it; they regarded his practice of reading his sermons from manuscript as a "heinous crime." When he was appointed Lecturer in Humanity at Cambridge, Barrow told his pupils his unascetic philosophy of education:

> You will not be expected to torture your tender brains by having to unravel any Aristotelian knots. . . . Attic honey, milk from the swelling breasts of the Muses, and wholesome juices of wisdom pressed from the ever-verdant olive of Minerva, will be set before you for your morning refreshment. Of all the authors whom we

> might read together, I have chosen Ovid . . . with his inexhaustible copiousness of invention, his perspicuity of meaning, his sumptuous store of stories. . . .

In his youthful M.A. thesis, written in 1652, Barrow hailed "our own times" as those in which "human minds seemed to be aroused out of a natural slumber."

Newton's teacher regarded himself as a follower of Francis Bacon; when he rejected Descartes's physical hypotheses, it was as a disciple of

> . . . the supreme champion on this battlefield, our own Verulam, a man of indisputable judgment and repute, who damned this philosophy before it was born. For several times in his *Organum* he most carefully warned us against all such general hypotheses. . . .[27]

If we look for a lineage to Newton's famous maxim, "*Hypotheses non fingo*," it will take us through his teacher Barrow to Francis Bacon, and the underlying psychology of the hedonist-libertarian recovery of the sense of reality.

William Whiston, Newton's successor, was likewise expelled from the professorship in 1710. He was persecuted, Whiston said, "for the very same Christian doctrines, which the great Sir Isaac Newton had discovered and embraced many years before," and for which Newton would have been similarly treated "had he ventured as plainly and openly to publish them to the world. . . ." Whiston had no use for Calvinist principles. The "original . . . fundamental doctrines of Christianity," he held, did not include any dogma of predestination. Rather, they contain a belief in "God's dealing with Men according to their Works only, and not according to Election and Reprobation." Peter, wrote Whiston, knew nothing of "calling and Election. . . ." Calvin had disregarded the plain Scriptural sense "to the unspeakable Mischief of the Church of Christ. . . ." As for Paul's doctrines of original sin, they seem, said Whiston, "to have been no Part of Christ's Revelation to him; but rather certain Reasonings of his own accommodated to the weak Roman Jews at that time only." [28] This was the radical rejection of Calvinist theology which Newton evidently shared with Whiston.

☙ Isaac Newton

ISAAC NEWTON, GREATEST OF SCIENTISTS, suspicious, morbidly sensitive to criticism, detesting the competitive strife among scientists, withholding his discoveries, presents an extraordinary enigma.* Freud might have found in him a worthy challenge to all his powers of insight. Newton could give vent to the most extraordinary suspicion, as when he wrote to John Locke in 1693:

> Being of an opinion that you endeavoured to embroil me with women and by other means, I was so much affected with it, that when one told me you were sickly and would not live, I answered 'twere better if you were dead.

Newton suffered a severe nervous breakdown in middle age—"Newton's madness," it was called. He recovered, but only to make science henceforth a secondary, and even tangential, activity in his life; he assumed in 1696 the Wardenship of England's Mint.[29] What was the underlying cause of Newton's collapse? According to another Cambridge man, John Maynard Keynes, Newton's genius was sacrificed to the intellectual repressions that were still part of English academic and religious life. Keynes dipped into the more than a million words, much still unpublished, that Newton wrote on religious questions. He then reported an intellectual tragedy:

> Very early in life Newton abandoned orthodox belief in the Trinity. . . . He was rather a Judaic monotheist of the school of Maimonides. . . . But this was a dreadful secret which Newton was at desperate pains to conceal all his life. It was the reason why he refused Holy Orders, and therefore had to obtain a special dispensation to hold his Fellowship and Lucasian Chair, and would not be Master of Trinity. Even the Toleration Act of 1689 excepted anti-Trinitarians. . . . It was a blot on Newton's record that he did not murmur a word when Whiston, his successor to the Lucasian Chair, was thrown out of his professorship and out of the University for publicly avowing opinions which Newton had secretly held for upwards of fifty years past. That he held this heresy was a further aggravation of his silence and secrecy and inwardness of disposition.[30]

* Cf. Appendix B: The Enigma of Newton, p. 411.

Newton, like the philosopher Locke, remained within the Church of England. But we cannot attach much weight to the formal religious affiliations of scientists in the seventeenth century. In an age when men cannot speak their opinions freely, a formal religious adherence is often an indication of a desire not to be molested rather than a sign of belief. Heresy, heterodoxy, and even atheism were rampant among men of science, who were prudent enough to reserve their opinions for the private hearing of their friends. Newton, according to Louis T. More, was deeply affected between 1642 and 1660 by the Protestantism of the Commonwealth. The editor of Newton's theological manuscripts, H. McLachlan, however, affirms that "there is no evidence that in early manhood Newton underwent any conversion in his religious and political opinions," He remained impervious to Puritan influences, though he shared their hostility to Roman Catholicism. Newton was an Arian, or as we would say today, a Unitarian. Jesus, to his mind, was a prophet only, and not of God's substance; Jesus's claim to pre-eminence was solely in the immediacy of his message. Therefore, said Newton, "We need not pray to Christ to intercede for us. If we pray the Father aright, he will intercede." [31]

Newton was evidently in his Cambridge years indifferent to the social world and its pleasures; all his energies were concentrated on science. In later years, he enjoyed "agreeable company" and discussions at the Grecian Coffee-House.[32] In principle, Newton would have subscribed to the ethics of happiness; his philosophical spokesman, Samuel Clarke, was a theological hedonist.[33]

Newton's philosophy is generally regarded as allied to that of the Cambridge Platonists. Cambridge Platonism arose, says the historian F. J. Powicke, from the workings of the "law of reaction" against Calvinism, which had had a considerable strength toward the end of the sixteenth century. "The very stringency of Puritan and Calvinist rule would tend to create exceptions to it, and drive men of an independent or antipathetic temper into revolt." The Cambridge Platonists were especially repelled by the dogma of predestination, which they found incompatible with their faith in the absolute goodness of God. Ralph Cudworth, the most learned of the Cambridge men, wrote that he found it impossible to believe that God for his mere pleasure would damn men to eternal torments for no fault of their own. Benjamin Whichcote, Vice-

Chancellor of the university, spoke for his fellow-Platonists when he rejected the dismal Calvinist view of human nature; God, said Whichcote, did not make "a sorry worthless piece fit for no use, when he made man." "*Non sum Christianus alicuius nominis*" ("I am not a Christian of any denomination"), said Whichcote to a friend who sought to bring him back to Puritanism. The Cambridge Platonists were highly selective in what they took from Plato, and indeed they reconstructed the Platonic philosophy to accord with their needs. They made "love the central motive of God and for man," and held out "a welcoming hand" to the "New Philosophy" of Francis Bacon, with its homely appeal to sense perception.[34] The classical Platonist denigration of the lowly sensory facts was absent from their perspective. Their Platonism was a cosmic poetry touched with empiricism, and suffused with benevolence.

As a Cambridge man, Newton became an intimate friend of the philosopher and poet Henry More, inspirer of their philosophic circle. Newton's speculation that space was "the boundless, uniform sensorium of God" was probably derived from More's writings. More's Platonism was a cosmological hedonism. In 1646 he wrote a poem, *Democritus Platonissans: or An Essay Upon the Infinite of Worlds*, whose excited, intense verse has been described by Marjorie Nicolson as a burst of "praise of the new freedom which comes to man from the conception [of infinity]." More wrote poems on his "enlarg'd delight" in the "unbounded joys" in the "boundless universe"; he was moved by "an all spreaden love to the vast Universe."

> Then all the works of God with close embrace,
> I dearly hug in my enlargèd arms.

God became for More the kind guarantor of human knowledge; "then all the inquisitions after knowledge are as safe as sweet," he wrote his correspondent Anne Conway, and man presses forth "in divine joy and triumph, praysing God in all his works." Devoted to Anne Conway, as Swift was to Stella, More, for nearly thirty years, "labored" for her approbation.[35]

The ethic of the Cambridge Platonists was thus the mildly Epicurean one—"a good mind and a good life." More, "an apostate from Calvinism," held that the human passions are good, provided that their satisfaction is in accordance with the laws of nature. He put this hedonism in mystical terminology, saying that nature's law is "a whisper of the divine law." He had small use for the Puritans. All through the years of Cromwell's rule, he defiantly used the Anglican Book of Common Prayer. His friends and relatives were Royalists, and he himself was overjoyed when Charles II was restored to the throne. "I am above all Sects whatsoever as Sects," said More. "For I am a true and free Christian. . . ." The Cambridge fellows generally were hardly an ascetic lot. For a while, they actually hesitated about giving Henry More a fellowship because it was rumored he was "a melancholy man." But when his friends showed that "he was very fond of entertaining people to a cup of ale, wine, or sack, and a song on the theorbo," the difficulty was overcome. Platonism for the Cambridge thinkers was, beginning with Whichcote, a philosophic instrument for attacking "the barren dogmatism of the Calvinists." [36]

Although the personality of Newton is in many respects an enigma, one important phase of his personal life reveals an underlying sympathy on his part for the hedonistic ethic. Newton evidently departed so far from the Protestant ethic that he accepted with equanimity and even approbation his niece's liaison with a man known as a notorious libertine. Newton's biographers have long puzzled over the nature of this relationship of Newton's favorite niece, Catherine Barton, to Newton's benefactor, Lord Halifax. Voltaire echoed mistaken gossip when he said that Newton owed his appointment as Master of the Mint to the fact that his niece had won the favor of Halifax, the Chancellor of the Exchequer. It seems clear, however, that Catherine Barton, who had for several years been in Newton's household, did later live with Halifax "in some capacity," as Louis T. More says, for about nine years. Halifax left her a comfortable legacy "as a small recompense," as he wrote in his will, "for the pleasure and happiness I have had in her conversation." The word "conversation" was commonly used in the early eighteenth century to signify sexual intercourse. Halifax, "almost universally characterized as a shameless libertine," was nonetheless Newton's close and admired friend.

Newton's biographers, who have sometimes lacked objectivity in their accounts, have preferred to think that Halifax was secretly married to Catherine; it was, they surmise, to avoid ridicule for his marriage to a woman from a parvenu family that he chose to keep their union secret. The brilliant Victorian logician, De Morgan, first proposed this theory to "exonerate," as far as he could, Newton's reputation:

> The more anyone reads of the social life of the time of Anne, the more will he feel that no inference can be drawn by help of impressions derived from the manners of our own day. The first elements of decency were engaged in a reactive struggle with ungodly brutality, itself a reaction against the godly brutality of the Puritans. The reigning school of life delighted to call itself "The Town"; just as all the vice and all the meanness which is now tolerated delights to call itself "The World." There was a great deal of religion afloat, but it was, in all ranks, much tinctured by a principle of relaxation. . . . Few men of fashion could bear the satire of the coffeehouse gang, which may have formed the larger part of genteel society, but which at any rate, by its noise and impudence, appeared to be the larger part. Nothing was so ridiculous, so utterly below a man of condition, as an unequal marriage.

And Newton, according to De Morgan, was sufficiently a man of the world to join with his friend Halifax in concealing the marriage to his niece from the "coffeehouse gang":

> He [Newton] was very much the man of the world; he stuck to the main chance, and knew how to make a cast. He took good care of his money, and left a large fortune, though very—even magnificently—liberal on suitable occasions, especially to his family.

In both theories concerning the relations of Catherine Barton to Lord Halifax, Newton appears as a man who shared in large measure, at this time of his life, the hedonist outlook of his age. The theory which avers that there was a secret marriage does not quite explain why Halifax did not at least reveal in his will after his death the true state of the facts. He would have been beyond the wits' ridicule, and have then spared Catherine the public reference to her in the language reserved for mistresses. This theory would require us to have Newton acquiescing to his favorite niece being regarded in people's eyes as Halifax's mistress simply to help Halifax's way among his fellow-libertines. There is a letter in which Newton, in declining a social invitation after Halifax's death, refers evasively to "the circumstances in which I stand related to his family." Nothing would have been easier than for Newton to have said plainly that he had to remain for the funeral of his niece's husband, and the circumlocutory evasion seems to be a way of indicating the truth—that Catherine was Halifax's mistress—in a way less offensive to Newton himself. In any case, Newton was prepared to accept the practice of the hedonist-libertarian ethic of his time; he engaged in no moralistic reproach.[37]

Halley and Flamsteed

WITHOUT THE CAJOLERY and encouragement of Edmond Halley, the epoch-making *Principia* of Isaac Newton would never have been written. He was, as De Morgan said, "the guardian angel of the work." When Halley, then Astronomer Royal, learned how much progress Newton had made on the problem of gravitation, he prodded him for further publication, brought to bear the urging of the Royal Society, then saw the manuscript through the press, and paid for the cost of printing. No wonder Newton said to Halley that the *Principia* was "your book."

Now, Halley was a hedonistic skeptic—indeed, probably an unbeliever. Bishop Rawlinson called Halley "a *very* free thinker"; Halley ridiculed the arguments that a religious-minded friend adduced against atheism. This reputation was the cause for Halley's failure to secure the vacant Savilian Chair of Astronomy in 1691. As Whiston wrote:

> Mr. Halley was then thought of . . . to be in a mathematick professorship at Oxford; and bishop Stillingfleet was desired to recommend him at court; but learning that he was a skeptick, and a banterer of religion, he scrupled to be concern'd. . . . But Mr. Halley was so sincere in his infidelity, that he would not so much as pretend to believe the Christian religion, tho he thereby was likely to lose a professorship; which he did accordingly. . . .

Halley was a man of courage and determination. At the age of twenty-one, he had gone to the ocean-isolated island of St. Helena for two years to chart the Southern Stars. He immortalized Charles II by naming a constellation Charles' Oak. Jovial, almost boisterous, Halley on occasion would express his irreverence in colorful language. When Whiston once declined to drink wine with him, Halley told him he "had a Pope in his belly." Puritanism cannot by any exercise of terminology claim Edmond Halley among its own.[38]

John Flamsteed, unlike Halley, was a genuinely religious man. Illness pursued him all his life. At the age of fourteen, in 1660, "it pleased God," he tells us, "to inflict a weakness in my knees and joints upon me." He was too frail to pursue the clerical career he desired. He acquiesced in God's decision, and went on to a life of distinguished scientific service. The grandson of an ironmonger, Flamsteed had literally grown up with a telescope; he became the first Astronomer of the Greenwich Royal Observatory. It was to Flamsteed that Newton turned in 1685 and 1686 for the observations on Jupiter and Saturn that he needed for his *Principia*.

There were gentle colors in Flamsteed's conception of the Deity. God's wish, he wrote, is that man "add (if it might be) some lustre, grace, or conveniency to that place which, as well as he, derived its original from the Creator." He did not conceive of work as a burden which man, in his guilt, must bear. There is a joy in work, in the activity of creation, says Flamsteed. Even in Paradise, Adam would "till, prune, and dress his pleasant verdant habitation" to avoid the tedium of "idleness." We, who are Adam's heirs, observe "that those are generally worst employed who have least to do. . . ." By working, wrote Falmsteed, I "recreate myself." Work is not irksome, it is not a curse. Gone is the Calvinist conception of man predestined to toil by the sweat of his brow. Rather, work is the opportunity for "man's active soul" to express itself.[39]

☙ Robert Hooke

ROBERT HOOKE WAS SOMETHING of a gadfly to Isaac Newton, whom he provoked by criticism into tackling the problem of gravitational synthesis. Hooke was the Curator of the Royal Society, to which post he was recommended after he had "contriv'd and perfected the Air-Pump for Mr. Boyle."

"There can be no doubt," write his editors, "that Hooke was the one man who did most to shape the form of the new Society and to maintain its active existence. Without his weekly experiments and prolific work the Society could scarcely have survived, or, at least, would have developed in a quite different way. It is scarcely an exaggeration to say that he was, historically, the creator of the Royal Society." He had an extraordinary mechanical knack; his father, not thinking him otherwise endowed, had meant him to be a watchmaker's apprentice. Hooke nevertheless managed to get to Oxford. The workingman's touch remained with him, however. To the embarrassment of some of his later colleagues in the Royal Society, Hooke regarded as among his friends and collaborators a motley group of contractors, plumbers, and instrument makers.

Hooke thrived in the atmosphere of the coffeehouses, which Calvinist critics condemned as "nurseries of Idleness and Pragmaticalness," and which Richard Bentley later assailed as rife with atheism. Hooke used to meet his personal friends and listen to stories at Jon's, used to foregather with Wren or Halley at Child's, while the rest of "the gang," as the elite of the Royal Society was known, could generally be found cheerfully holding forth at Pontack's or Jeremy's. "Great drinkers of coffee" was the way one pamphleteer characterized Hooke and Wren, and the list of coffeehouses Hooke frequented was, indeed, imposing. His diary entries record sessions at Atkins, Bill, Bird's, Carolina, Cheapside, Child's, Coleman St., Cropper's, Jonathan's, Leonnard's, Man's, Pontack's, Rainbow, Sam's, Tom's, Tarts, Vigors, and Virgines. During the years from 1672 to 1680, indeed, Hooke's diary recorded doings of himself and his friends at no less than a hundred and fifty-three taverns and coffeehouses. There they could gather, talk science, gossip, hear the latest news and rumors, sip their coffee, chocolate, tea, or cider, according to the season, and, in winter, sit by a great fire, and smoke for two hours, all for only twopence and the costs of one's drinks. "With Sir Ch. Wren . . . to the Playhouse Saw Tempest," is a typical entry in Hooke's *Diary*. Hooke was a man of the Restoration, pleasure-loving and gregarious. A succession of his maids—Nell Young, Doll Lord, Betty Orchard—were also his successive mistresses, for periods varying from four to fourteen months, but always with an unconcern for theological reproach.

Hooke was content with religious conventionalities. His early biographer tried to picture Hooke as devout: "He always exprest a great Veneration for the eternal and immense Cause of all Beings, as may be seen in very many Passages in his Writings." Hooke, he continues, never made an important discovery, "without setting down his Acknowledgment to the Omnipotent Providence, as many places in his Diary testify, frequently in these or the like words, abbreviated thus, D O M G M. . . ." The Oxford volume of the *Diary*, however, contains only four references to "D O M G," two of which occur on his birthday; the letters stand for the conventional phrase "*Deo omnipotente meae Aetatis Gracias*." Compared to the long array of coffeehouses, the religious entries seem entirely unimpressive. The hedonist in Hooke had a daily ascendancy. Although a parson's son, Hooke eschewed religious controversies. His philosophy was, in his simple statement, "to doe good to friends while Alive." [40]

To the Calvinist, man fell when Adam tasted the forbidden apple, and only God's grace could help him. To Robert Hooke, however, scientific research was a practical way of undoing original sin. There was no edict of predestination:

> And as at first, mankind fell by tasting of the forbidden Tree of Knowledge [says Hooke], so we, their Posterity, may be in part restor'd by the same way, not only by beholding and contemplating but by tasting too those fruits of Natural Knowledge, that were never yet forbidden.

Man can save himself by science—that was the simple theology of the Curator of the Royal Society.

Calvinist doctrine, furthermore, stressed man's natural infirmities, the weakness of the flesh, the frailty of the senses. Hooke, the skilled technician, held, however, that the use of scientific instruments would make up for the limitations of the human organism.

> By the addition of such artificial Instruments and methods [he wrote], there may be, in some manner, a reparation made for the mischiefs, and imperfection, mankind has drawn upon itself . . . whereby every man, both from a deriv'd corruption, innate and born with him, and from his breeding and converse with men, is very subject to slip into all sorts of errors.

It was Hooke's faith as a scientist that "the World may be assisted with a variety of Inventions" at the same time as man's senses "may be wonderfully benefited by it, and may be guided to an easier and more exact performance of their Offices."

In this spirit, Hooke, like his colleagues in the Royal Society, hailed the Restoration for the happiness it brought England. His *Micrographia*, in 1665, began with a warm Dedicatory Epistle to Charles II:

> Amidst the many felicities that have accompanied Your Majesties happy Restauration and Government, it is none of the least considerable that Philosophy and Experimental Learning have prosper'd under your Royal Patronage.

And among the "felicities" to which the Royal Society was devoted were "the Improvement of Manufactures and Agriculture, the Increase of Commerce, the Advantage of Navigation."

The linkage of science to the tradesmen of England, affirmed Hooke, was helping to liberate "the Mechanick Arts" from their subterranean dwelling among the lowly artisans. Hooke had an especial encomium for the businessman Sir John Cutler, who had seen "that the Arts of Life have been too long imprison'd in the dark shops of Mechanicks themselves," and had endowed a Lectureship to bring them to the light of day. The merchants' interest in science was a good omen, wrote Hooke; "their attempt will bring Philosophy from words to Action, seeing the men of Business have had so great a share in their first foundation." [41]

Thus the human senses were rising from their hitherto humble status. The skilled artisan might hope to find his place in the Royal Society. The senses touch and sight, his homely specialties, rose with him. It was an age of social mobility and epistemological mobility, too. With the spread of the hedonistic spirit, the senses took a place at least the equal of intellect and intuition as a means to knowledge, while revelation was largely superseded.

Coffeehouses and Scientific Women

The coffeehouse, the cradle of the Royal Society, was an institution of immense political and social significance in its time. When the English scientists drank their coffee, they were partaking in a rite of communion with the liberal spirit of their times.

Coffee was first imbibed at Oxford by Royalist hedonists, and the beverage for many years was associated with this social flavor. A Jew, Jacob, opened in 1650 the first coffeehouse in England; it "was, by some who delighted in noveltie, drank." Those were gloomy days at Oxford, for the scholars were undergoing the purges of a loyalty-oath regime; they were, moreover, under orders to refrain from such vanities as sportsmen's clothes, powdering their hair, wearing ribands, and keeping hounds and horses. Coffee-drinking was among the lesser vanities, and evoked many a Puritan diatribe. The first coffee-drinker, Conopius, was, indeed, "expelled [from] the university by the barbarians—I mean the Parliamentary Visitors," wrote Wood.

Nonetheless, a society of young students in the year 1655 encouraged an apothecary, Arthur Tillyard, known as a "Great Royallist," to sell "coffey publickly in House against all Soules College." Coffee-drinking found its protective alma mater in a college that had strenuously resisted "the reforming zeal of the Puritans." The members of this earliest coffee club included names that were later among the founders of the Royal Society—the Royalist Wren family, Christopher, Matthew, and Thomas; Peter Pett, who became Advocate-General to Charles II; and William Bull (probably William Balle), who was a companion in a "mad frolic." Their companion, John Lamphire, a physician, was a "natural Droll," "free from pharisaical leven," who had been ejected from his fellowship.

Coffeehouses soon multiplied. The coffeehouse was a place where one could escape the political and religious passions of the Commonwealth. It became an oasis of freedom of speech. As Charles II was later reminded, "the king's friends had used more liberty of speech in those places than they durst do in any other." Here, speculative politicians could retire "to talk Nonsense by themselves about State Affairs." Above all, Puritans were outraged by the utter worldliness, vanity, and carefreeness of the coffeehouse men:

> Beau Fools in Clusters here Resort
> And are so saucy grown,
> They'll ask my lord, What News from Court?
> Who smiles, and Answers none.

To be inform'd few caring less
But ask as 'tis the Mode;
No knowledge seek, but how to Dress;
Their Taylor is their god.

When a proposal was made in 1673 that the coffeehouses be closed, it proponents availed themselves of the Puritan critique. The coffeehouses, they said, "have undone many of the king's subjects, for they being great enemies to diligence and liberty, have been the ruin of many serious and hopeful young gentlemen and tradesmen," who sit "talking three or four hours"—indeed, with renewed breath, "five or six hours together"—"all of which time their shops . . . their business . . . their servants . . . their customers' have been alike neglected!" Another critic complained sadly that coffee, tea, and chocolate were subversive forces, for their drinkers decry their rulers, magnify "their own parts, knowledge and wisdom," all of which "may prove pernicious and destructive." The first coffeehouse at Cambridge was described like its Oxonian counterpart, as a place where

> . . . Scholars are so greedy after News (which is none of their business) that they neglect all for it . . . a vast loss of Time grown out of a pure Novelty; for who can apply close to a subject with his Head full of the Din of a Coffee House?

Things came to such a pass that the university in 1664 forbade its undergraduates from going to the coffeehouses unless escorted by their tutors. Whereupon a member of the Royal Society came stoutly to the defense of the coffeehouses, saying that they were as good as the university itself, "that coffeehouses had improved useful knowledge, as much as they [the universities] have. . . ." [42]

The search for pleasure and freedom, however, was what was most distinctive in the coffeehouses. Their philosophy found characteristic expression in two pamphlets that were exchanged in polemical warfare in 1674. For this was an age of pamphlet battles, and the two pamphlets in question, *The Womens Petition Against Coffee* and *The Mens Answer to the Womens Petition Against Coffee* were missiles wrought in a language free and sensual, so that one historian held them "so vulgar and obscene" as to resist quotation. The spokeswoman for her sex charged that coffee-men were remiss as husbands. She said that the power of "this ugly Turkish

Enchantress," this "little base, black, thick, nasty, bitter, nauseous Puddle water," was such as to render their men impotent. Coffee has "Eunucht our Husbands and Crippled our more kind Gallants," deprived the "Codpiecepoint of its Charm" so that "their Ammunition is wanting." The Woman in the Nuptial Bed, said the writer sadly, meets no more "Sprightly Embraces" to "Answer the Vigor of her Flames."

The spokesman for the male sex replied with a powerful hedonistic rebuttal.

> Coffee [he said] collects and settles the Spirits, makes the erection more Vigorous, the Ejaculation more full, adds a spiritualescency to the Sperme, and renders it more firm and suitable to the Gusto of the womb, and proportionate to the ardours and expectations too, of the female Paramour.

The spokesman appealed to the facts of the comparative anthology of sexual prowess.

> Coffee is the general Drink throughout Turkey, yet no part of the world can boast more able or eager performers, than those Circumcised Gentlemen, who (like our modern Gallants) own no other joys of Heaven, than what consists in Veneral Titillations.[43]

The men of the Royal Society took no part in this particular debate, but their allegiance to the coffeehouse, with its atmosphere of freedom, was firm and unshaken.

The Puritans, sorely perturbed by these gathering places in which, as Wood said, men "spend all their time; and in entertainments," tried to place them under a social ban. One Puritan mayor, for instance, in 1680 ordered all the coffeehouses to be closed on Sundays. But even Puritans had to bend before the historical inevitability of the "bitter black drink." Gradually, they began to devise an ideology of accommodation to the coffeehouses. Puritans tasted of the forbidden beverage, and found it good. Presumably no Eve ministered to their downfall; rather, they themselves began to assemble in a "coffee-academy instituted . . . for the advance of Gazett Philosophy." The gazette philosophy—this was how they aptly denoted the merely temporal and temporary, the here and now, which was supplanting the eternal and everlasting, the otherworldly philosophy. It began to be observed that coffee was conducive to the virtues of business and industry, for "whereas formerly Apprentices and clerks" were rendered by their morning drinks of ale, beer, or wine "unfit for business," coffee, on the contrary, was a "wakeful and civil drink," and its innovator worthy of "much respect of the whole Nation." But evidently the commercial virtues did not exhaust the charms of coffee. She made men happy. In the soothing aroma of the coffeehouse, even Presbyterians became cheerful, "though their cause is well-nigh desperate out of doors." The democracy of the coffeehouse, moreover, brought a truce to the political and class conflicts of the time. The equality of classes was celebrated in the verse of *The Rules and Orders of the Coffee House:*

> First, Gentry, Tradesmen, all are welcome hither,
> And may without affront sit down together;
> Pre-eminence of place, none here should mind,
> But take the next fit seat that he can find:
> Nor need any, if Finer Person come,
> Rise up to assigne to them his room; . . .
> Let Noise of loud disputes be quite forborn. . . .
> On Sacred Things, let none presume to touch. . . .[44]

Such then were the coffeehouses—centers of free thought and the free life, where the smoke of religious and partisan debate was dispelled by the taste and smell of coffee. The hedonistic movement had found its symbolic beverage—not the torpor of whiskey's escape, but the sharp stimulant of the drink which could be endlessly consumed. And in the coffeehouses, the English scientists found their meeting places and conventicles.

Excluded from the coffeehouses, women, however, achieved in other places a new unwonted eminence. The hedonistic ethics that presided over the origins of modern science also promoted the entry of women into scientific life. Women's participation in scientific readings and pursuits became part of their social role in the salon. The Duchess of Newcastle early managed to get herself invited to a meeting of the Royal Society, at which she was shown sundry instruments and experiments. In 1663, the Duchess indeed came out in favor of the education of women. Her argument was much the same as the one John Stuart Mill used two centuries later. Englishmen, she wrote, were in danger of becoming "Irrational as Idiots . . . through the Careless Neglects and Despisements to the

Female"; women, she added, were confined to idleness "like Birds in Cages, to Hop up and down in Houses." She had called on women the year previously to organize themselves "that we may unite . . . to make our Selves as Free, Happy, and Famous as Men." Her contemporaries called this *femme savante* Mad Madge. Nevertheless, her scientific writings for the female audience, the *Observations Upon Experimental Philosophy* and her scientific utopian romance, *The Description of the New Blazing World*, were infused with the emancipative spirit of the new movement.

The Duchess and her husband had shared the exile of Charles II in Holland, and employed those years to dabble in natural philosophy. The Duchess had meditated how a beautiful lady, as seen under a microscope, "would not only have no Lovers, but be rather a Monster of Art. . . ." She wrote poems concerning other worlds and distant stars, the compass and the microscope. The Duchess was not alone in her scientific and artistic activities. The decade of the 1650's saw these interests burgeoning in the bosoms of many distinguished ladies—Mrs. Philips, Mary North, Dorothy Osborne, Margaret Blagge, Lady Pakington, the Countess of Warwick, and Mrs. Hutchinson. No gloomy Calvinist matrons, they were Restoration women who restored science together with the life of the senses.[45]

Manifestoes of Thomas Sprat and Joseph Glanvill

THE UNDERLYING HEDONISTIC ETHICS of English science found its most vigorous and comprehensive expression in the classical work of Thomas Sprat, *The History of the Royal Society*. Sprat took orders in 1660, served as Prebendary until 1669 at Lincoln Cathedral, and rose in 1684 to be Bishop of Rochester. As the Society's spokesman, Sprat undertook to reply to the proponents of the austere ethics of asceticism, and to justify the scientific movement in terms of its contributions to earthly human happiness.

The advocates of asceticism regarded science with hostility. The ascetic divines, writes Sprat, tell us that Scientific studies will interfere with "the mortifying of our Earthly desires."

> And here the men of retyr'd and severe devotion are the loudest: For they tell us, that we cannot conquer and despise the World while we study it so much; that we cannot have sufficient leisure to reflect on another life, while we are so taken up about the Curiosities of this. . . .

Sprat replies that genuine religion is consistent with the hedonistic way of life:

> . . . the true and unfain'd Mortification is not at all inconsistent with men's consulting of their happiness in this world, or being emploi'd about earthly affairs. The honest pursuit of the conveniences, decences, and ornaments of a mortal condition . . .

is not contradictory to Christian duty. Christian virtues, Sprat holds, are not exhausted by faith and repentance; there are other divine graces, "Charity, Affability, Friendship, and Generosity. . . ." Scriptures, he affirms, are

> . . . to be understood in a moderate sense. . . . Seeing the Law of Reason intends the happiness and security of mankind in this life; and the Christian Religion pursues the same ends, both in this and a future life. . . .

The state of Grace is misconceived, says Sprat, when it is believed to require men to "cast away all the thoughts and desires of humanity." Was not Jesus himself concerned with helping people to be happy?

The men of the Royal Society, Sprat declares, don't meddle with "divine things." If they did, "they would be in danger of falling into talking, instead of working, which they carefully avoid." Rather, they seek to advance human happiness much as Jesus did: they

> . . . here may behold the Whole Doctrine of Future Happiness, introduc'd by the same means; by feeding the Hungry, by curing the Lame, and by opening the eyes of the Blind: All of which may be called Philosophical Works, perform'd by an Almighty hand.

The scientists study Nature to increase the joys of living: "they wander, at their pleasure: In the frame of Mens bodies, the ways for strong, healthful, and long life: In the Arts of Mens Hands, those that either Necessity, convenience, or delights have produc'd. . . ." Nature is studied for "the uses of humane society." [46] Sprat adds incidentally that the Wisdom and Power of God are appreciated as one perceives the order and workmanship of his Creatures. But with this almost ritualistic remark, he quits theology; a statement or two has served to safeguard against inquisitorial divines.

The angry, fruitless religious disputations of the civil war, Sprat rejoiced, could now be forgotten. A new age had come with the Restoration of Charles II, one in which Englishmen could work for their well-being:

> But now since the King's return, the blindness of the former Ages, and the miseries of the last are vanished away: now men are generally weary of the Relicks of Antiquity, and satiated with Religious Disputes: now not only the eyes of men, but their hands are open, and prepar'd to labour: Now there is a universal desire, and appetite after knowledge, after the peaceable, the fruitful, the nourishing Knowledge: and not after that of antient Sects, which only yielded hard indigestible arguments, or sharp contentions instead of food.

Now that the minds, hands, and eyes of Englishmen had been freed from the Calvinist yoke, England could be made beautiful and comfortable. ". . . Since the King's return," said Sprat, "there have been more Acts of Parliament, for the clearing and beautifying of Streets, for the repayring of Highways, for the increase of Manufactures. . . ." Not only was Sprat's ethic one of liberated utilitarian and aesthetic values. He rejoiced in science with a patriot's love of country. The Royal Society, he wrote, "proposes an infallible course to make England the glory of the Western World." The greater glory of God was being superseded among the avowed motivations of English scientists.

The scientific temper, Sprat affirmed, is not the child of asceticism and dogma; it is the offspring of freedom and doubt. "The present Inquiring Temper of this Age was at first produc'd by the liberty of judging, and searching, and reasoning, which was us'd in the first Reformation." Sprat, moreover, was alert to the economic promise of the new scientific movement. He warned the Church of England "that it is not the best service that can be done to Christianity to place its chief Praecepts so much out of the way, as to make them unfit for men of business." The Church, he declared, should not be "an Enemy to Commerce, Intelligence, Discovery, Navigation, or any sort of Mechanics. . . ." It should not contravene the English genius for these pursuits. At the same time, however, Sprat rejected any ideology of business pragmatism. If science was not the handmaiden of theology, neither was she the mistress of economics. There have been writers who have regarded the Royal Society as simply and exclusively exemplifying the business ideology of the rising middle class of England. Sprat, however, was aware that an overpractical direction of research is self-defeating because it leaves unplanted the pure seed that yields even greater fruit. He was therefore glad that so many of the Royal Society were "gentlemen," members of the leisure class, for this meant that the Society would be impervious to demands that it produce economically profitable results. "Gentlemen" were immune to the pressures of the market place. "By the freedom of their education, the plenty of their estates, and the usual generosity of Noble Bloud, [they] may be well suppos'd to be the most averse from such sordid considerations." Moreover they were also not to be seduced by the groves of academe; neither professors nor pupils, they were free from fears, fealties, and timidities that beset the academic mind. The academic relationship, according to Sprat, "does very much suppress and tame mens Spirits"; it makes for good "Discipline," but not for "free Philosophical Consultation." In short, the purity of science was safeguarded by the ingredient of leisure-class mentality, which "gentlemen" contributed to the Royal Society:

> But, though the society entertains very many men of particular Professions; yet the farr greater Number are Gentlemen, free, and unconfin'd. By the help of this, there was hopefull Provision made against two corruptions of Learning, which have been long complain'd of, but never remov'd: The one, that Knowledge still degenerates to consult present profit too soon; the other, that Philosophers have bin always Masters and Scholars; some imposing, and all the others submitting; and not as equal observers without dependence.
>
> The first of these may be call'd the marrying of Arts too soon; and putting them to generation, before they come to be of Age; and has been the cause of much inconvenience. It weakens their strength; it makes an unhappy disproportion in their increase;

which not the best, but the most gainfull of them flourish. But above all, it diminishes that very profit for which men strive. It busies them about possessing some petty prizes; while Nature it self, with all its mighty Treasures, slips from them. . . .[47]

What informs Sprat's whole work is the spirit of freedom and happiness. He is proud that the merchants of England do not live with that ascetic frugality which characterizes their Dutch competitors: "The Merchants of England live honourably in foreign parts; those of Holland meanly, minding their gain alone. . . ." The English merchants, Sprat boasts, live amply, as befits the descendants of an aristocratic leisure class;

. . . ours . . . having in their behaviour, very much of the Gentility of the Families, from which so many of them are descended: . . . This largeness of ours, and narrowness of their living, does, no doubt, conduce very much to inrich them; and is, perhaps, one of the Reasons why they so easily undersell us: But withall, it makes ours the most capable, as theirs unfit, to promote such an Enterprise, as this of which I am now speaking.

The Calvinist virtues, according to the historian of the Royal Society, do not contribute to the rise of a scientific movement. Asceticism, frugality, and thrift may confer a competitive advantage in the strife of the market but they do not provide the free soil in which science grows.

The Platonic-Calvinist tradition was hostile to the empirical spirit. Its narcissist preoccupation with the soul's salvation had involved a withdrawal of libidinal energies from the natural world. It had deprecated sensory experience as a source of truth, and had elevated pure intellect, unsullied by manual contacts, into the highest form of knowledge. The spokesman of the Royal Society rejected this tradition in words that are a manifesto of empiricism:

It was said of Civil Government by Plato, that then the World will be best rul'd when either Philosophers shall be chosen Kings, or Kings shall have Philosophical Minds. And I will affirm the like of Philosophy; it will then attain of Perfection, when either the Mechanic Labourers shall have Philosophical Heads, or the Philosophers shall have Mechanical Hands. . . .

With the newly found confidence in the senses, there arose the desire for a simple, matter-of-fact language. The men of the Royal

Society wished to get away from the "outlandish phrases" and "fantastical terms" "introduced by our Religious Sects." The new language avoided the pitfalls of the clerical idiom. "Eloquence" said Sprat, "ought to be banished out of all civil societies." The Royal Society

> . . . have exacted from all their members a close, naked, natural way of speaking, positive expressions, clear senses, a native easiness, bringing all things as near the Mathematical plainness as they can, and preferring the language of Artizans, Countrymen, and Merchants, before that of Wits or Scholars.[48]

The language of science was the speech of the senses, bare and unadorned. It did not aim to repress the workaday world, but to express it, in a curious and friendly way. The hedonistic ethics gave men the courage to dare to be empirical.

The free philosophy of the Royal Society was eloquently expounded in still another tract on behalf of science, the *Plus Ultra* of Joseph Glanvill. It was written at the direct behest of the Society's secretary, Henry Oldenburg. For Sprat's book had failed to please all the members, some of whom felt that it had failed to recount the scientific advances achieved by the society. Oldenburg therefore encouraged Glanvill, a vigorous young Oxford graduate, to such a work. Glanvill was the author of a powerful tract, *The Vanity of Dogmatizing* (1661), which had won him a place in the Royal Society. He was provoked in 1666 to enter the literary battle of science when an elderly Puritan divine, Robert Crosse, charged that the Royal Society was a Jesuit conspiracy to destroy the English church, and that its science was far inferior to Aristotle's. When Glanvill rebutted this assertion, the "Grave Man" laid against him "the most dreadful and most injurious censure of Atheism." Glanvill's atheism, he later alleged, was the only "Subject handled on Ale-benches and in Coffee-Houses." Also it was charged "that the Universities are undermined by this new Philosophical Society." Thereupon Glanvill began to write a reply that grew into the *Plus Ultra: or, The Progress and Advancement of Knowledge Since the Days of Aristotle*, published in June, 1668.

If Sprat emphasized the homespun quality of the Society's science, Glanvill more glowingly described its spirit of freedom.

The Royal Society was dedicated, said Glanvill, to the "sweet humors" of the "Free Philosophy." It was a "Great Body of Practical Philosophers," who were modest in temper and secure from the quarrelsome genius. For "the Free and Real Philosophy makes men deeply sensible of the infirmities of humane intellect," wrote Glanvill. The old world of the disputers and scholars had closed the door to questions, and had prided itself on its "Omniscience and Infallibility." But the new Society stood for an "inquisitive World," and had liberated curiosity in "this late Age of Inquiry." The "Free Philosophy," moreover, would promote the happiness of mankind. It would show:

> That the Goods of Mankind may be much increased by the Naturalist's insight into Trades; that the Naturalist may much advantage men, by exciting and assisting their curiosity to discover, take notice, and make use of the home-bred riches and Advantages. . . . That a ground of high expectation from Experimental Philosophy is given, by the happy Genius of this present Age, and the productions of it; That a ground of expecting considerable things from Experimental Philosophy is given by those things which have been found out by illiterate Tradesmen, or lighted on by chance. . . . That the uses of scarce one thing in Nature, to Humane Life, are yet thorowly understood. . . .

In a passage of philosophical autobiography typical of the intellectual self-liberation of many of the "free philosophers," Glanvill told how he had begun to question the "discipline I underwent in my younger days," which had bred in him "a dread of dissenting in the least Article." He had reflected on the diversity of opinions and religions, each of them confident it possessed the truth, though all had "nothing but their education for their inducement." The schoolmen, the Peripatetics, the Aristotelians—what Glanvill called the "notional philosophers"—were similarly bound by their "first education," and were indignant with the free philosophers who had outgrown their "cherry-stones and rattles." The "notional philosophers" continued to dispute about "quiddities and haecceities," "Homogeneities and Heterogeneities," predicaments and predications. "But," said Glanvill, "after I spent some years in those Notional Studies . . . I began to think *cui bono*, and to consider what these things would signifie in the World of Action and Business. . . ." All the followers of the "Free and Experimental Procedure . . . have been very well instructed in the Peripatetick Doctrines which they have deserted, and most of them much better than those who are yet zealous Contenders for them." The "free philosophy," in the fashion of the mechanics and tradesmen, held, with Robert Boyle, "that motion, figure, and disposition of parts, may suffice to produce all the secondary affections of Bodies, and consequently that there is no need of the substantial Forms and Qualities of the Schools." The psychological revolution had indeed strengthened the sense of reality; with the emergence of the hedonist-libertarian ethic, with the disenthrallment of the senses, feelings, and intellect, the non-sensory character of the received "notional philosophy" made it seem empty, useless, a pretentious chatter of words disconnected from realities.

Finally, Glanvill replied to the accusation of atheism. "Narrow, angry people," he observed, "take occasion to charge the freer spirits with Atheism, because they move in a larger Circle," and are not fettered to opinions. But, said he, the fullest arguments for God's existence would finally be provided by the free philosophers, "the humblest and deepest Inquisitors into the works of God." Glanvill's faith consisted of what he called "a few practical Fundamentals." He prided himself on a "modest indifference," which secured "charity for all the diversities of belief," and friendship "to the several Sects and Persuasions, that stick to the plain Principles of the Gospel and a Vertuous Life." Critics charged him with "Scepticism and cold Neutrality." Glanvill replied as befitted the spokesman of the scientific intellectuals; the Scriptures had been written in their time to help those of "Plebeian Capacities," not to bind the minds of the free philosophers. The future belonged to the new "numerous Company of the deep, wary, diligent, and eagle-ey'd Philosophers," who had learned to work as co-operative groups and whose thoughts were rooted in an accumulation of observations.

In our time, when spectacular massive research projects engage people's attention, scientists have regretted the passing of the individual entrepreneurial investigator. The founders of the Royal Society, however, were fascinated by their discovery of the advantages of "group-research teams." "Single inquisitors can receive but scant and narrow informations," wrote Glanvill.[49] Such fellows as Glisson, Willis, and Petty had already headed co-operative research projects before the Society was incorporated. In 1664, eight committees were organized to direct the Society's activities and to see what experiments had to be done. Wilkins worked with Petty, Goddard, and Rooke on the compression of water, and there were committees to study "the rising of liquors in small pipes," the pendulum, waterworks, and the vacuum pump. Wilkins' essay toward a philosophical language was assisted similarly by several co-workers, and was "distinctly a co-operative enterprise," as Dorothy Stimson has said.

A feminine narcissism, according to Glanvill, was the psychological basis of the traditional "notional philosophy," the "Aristotelian philosophy." "The Woman in us," wrote Glanvill in his *The Vanity of Dogmatizing*, "still prosecutes a deceit, like that begun in the Garden: and our Understandings are wedded to an Eve, as fatal as the Mother of our Miseries." "The Gusto of the fond Feminine" seduces our understanding, "for every man is naturally a Narcissus," and when "passion hath the casting voice, the case of Truth is desperate." "Yea, we love nothing but what hath some resemblance within our selves . . . then, the beloved Opinion being thus wedded to the Intellect; the case of the espoused self becomes our own." In short, as we would say, but with a more psychoanalytical overtone, the "notional philosophy" was the outcome of a feminine, masochist asceticism; the reviving healthy sense of reality of the "free philosophers," the scientific movement, had begun with the revolt against this masochist asceticism.[50]

Although himself a clergyman, Joseph Glanvill in his personal ways had moved far from the ethics of Christian asceticism. Samuel Pepys thus tells how, in 1665, he and his friend Captain Cocke went several times to Glanvill's, and "there he and I sat talking with Mrs. Pennington, whom we found undrest in her smocke and petticoats by the fireside, and we drank and laughed. We staid late. . . ." The biographer of Glanvill, Ferris Greenslet, observes discreetly that "the presence of this fascinating Mistress Pennington in Glanvill's house is shrouded in mystery," but that evidently it "was very hospitable, and frequented by genial company."

Glanvill was prepared to acknowledge that our senses were weak and deceptive. Adam's naked eyes had had the power of Galileo's tubes, but we were not in that happy state. Nevertheless, the senses were our one avenue to knowledge. "The knowledge we have comes from our Senses, and the Dogmatist can go no higher for the original of his certainty." Mathematics and the Mechanic Arts owed their "progress" to the fact that they had not allowed a "reverential awe" for the past to displace their respect for their own senses and judgment. Perhaps, said Glanvill, with a terminology that foreshadowed Durkheim, "our purer intellectuals, or only our impetuous affections, were the prime authors of the anomie." [51] It was this anomie of original sin and masochist asceticism that the free philosophers of the Royal Society had in their own lives overcome, as they achieved the clarity of a hedonist-libertarian ethic.

☙ The Scientific Journals

ON MARCH 1, 1664, THE COUNCIL of the Royal Society made a decision far more momentous than it realized. It authorized Henry Oldenburg to publish a scientific periodical which, though his private venture, was under its patronage. The next year the *Philosophical Transactions* commenced publication. The year 1665 ended an era during which the scattered scientific intellectuals had been knit into a community primarily by private letters, with all the loss of time and irregularity that correspondence then involved. The growing new movement of scientific intellectuals had now invented its own form of communication. Monks had written metaphysical tomes; religious revolutionaries and dissenters had published endless pamphlets and sermons; but the new international community of scientific intellectuals created its own distinctive literary form—the scientific journal, printed periodically, with a variety of contributing authors, and administered by editors. Between 1665 and 1730, more than three hundred journals were founded, of which thirty were devoted to the natural sciences; the most important were the *Journal des Sçavans* and the *Philosophical Transactions*, both established in 1665 at Paris and London, respectively, and the *Acta Eruditorum* in Berlin in 1682. Eighteen journals were devoted to the natural sciences generally, eleven were medical, and one specialized in mathematics and physics. Among the scientific journals were one weekly, fifteen monthlies, one bi-weekly, one semi-annual, and five annuals. Only six of the thirty scientific journals were organs of important academies of science. The journals' popularity was immense, their circulations considerable. Many issues were reprinted from two to five times; the *Journal des Sçavans* at times was published like a modern news weekly, with editions in Paris, Amsterdam, Lyon, Cologne, and Leipzig. In Germany, a standard edition evidently ran to a thousand copies. The journals, moreover, printed vernacular summaries of Latin and foreign books. They opened the sciences to the people at large. Cultivated gentlemen and ladies prepared themselves for conversation in their *salons* by subscribing to one of the scientific journals or, better still, to one of the thirty magazines that merely popularized science, or perhaps one of those six that specialized in reprinting the best articles from other journals. By 1721, a contemporary could say "there is scarcely any literature better received by the public, nor read with more eagerness than that of journalists."

The *Journal des Sçavans* in its first issue introduced the novelty of a publication that disclaimed any necessary agreement with its contributors. There was to be no *imprimatur* or *nihil obstat* for the scientific intellectuals. Denis de Sallo, the first editor of the first scientific journal, wrote in the first issue:

> *Personne ne doit trouver estrange de voir icy des opinions différentes des siennes, touchant les sciences, puisqu'on fait profession de rapporter les sentiments des autres sans les garantir. . . .*
>
> (Nobody should find it strange to see here opinions different from his own concerning the sciences, because we aim to report the ideas of others without guaranteeing them. . . .)

Jean Le Clerc, the noted editor from 1686 to 1693 of the *Bibliothèque Universelle et Historique*, which was sold in London and eight Dutch towns, in his latter years looked back with assurance that the truths his magazine had published "*commencent à faire quelque progrès dans le monde, malgré le zèle excessif de ceux qui ne les aiment pas*" ("are beginning to make some progress in the world, despite the excessive zeal of those who don't like them"). He would see only the aurora of this light of Liberty, he wrote, but posterity would see all its glory. Editors could be worried, however, by the rashness of their authors. When Jacques Bernard, editor of *Nouvelles de la République des Lettres*, received in 1700 an essay of Biblical criticism from Desmaizeaux, a follower of

Boyle resident in England, he pleaded with Desmaizeaux that he needed "the prudence of a serpent. We do not dare to speak in this country as in the place where you are." Bernard warned his contributor that "we live in a country where we are not so *libertins* as you are in England." [52] In that word "*libertins*," one had an indication of the underlying hedonist-libertarian ethic of the scientific movement.

Critique of the Puritan Thesis

The picture I have drawn of the influence of the hedonistic ethics on the rise of science in seventeenth-century England is at variance with that presented by several distinguished scholars. Robert K. Merton, for instance, is convinced, as we have mentioned, that the evidence confirms Weber's insight:

> Puritanism and ascetic Protestantism generally, emerges as an emotionally consistent system of beliefs, sentiments and action which played no small part in arousing a sustained interest in science.[53]

My foregoing analysis has shown the determining contribution of the hedonistic-libertarian ethic in the rise of modern science. I should like now to show how the "evidence" submitted on behalf of the Puritan thesis fails to withstand analysis.

"It is hardly a fortuitous circumstance," writes Merton, "that the leading figures of the nuclear group of the Royal Society were divines and eminently religious men. . . ." The largest active professional group in the Royal Society, on the contrary, was that of the physicians. When the Society was being organized in 1660, it devoted one meeting on December 12th to the formulation of the requirements for membership. It invited members of the College of Physicians to join. This body numbered sixty-two licentiates at the time of the Restoration; twenty-seven of them joined as original fellows of the Royal Society, and twelve more during the next years. All in all, nearly two-thirds of the College of Physicians joined the Royal Society. The College, since its foundation in 1518, had had a distinguished scientific tradition. In 1616, William Harvey first presented to it his discovery of the circulation of the blood. The interests of its members tended often to be broadly scientific. Of its eighty-two members during 1603 to 1625, twenty-seven of them actively pursued scientific studies in such non-medical branches as astronomy, mathematics, chemistry, physics, mineralogy, botany, entomology, and psychology. Moreover, the physicians were not passive or decorative members of the Royal Society. In the person of such men as Petty, Merret, Willis, Glisson, Goddard, and Scarbrough, they were among its circle of scientific leaders. Among the hundred and seventy-one projects on which the Royal Society was engaged in 1661, physicians were involved in ninety-two. The physicians were Baconian optimists who had completed their own revolt against the authority of Galen. They had a reputation, moreover, for freethinking. The proverb "*Ubi tres Medici, duo Athei*" ("Where there are three physicians, there are two atheists") was so current that Joseph Glanvill tried to reply that it was a slander.[54]

How many divines, on the other hand, were there among the founders of the Royal Society? In 1668, Joseph Glanvill, writing his *Plus Ultra* to defend the Royal Society against the suspicions of atheism and irreligion, and to prevent "those panic, causeless Terrors" that the Royal Society was arousing among the clergy, listed the "Venerable and Worthy Ecclesiasticks" who were among its members:

> I find therefore in their Catalogue, The Most Reverend the Lords Archbishops of Canterburie and York, the Right Reverend the Lords Bishops of Ely, London, Rochester, Sarum, Winton; and those other Reverend Doctors, Dr. John Wilkins Dean of Rippon, Dr. Edward Cotton Archdeacon of Cornwall, Dr. Ralph Bathurst President of Trin. Coll. Oxon., Dr. John Pearson Margaret Professor of Cambridge, Dr. John Wallis Professor of Geometry in Oxford, Dr. William Holder, Dr. Henry More, Dr. John Pell; and . . . Dr. John Beale.[55]

Of this group, only Wilkins, Cotton, Bathurst, Wallis, Holder, and Pell were among the initial members of the Royal Society, and to their names we should add those of the freethinking Seth Ward, who took his doctorate of divinity at Oxford in 1654, and Thomas Sprat, Prebendary at Lincoln Cathedral when he was elected to the Royal Society. Martha Ornstein in her notable book *The Role of Scientific Societies in the Seventeenth Century* counted five of the original Fellows as doctors of divinity. Our more liberal estimate is eight divines, but nonetheless the group was a small minority in the Royal Society. Ecclesiastical dignitaries were later added to the Society's members, probably to offset the continual polemics against the Society from the clergy.

Moreover, how serious were divinity's attractions? In the seventeenth century, and for many years thereafter, scholars and scientists became divines for practical economic reasons. The stipends of Oxford and Cambridge dons were seldom more than ten pounds a year, unless supplemented by the revenue of chaplaincies or lectureships. "In consequence," writes David Ogg, "even the poorest of college benefices were eagerly sought after, and vacancies were the occasion for expert negotiation." The church could not, of course, always provide a lucrative career. If there were well-endowed bishoprics, amply sustained by coal royalties, there were also poor ones like Exeter. The livings of ordinary parsons varied in accordance with the wealth of their parishes. But if a young man aspired to be a scientist, scholar, writer, or professor, the taking of clerical orders offered the assurance of a minimal income. The divines of the Royal Society, men such as Wilkins and Seth Ward, writes Dorothy Stimson, "found in the service of the Anglican Church of those days, not only financial support and a certain amount of leisure, but also a comfortable indifference to their scientific concerns." [56] Theological conviction was not the controlling factor in the decision to accept holy orders.

There were a few who rebelled against the clerical avenue to financial respectability. Robert Boyle was urged to take orders, and was offered the highest emoluments of the church as an inducement. But Boyle was a wealthy man, and able to decline the clerical career on the ground that he would be more useful outside the church. Newton did not take orders though his financial situation was pressing; when he resigned from the Royal Society in 1674, the secretary told the Fellows that it was because he couldn't afford the weekly dues of one shilling. He refused the Mastership of Trinity College rather than become a cleric, and he secured special dispensations, as we have mentioned, for holding his fellowship and professorship without relinquishing his lay status.[57] Men cast in a less gigantic mold, men like Wilkins and

Ward, schemed for appointment to deaneries and bishoprics. Even Jonathan Swift, the genius of hatred for the human species, was immersed in intrigue to obtain ecclesiastical sinecures. Scientific talent was not yet able in the seventeenth century to stand in its own right; it had recourse to clerical patronage. The church paid the piper, but it did not call the tune. The scientific divines were not moved by the Puritan philosophy, and their divinity was economic expediency.

Moreover, a tension persisted between the experimentalists and the clergy. A Cambridge divine, John Eachard, thus protested against the experimentalists who sneered at the divines. He complained of

> . . . the small ingenioso or experimenter, who, having perhaps blown a glass, seen a paper-mill or a bell-run, that knows within two houses where the best chemist in town dwells, and dined once where one of the Royal Society should have been, and looked another time into the door at Gresham when the company was sitting,

then felt himself entitled to jeer at the "Aristotelian parson."

The Puritan thesis has been defended on the purported ground of statistical evidence. Such a study by Dorothy Stimson has been pronounced by Professor Merton to be "brief, but meticulous and convincing." According to Miss Stimson, ". . . among the original list of members of the Royal Society in 1663, forty-two of the sixty-eight for whom information pertaining to religious leanings is available, were clearly Puritan." [59] And it is a "fact," Miss Stimson adds, that out of the ten men who constituted the "invisible college" in 1645, only one, Dr. Scarborough, was definitely Royalist.

We shall be disappointed, however, when we sift into the grounds of Miss Stimson's enumerations. Of many of the original hundred and nineteen Fellows of the Royal Society, as Miss Stimson tells us, "little or nothing is known." We must remember, however, Sprat's description that they were mostly "gentlemen, free and unconfin'd," men who "by the freedom of their education, the plenty of their estates and the usual generosity of noble bloud, may be well suppos'd to be most averse from sordid considerations." These facts alone would suffice to make us expect that the majority of the Royal Society would be Royalist in politics and anti-Calvinist in religion.[60]

Royalist personages, indeed, held the positions of power in the Royal Society. Lord Brouncker, "one of the most active promoters of the Royal Society," became its first president. A distinguished mathematician, he was also eminent among the noble adherents of Charles II. Brouncker helped prepare for the Restoration, and became Chancellor of the Queen Consort. John Evelyn, another Fellow, said that "Brouncker, Boyle, and Sir R. Moray were above all others the persons to whom the world stands obliged" for surmounting all the obstacles to the furtherance of scientific knowledge. Moray was the Society's president immediately before its incorporation. He had intrigued on behalf of Charles I, and after the Restoration, Charles II elevated him to the Privy Council. His influence with the monarch counted for a great deal in the chartering of the Society, and Bishop Burnet called him "the life and soul of the body." As Weld said, ". . . the year of the Restoration was peculiarly favorable to the establishment of a scientific society, and the study and investigation of science."[61] John Evelyn, who joined the early circle at Gresham College together with Brouncker, served the Royal Society on its council in 1662, and became its secretary in 1672. Evelyn, too, was a staunch Royalist who had been "threatened" for his Royalist writings in 1649. He was at home in the Church of England, with no inclination to Calvinist metaphysics. His devotion to science was genuine; in 1659 he proposed to Robert Boyle that a college be founded near London where a few men of science could join in "the promotion of experimental knowledge."

Let us, however, examine further the details of Miss Stimson's statistical survey. Concerning thirty-two of the original hundred and nineteen Fellows, she "can find no information whatever," and of nineteen more she cannot ascertain where their political sympathies lay before 1660. Her positive finding follows:

> Forty-two of the remainder are Puritan in their training or parliamentary in their affiliations or both, even though they later accepted the Book of Common Prayer along with the Restoration and were conforming to the Church of England. Only twenty-six were definitely royalist before 1660.

Miss Stimson's census, however, makes use of a criterion for "Puritan" which is vague and loose. A man can reject his early training, as did, for instance, Descartes, Spinoza, Hobbes, and Leibniz; indeed, such rejection of one's upbringing is characteristic of a revolutionary age. Moreover, affiliations in a revolutionary period can be expedient, temporary, superficial, and even deceptive. Miss Stimson regards Wilkins as an outright Puritan, and mentions by way of evidence that he was chaplain to the Prince Elector Palatine. Goddard is taken as a Puritan because he received his wardenship from a Parliamentary commission. Boyle is said to have derived from "European travel with his tutors an education that made him strongly Puritan." Glisson is regarded as tinged with Puritanism because he went to London after Colchester fell to the Parliamentary forces. Bathurst is classified as "trained under Puritan influences," and George Ent is similarly pigeonholed. Professor Merton broadens Miss Stimson's classification by using an overextended criterion for Puritanism through diffusion. "Wilkins' influence as Warden of Wadham College was profound; under it came Ward, Rooke, Wren, Sprat. . . ." Wallis is taken as "a clergyman with strong leanings toward Puritanism," and Petty falls into place as a "moderate Puritan." [62]

The Stimson-Merton taxonomy belies the weight of the actual facts we have adduced. Thus, Wilkins, the friend of Charles II, bishop in 1668, advocate of flexible yielding to the dominant political force, doesn't fit easily under the Puritan rubric. Wilkins was indeed chaplain to the Elector Palatine, but Charles Ludwig, a picturesque figure, was no Calvinist partisan.[63] The Elector's family was Calvinist, and they sought English help to restore their throne. But Charles Ludwig was drawn in other directions. He loved Shakespeare, and even prepared a play of Ben Jonson's for production. As a refugee in England, he stayed with Christopher Wren's Royalist father. In 1642, he took his stand by the king's standard. Subsequently, he took the Covenant, but evidently it was political expediency rather than Puritan conviction that guided him. For when Charles Ludwig returned to his Electorate, he amazed Europe with his liberalism. He founded a Church for Holy Concord, in which Lutheran, Calvinist, and Catholic clergy shared at the opening ceremony. He insisted on freedom of religion for Mennonites, Jews, and Anabaptists, and in so doing defied the

Calvinist pastors. He introduced free trade into his domain, and broke with the Calvinist-approved policy of regulation. He brought a liberal faculty to the University of Heidelberg, promoted its free thought, and even invited the famed scientific philosopher Spinoza, in 1673, to become one of its professors. Wilkins' chaplaincy to the young Elector is scarcely evidence of Puritan proclivities.

Nor can we feel secure about classifying Goddard, the wine-drinking clubman, as a Puritan of conviction. As for Robert Boyle, when he returned from his European sojourn he was bitter against all doctrinal argument, would have nothing of Calvinist theology, and espoused a universalist religion of peace and charity. Glisson was an emissary of the Royalist forces, and physician to Lord Shaftesbury. Bathurst admired Hobbes, and hid the painted glass of the Oxford library to save it from the Parliamentary committee. George Ent said sardonically, "a pox take parties." Seth Ward was ousted from Cambridge as a Royalist; Rooke, the king's friend, made him his heir. Wren was a tolerant Mason with a Cavalier background; Sprat inveighed against Puritan theologians; Wallis tacked his sails to the prevailing wind; Petty disliked all sects, and was concerned with the art of happy living. Only Samuel Foster, of all those named by Miss Stimson, may possibly have been a convinced Puritan.[64] He was Professor of Astronomy at Gresham College, but he died in 1652, several years before the movement that led to the Royal Society reached its height.

It has been suggested in all seriousness that the Puritan emphasis on high-minded living kept solid men away from the Restoration theatre, and thereby encouraged the pursuit of science as a kind of substitute activity.[65] There is no evidence, however, that the Fellows of the Royal Society were more averse to the playhouse than was the citizenry at large. Indeed, Wren's letter to Sprat indicates that they delighted in the poetical bees, comedies, tragedies, and burlesques. And if the Restoration coffeehouses had been closed down, the Royal Society would have been virtually homeless.

Every hypothesis confronted with contrary evidence can try to save itself with devices of redefinition and qualification. Miss Stimson does beforehand carefully qualify her thesis with the statement that it was the "moderate Puritans" who produced the scientific ferment in the seventeenth century. A hypothesis can, however, be qualified out of scientific existence. What is a "moderate Puritan"? If he is so "moderate" as to abandon the distinctive principles of Puritan theology; if his moderation has become an antagonism to dogma, a belief in a religion of peace, tolerance, and charity; if he has extended a warm approval to the joys of the coffeehouse and tavern; if, finally, he is basically free of a sense of original sin and its burden of guilt, then the "moderate Puritan" has ceased, for all practical purposes, to be a Puritan and has become a hedonist.

Finally, my own study of the biographical facts indicates that of the ninety-four Fellows concerning whom we have evidence, only five can be regarded as adherents to the Puritan ethics, while at least fifty-four were liberal hedonists. Sixty-eight were royalists in their political attitudes or actions, while only twelve were Parliamentarians.*

It is clear, after all allowances for error have been made, that the dominant temper of the membership of the Royal Society on May 20, 1663, was not that of the Puritan ascetic virtues; it was hedonist-libertarian. Science became the fashion in a pleasure-loving age. In Macaulay's vivid words:

> The year 1660, the era of the restoration of the old Constitution, is also the era from which dates the ascendency of the new philosophy. In that year, the Royal Society . . . began to exist. In a few months, experimental science became all the mode. The transfusion of blood, the ponderation of air, the fixation of mercury, succeeded to that place in the public mind which had been lately occupied by the controversies of the Rota. . . . All classes were hurried along by the prevailing sentiment. Cavalier and Roundhead, Churchman and Puritan, were for once allied. . . . Chemistry divided for a time, with wine and love, with the intrigues of a courtier and the intrigues of a demagogue, the attention of the fickle Buckingham. . . . It was almost necessary to the character of a fine gentleman to have something to say about air-pumps and telescopes; and even fine ladies, now and then, thought it becoming to affect a taste for science, went in coaches

* See Appendix C, The Membership of the Royal Society, p. 420.

and six to visit the Gresham curiosities, and broke forth into cries of delight at finding that a magnet really attracted a needle, and that a microscope really made a fly look as large as a sparrow. . . .

The spirit of Francis Bacon was abroad. . . . There was a strong persuasion that the whole world was full of secrets of high moment to the happiness of man, and that man had, by his Maker, been intrusted with the key which rightly used, would give access to them.[66]

The ideal society, as conceived by the men of the Royal Society, was one in which "the arts of Wit, Reason, and delight were in their highest perfection." Among all the ages of history, Sprat and his friends would have preferred life in the Rome of Augustus. They looked back to that time with the same admiring spirit as did the skeptical, hedonistic Gibbon during the following century. Sprat addressed Christopher Wren:

You may perhaps remember, that we have sometimes debated together, what place and time of all the past, or present, we would have chosen to live in, if our fates had bin at our own disposal. . . . We both agreed, that Rome, in the Reign of Augustus was to be preferr'd before all others . . . that Emperor had the good fortune to succeed a long civil war: the minds of all men were easily compos'd into obedience by the remembrance of their past misfortunes: the arts of Wit, Reason, and delight were in their highest perfection: the Court was the place of resort, for all the Lovers of generous knowledge: and such was the freedome of their manners, that Virgil, Horace, and Varius were admitted into the privacies, and friendship, of Agrippa, Mecaenas, and Augustus.[67]

There could be "nothing pleasanter to a Philosophical mind," wrote Sprat, than thus to live "according to the convenience, and Rules of Nature." Thus was defined the hedonistic-libertarian ethics of the English scientist in the seventeenth century.

NOTES

1. Charles Richard Weld, *A History of the Royal Society* (London, 1848), Vol. I, p. 101.
2. Thomas Sprat, *The History of the Royal Society of London, for*

the Improving of Natural Knowledge (London, 1667), pp. 53, 55-6.

3. *Ibid.*, vs. 5, B-2. Dorothy Stimson, "Amateurs of Science in 17th Century England," *Isis*, XXXI (1939), 34-5.

4. Thomas Sprat, *op. cit.*, pp. 55, 57-9.

5. Dorothy Stimson, "Ballad of Gresham Colledge," *Isis*, XVIII (1932), 109-17.

6. Raymond Phineas Stearns, "The Scientific Spirit in England in Early Modern Times (c. 1600)," *Isis*, XXXIV (1943), 298. Francis R. Johnson, "Gresham College: Precursor of the Royal Society," *Journal of the History of Ideas*, I, (1940), 413-38. Sir Thomas Gresham, founder of the college, is a distinguished name in the history of economic science. Cf. Thomas Willing Balch, *The Law of Oresme, Copernicus, and Gresham* (Philadelphia, 1908), pp. 1-21. F. R. Salter, *Sir Thomas Gresham (1518-1579)* (London, 1925), pp. 29 ff.

7. Dorothy Stimson, "Amateurs of Science in 17th Century England," p. 42. Dorothy Stimson, "Comenius and the Invisible College," *Isis*, XXIII (1935), 377, 385. Francis R. Johnson, *op. cit.*, pp. 420-1. John William Burgon, *The Life and Times of Sir Thomas Gresham* (London, 1839[?]), Vol. II, p. 519.

8. J. F. Fulton, "Robert Boyle and his Influence on Thought in the Seventeenth Century," *Isis*, XVIII (1932), 84. Louis Trenchard More, *The Life and Works of the Honorable Robert Boyle* (New York, 1944), pp. 132, 151-2, 161, 164. Thomas Birch, *The Life of the Honourable Robert Boyle*, in *The Works of the Honourable Robert Boyle* (London, 1772), Vol. I, p. cxli. Harold Fisch, "The Scientist as Priest: A Note on Robert Boyle's Natural Theology," *Isis*, XXXXIV (1953), 252 ff.

9. Robert Boyle, *A Free Enquiry into the Vulgarly Receiv'd Notion of Nature* (London, 1685), pp. 4, 35, 11.

10. *The Philosophical Works of the Honourable Robert Boyle Esq.* (2nd ed.; corrected by Peter Shaw, London, 1738), Vol. I, pp. 110-12, 129-30.

11. P. A. Wright Henderson, *The Life and Times of John Wilkins* (Edinburgh, 1910), pp. 55-7. Charles Edward Mallet, *A History of the University of Oxford* (London, 1924), Vol. II, p. 264.

12. *The Life and Times of Anthony Wood, antiquary of Oxford, 1632-1695, described by Himself*, collected by Andrew Clark (Oxford, 1891), Vol. I, p. 148.

13. *Aubrey's Brief Lives*, ed. Oliver Lawson Dick (Ann Arbor, 1957), p. 318.

14. John Wilkins, *An Essay Towards a Real Character and a Philosophical Language* (London, 1668), p. 13; Dedicatory Epistle, p. 4.

15. John Wilkins, *Discovery of a World in the Moone* (London,

1638), p. 175, as quoted in Dorothy Stimson, "Comenius and the Invisible College," p. 382. Dorothy Stimson, "Dr. Wilkins and the Royal Society," *The Journal of Modern History*, III (1931), 542-3, 555, 563. *Aubrey's Brief Lives*, p. 319. *Diary of John Evelyn*, ed. William Bray (London, 1879), Vol. II, p. 57.

16. John Aubrey, *"Brief Lives," Chiefly of Contemporaries, set down by John Aubrey, between the years 1669 &1696*, ed. Andrew Clark (Oxford, 1898), Vol. II, pp. 140, 143; Vol. I, p. 368. Lord Edmond Fitzmaurice, *The Life of Sir William Petty* (London, 1895), pp. 16, 96, 106, 118, 120, 223. *Diary of John Evelyn*, Vol. II, pp. 307-308. *The Economic Writings of Sir William Petty*, ed. Charles Henry Hull (Cambridge, 1899), Vol. I, p. 79.

17. Lord Edmond Fitzmaurice, *op. cit.*, pp. 114-115, 117, 120-21, 299, 302-3. *Aubrey's Brief Lives*, p. 240. E. Strauss, *Sir William Petty: Portrait of a Genius* (London, 1954), p. 153. *The Diary of Samuel Pepys*, ed. Henry B. Wheatley (London, 1904), Vol. IV, pp. 293, 330. Dorothy Stimson, "Dr. Wilkins and the Royal Society," p. 557.

18. Martin S. Briggs, *Wren the Incomparable* (London, 1953), pp. 23, 274, 276. James Elmes, *Sir Christopher Wren and His Times* (London, 1852), pp. 117, 165, 347-8.

19. Anthony Wood, *op. cit.*, p. 363. Aubrey, however, says that Ward was "put out of his fellowship at Sydney College" because of loyalty "for the king's cause." John Aubrey, *op. cit.*, Vol. II, p. 284. George Croom Robertson, *Hobbes* (Edinburgh, 1886), p. 169. *The Dictionary of National Biography* (London, 1921-22), Vol. XX, pp. 793-6.

20. James Elmes, *Memoirs of the Life and Works of Sir Christopher Wren* (London, 1823), pp. 4-6, 312-13.

21. John Aubrey, *op. cit.*, Vol. I, p. 269. Charles C. Gillispie, "Physick and Philosophy: A Study of the Influence of the College of Physicians of London upon the Foundation of the Royal Society," *Journal of Modern History*, XIX, (1947), 219. *The Dictionary of National Biography*, Vol. VIII, pp. 24-6.

22. *The Dictionary of National Biography*, Vol. I, pp. 1329-31. John Aubrey, *op. cit.*, Vol. II, pp. 24, 141, 158; Vol. I, pp. 371, 377. James Elmes, *Memoirs of . . . Sir Christopher Wren*, pp. 171-172.

23. *Ibid.*, pp. 94-95. John Ward, *The Lives of the Professors of Gresham College* (London, 1740), pp. 91-95. John Aubrey, *op. cit.*, Vol. I, p. 365; Vol. II, p. 288.

24. Erik Nordenskiöld, *The History of Biology*, trans. L. B. Eyre (New York, 1932), p. 148. Sir Michael Foster, *Lectures on the History*

of Physiology (Cambridge, 1901), p. 269. Charles C. Gillispie, *op. cit.*, p. 221.

25. John Aubrey, *op. cit.*, Vol. I, p. 373; Vol. II, pp. 281-282. *The Dictionary of National Biography*, Vol. XX, pp. 598-602. Cf. the temperate summary in John Laird, *Hobbes* (London, 1934), pp. 15, 19-20. Hobbes told Wallis: ". . . there is nothing in my verses that do *olere hircum* as much as that of yours." *The English Works of Thomas Hobbes*, ed. Sir William Molesworth (London, 1839-1845), Vol. VII, p. 389.

26. John Wallis, *A Defence of the Royal Society* (London, 1678), pp. 7-8.

27. R. T. Gunther, *Early Science in Cambridge* (Oxford, 1937), p. 39. Louis T. More, *Isaac Newton* (New York, 1934), p. 37. Percy H. Osmond, *Isaac Barrow: His Life and Times* (London, 1944), pp. 18, 71, 144, 148, 78-9, 97, 28, 44, 30, 61-2, 74.

28. William Whiston, *Historical Memoirs of the Life of Dr. Samuel Clarke* (London, 1730), p. 24. R. T. Gunther, *op. cit.*, p. 46. L. T. More, *Newton*, pp. 560-561. H. McLachlan, *The Religious Opinions of Milton, Locke, and Newton* (Manchester, 1941), p. 129. *Memoirs of the Life and Writings of Mr. William Whiston* (London, 1749), Pt. II, pp. 638-42.

29. Lord King, *The Life and Letters of John Locke* (London, 1884), p. 226. Sir John Craig, *Newton at the Mint* (Cambridge, 1946), pp. 119-20.

30. Lord Keynes, "Newton the Man," *Newton Tercentenary Celebration* (Cambridge, 1947), pp. 30-1.

31. Sir Isaac Newton, *Theological Manuscripts*, ed. H. McLachlan (Liverpool, 1950), pp. 10, 13. For Newton's essay "Ex Maimonides de Cultu Divino," *ibid.*, pp. 16-17. L. T. More, *Newton*, pp. 134, 624, 629, 644. Also, Augustus De Morgan, *Newton: His Friend: and His Niece* (London, 1885), p. 107.

32. *The Diary of Robert Hooke (1672-1680)*, ed. Henry W. Robinson and Walter Adams (London, 1935), p. 467.

33. Samuel Clarke, *A Collection of Papers which passed between the Late Learned Mr. Leibnitz and Dr. Clarke* (London, 1717), p. ix. Cf. Samuel Clarke, *A Discourse Concerning the Being and Attributes of God* (6th ed., London, 1725), p. 123.

34. Frederick J. Powicke, *The Cambridge Platonists: A Study* (London, 1926), pp. 3, 20, 25, 35, 61, 111-12. Ernst Cassirer, *The Platonic Renaissance in England*. trans. James P. Pettegrove (Edinburgh, 1953), p. 67.

35. L. T. More, *Newton*, pp. 11, 245, 345. *Philosophical Writings of Henry More*, ed. Flora Isabel Mackinnon (New York, 1925), p. 294. *Conway Letters: The Correspondence of Anne, Viscountess Conway, Henry More, and Their Friends, 1642-1684*, ed. Marjorie Hope Nicolson (New Haven, 1930), pp. 44-5, 54.

36. G. P. H. Pawson, *The Cambridge Platonists and Their Place in Religious Thought* (London, 1930), pp. 9, 11-12, 47, 50, 59. Ernst Cassirer, *op. cit.*, pp. 67-69.

37. L. T. More, *Newton*, pp. 467, 470-1, 473. Sir John Craig, *op. cit.*, pp. 28-9. Augustus De Morgan, *op. cit.*, pp. 49, 70-74.

38. Eugene Fairfield MacPike, *Hevelius, Flamsteed and Halley* (London, 1937), pp. 41, 45-52, 72-73. Augustus De Morgan, *Essays on the Life and Work of Newton* (Chicago, 1914), p. 22. L. T. More, *Newton*, p. 317. *Correspondence and Papers of Edmond Halley*, ed. Eugene Fairfield MacPike (Oxford, 1932), p. 264. R. T. Gunther, *op. cit.*, pp. 126-7.

39. John Flamsteed, "History of his own Life and Labors," in Francis Bailey, *An Account of the Revd. John Flamsteed* (London, 1835), pp. 7-8. L. T. More, *Newton*, p. 412.

40. *The Diary of Robert Hooke*, pp. xx, 108, 216, 463-70. Richard Waller, *The Life of Dr. Robert Hooke* (London, 1705), reprinted in R. T. Gunther, *Early Science in Oxford* (Oxford, 1930), Vol. VI, pp. 22, 66. John Aubrey, *op. cit.*, Vol. I, p. 411. L. T. More, *Newton*, pp. 298, 310-211. Margaret Espinasse, *Robert Hooke* (Berkeley, 1956), pp. 36, 110, 147. *The Life and Work of Robert Hooke*, in R. T. Gunther, *Early Science in Oxford* (Oxford, 1935), Vol. X, pp. xxv, 137, 151, 259.

41. Robert Hooke, *Micrographia* (London, 1665), reprinted in R. T. Gunther, *Early Science in Oxford* (Oxford, 1938), Vol. XIII, pp. 2, 5, 11, 12, 30.

42. Edward Forbes Robinson, *The Early History of Coffee Houses in England* (London, 1893), p. 73. Aytoun Ellis, *The Penny Universities: A History of the Coffee-Houses* (London, 1956), pp. 18, 19. Ellis errs in saying that Jacob's advent was after Cromwell allowed the Jews to return to England. That did not come till six years later. Edward Forbes Robinson, *op. cit.*, pp. 74-7, 156, 161, 163-4. Aytoun Ellis, *op. cit.*, pp. 27-9.

43. Aytoun Ellis, *op. cit.*, p. 88. *Old English Coffee Houses* (London, 1954), pp. 12-14, 22.

44. Aytoun Ellis, *op. cit.*, p. 24. Edward Forbes Robinson, *op. cit.*, pp. 80-1, 108, 110, 111, 117, 136.

45. Cf. Gerald Dennis Meyer, *The Scientific Lady in England 1650-1760* (Berkeley, 1955), pp. 1-17.

46. Thomas Sprat, *op. cit.*, pp. 365, 367, 366, 368, 82, 352, 83. Cf. Albert Rosenberg, "Bishop Sprat on Science and Imagery," *Isis*, XLIII (1952), 221.

47. Thomas Sprat, *op. cit.*, pp. 152, 78, 372, 377, 371, 67 9. Boyle like wise "undertook to persuade the nobility and gentry, who had the means and leisure to pursue such sorts of studies, to follow his example." Thomas Birch, *op. cit.*, p. lv.

48. Thomas Sprat, *op. cit.*, pp. 88, 397, 117-18.

49. Joseph Glanvill, *Plus Ultra: or, the Progress and Advancement of Knowledge since the Days of Aristotle* (London, 1668), reproduced with introduction by Jackson I. Cope (Gainesville, Florida, 1958), pp. viii, 13, 26-7, 105, 142-3, 117, 119, 123, 122, 95, 102, 139, 148, 146, 121, 141. Charles C. Gillispie, *op. cit.*, p. 220. Dorothy Stimson, "Dr. Wilkins and the Royal Society," pp. 552, 554, 559.

50. Joseph Glanvill, *The Vanity of Dogmatizing: or Confidence in Opinions Manifested in a Discourse of the Shortness and Uncertainty of our Knowledge, and its Causes* (London, 1661), reproduced with a bibliographical note by Moody E. Prior (New York, 1931), pp. 150, 118-20.

51. *Ibid.*, pp. 218, 212, 5, 11. Ferris Greenslet, *Joseph Glanvill: A Study in English Thought and Letters of the Seventeenth Century* (New York, 1900), pp. 103, 66-7.

52. Dorothy Stimson, "Hartlib, Haak and Oldenburg: Intelligencers," *Isis*, XXXI (1940), 321-3. *Diary of Samuel Pepys*, ed. Henry B. Wheatley, Vol. II, p. 568. Sherman B. Barnes, "The Editing of Early Learned Journals," *Osiris*, I (1936), 155-72. Sherman B. Barnes, "The Scientific Journal, 1665-1730," *Scientific Monthly*, March 1934, 257-60.

53. Robert K. Merton, "Science, Technology and Society in Seventeenth Century England," *Osiris*, IV (1938), Pt. 2, 494-5.

54. Charles C. Gillispie, *op. cit.*, pp. 210-25. Joseph Glanvill, *The Vanity of Dogmatizing*, p. 248.

55. Joseph Glanvill, *Plus Ultra*, p. 25.

56. David Ogg, *England in the Reign of Charles II* (Oxford, 1934), Vol. I, p. 134. L. T. More, *Newton*, p. 22. Dorothy Stimson, "Dr. Wilkins and the Royal Society," p. 541.

57. L. T. More, *The Life and Works of the Honourable Robert Boyle*, pp. 46, 168, 200.

58. Percy H. Osmond, *Isaac Barrow*, pp. 103-4.

59. Dorothy Stimson, "Puritanism and the New Philosophy in 17th

Century England," *Bulletin of the Institute of the History of Medicine*, III (1935), 330. R. K. Merton, *op. cit.*, p. 473. Dorothy Stimson, "Amateurs of Science in 17th Century England," p. 43.

60. Thomas Sprat, *op. cit.*, p. 67. George Macaulay Trevelyan, *England Under the Stuarts* (21st ed., London, 1949), p. 188.

61. C. R. Weld, *A History of the Royal Society*, Vol. I, pp. 56, 105, 125. Bishop Burnet declared that "the men that formed the Royal Society were Sir Robert Moray, Lord Brouncker, a profound mathematician, and Dr. Ward."

62. Dorothy Stimson, "Puritanism and the New Philosophy in 17th Century England," p. 329. R. K. Merton, *op. cit.*, pp. 471-72.

63. J. H. Clapham, "Charles Louis, Elector Palatine, 1617-1680," *Economica*, VII (1940), 387.

64. "From his will . . . he seems to have been a zealous nonconformist." *The Dictionary of National Biography*, Vol. VII, p. 502. There is no mention, however, of such leanings in the account given in John Ward, *op. cit.*, pp. 85-7.

65. Dorothy Stimson, "Puritanism and the New Philosophy in 17th Century England," p. 326.

66. Thomas Babington Macaulay, *The History of England from the Accession of James II* (New York, 1849), Vol. I, pp. 378-81. Arthur Bryant, *King Charles II* (London, 1931), p. 142.

67. Thomas Sprat, *Observations on Monsieur de Sorbier's Voyage into England* (London, 1665), pp. 283-5. Also cf. C. V. Wedgwood, "The Scientists and the English Civil War," *The Logic of Personal Knowledge: Essays Presented to Michael Polanyi* (London, 1961), p. 69.

III

The Nominalist Recovery of the Sense of Reality

THE SCIENTIFIC MOVEMENT IN ENGLAND DURING THE SEVENteenth century was, as we have seen, characterized by its attachment to the hedonist-libertarian ethics. This was the philosophy of the scientific intellectual, a rising new type in European civilization, with his own method, his own simple language, his freedom from theological fanaticism. The scientific intellectuals created their own new societies, where, for the first time in European history, matters of intellect could be discussed without reference to religious dogma. They began to displace the religious intellectuals in the leadership of the European community.

The psychological revolution among the European intellectuals that brought them to a hedonist-libertarian standpoint developed slowly before the seventeenth century. What was later a movement was in the latter Middle Ages only a growing trend among a handful of thinkers. The scientific revolution of the sixteenth and seventeenth centuries was preceded by a period of gestation during which European thinkers revolted against masochist asceticism, and slowly recovered their sense of reality.

The dominance of masochistic asceticism in the Middle Ages carried with it a distinctive philosophical expression: it gave rise to the philosophical movement that made its central tenet the belief in the reality of universals. "The whole philosophy of the Middle

Ages," says Etienne Gilson, "was little more than an obstinate endeavor to solve one problem—the problem of the Universals." [1] Today we find it hard to understand how the most powerful intellects of an age were troubled to prove that, apart from the ordinary tables or men whom we see and touch, there exists a "pure idea" or "essence" of Table or Man; we find it almost incredible that their emotional involvement with these "pure ideas" was such that they deemed them more real than the objects they perceived.

Every philosophy is based on the emotional state of a person's sense of reality. The order of realities which a philosopher constructs corresponds to his order of emotional involvements; those segments of existence that he has come to hate, and would destroy, he tries to prove unreal; those characteristics of existence that he prizes he tries somehow to elevate into a realm of higher reality. In the history of philosophy, there have been "proofs" that physical objects don't exist, that other persons' feelings are unreal or meaningless, that one's own consciousness is nonexistent, that the past is unreal, that the future is unreal, that the present is unreal, that time is unreal, that change is an illusion. All such "proofs" express the state of the affections and aggressions of their respective philosophers. A society that imposes upon itself great emotional deprivation will have a correspondingly distorted sense of reality; its inner frustrations will vent themselves in metaphysical aggressions against disturbing segments of existence. And as a neurotic's world is interspersed with fantasies and hallucinatory objects, so a sick society will expel realities from its philosophy and replace them with fantasia; the world of fantasia replaces the world of sense.

Realism, the doctrine of the reality of universals, was central to the philosophical creed called scholasticism. The latter was literally, as de Wulf has written, the "daughter of the schools"; its decline began in the fourteenth century as nominalism became influential.[2] What evidence is there, however, to show that medieval realism was an outcome of masochist asceticism?

To begin with, there is the striking correlation that realism was confined in the Middle Ages to the Christian philosophers; not a single one of their leading Jewish contemporaries shared their metaphysics. As Professor Abraham Wolf wrote, "The Jews, it is interesting to observe, were thoroughgoing nominalists." [3] Maimonides stated plainly the dominant view of the Jewish philosophers:

> It is an established fact that species have no existence except in our own minds. Species and other classes are merely ideas formed in our minds, while everything in real existence is an individual object, or an aggregate of individual objects.

Maimonides, the medical philosopher, said with simple straightforwardness that "only individual objects have real existence." [4] The Jewish philosophers lacked the central ingredient that made for scholastic realism; they were not celibates. There were no monks among the Jews, no extolling of sexual asceticism as the road to God; therefore the Jews were nominalists, for they cathected no frustrated sexual desires on fantasy-substitute objects.

Take any page of Maimonides' writings on ethics, and contrast it with a similar page from one of his Christian scholastic contemporaries. They sound as if they were written in different worlds. Maimonides writes about human problems in the spirit of a physician who wishes to advise people about how to lead as happy lives as they can. The Christian scholastics write in a spirit of mortification, self-hatred, self-denial, and self-immolation on behalf of their suffering Lord of the Cross. "Pleasure and guilt," said Edward Gibbon, "are synonymous terms in the language of the monks." [5] Maimonides, a scientist himself, launches into a remarkable attack on the ascetic ethics.

> [The] ignorant chastised their bodies with all kinds of afflictions, imagining that they had acquired perfection and moral worth, and that by this means man would approach nearer to God, as if He hated the human body and desired its destruction. It never dawned upon them, however, that these actions were bad and resulted in moral imperfection of the soul.

The Law, says Maimonides, recommends, rather, that men follow

> . . . the path of moderation, in accordance with the dictates of Nature, eating, drinking, enjoying legitimate sexual intercourse . . . and living among people in honesty and uprightness, but not dwelling in the wilderness or in the mountains, or clothing oneself in garments of hair and wool, or afflicting the body.

Against the ascetics, Maimonides lays down the principle of the bodily basis of mental health: "The well-being of the soul can only be obtained after that of the body has been secured." The preservation of the body in a healthy and perfect state is not only the way of life prescribed by God; it is also a condition for reaching wisdom and understanding. He urges the refreshing significance of a beautiful wife, beautiful pictures, and beautiful music:

> . . . one who suffers from melancholia may rid himself of it by listening to singing and all kinds of instrumental music, by strolling through beautiful gardens and splendid buildings, by gazing upon beautiful pictures. . . . Our Rabbis of blessed memory say, "It is becoming that a Sage should have a pleasant dwelling, a beautiful wife, and domestic comfort. . . ."

A man, said Maimonides, should keep his body "perfect and strong" not only to know the Lord but "because it is impossible for him to reflect and study the sciences when he is hungry, or ill, or any one of his limbs aches." The medical standpoint in ethics was explicitly defended by Maimonides, for through "the study of medicine . . . one learns to weigh one's deeds and thereby human activities are rendered true virtue." [6] This probing physician of the human soul even dared to speak scientifically concerning the incest taboo. It would not be true to affirm "I do not want to enter into an incestuous marriage"; rather, said Maimonides, with Rabbi Simeon ben Gamaliel, one should say, "I do indeed want to, yet I must not, for my Father in Heaven has forbidden it." And, with a curious logic, he held that the prohibition of incest did not apply to slaves: ". . . as long as he is a slave he may marry his own mother." [7] The emancipation from the ascetic mode of thought made Maimonides the pre-eminent scientific ethical thinker of the Middle Ages, and at the same time made scholastic realism seem to him like a mental aberration.

The celebrated poet-philosopher of twelfth-century Spain, Jehuda Halevi, wrote similarly in his dialogue *Kuzari:* "The Divine Law imposes no asceticism on us." The ascetic, he said, "has not achieved any association with any Divine light . . . nor has he acquired knowledge to absorb him and to enjoy as did the philosophers." He does not find God by repressing his "inherent powers of seeing, hearing, speaking, moving, eating, cohabitation, gain, house-managing, helping the poor. . . ." Solomon ibn Gabirol, his predecessor in the eleventh century, also conceived his ethics in the medical tradition. As his translator Stephen S. Wise has said, "Gabirol's object is to establish a system of purely physio-psychological ethics." The Jewish philosopher Gersonides is regarded as having stood closest to the scholastic mode of thought; he was the "Jewish scholastic par excellence," wrote Nima Adlerblum. But he, too, like Maimonides, was both a physician and married, and he too affirmed that universals have no real existence outside the mind, that the only really existing things are particular individuals.[8] The practice of Jewish physicians in the New East indeed involved them in the intensities of people's emotional lives. Maimonides, for instance, wrote treatises on sexual intercourse and poisons because the problems that harems raised and the fear of poisoning were live issues for Arab potentates.[9] Such concerns kept one's sense of reality involved with individual things.

By contrast, the realm of universals, purified of gross matter, was the projective universe of the celibate scholastics; it expressed their repression of sexuality. John of Salisbury, in his contemporary documentary account of the origin of scholastic realism, could not help perceiving this: "Bernard of Chartres," he writes, "used to say that 'whiteness' represents an undefiled virgin; 'is white' the virgin entering the bed chamber, or lying on the couch; and 'white' the girl after she has lost her virginity."[10] The pure universals were the desexualized realities, and as one descended to the ordinary world of individual objects, the dreaded sexuality intruded. Duns Scotus was the most renowned of the medieval realists. Little is known about his personal characteristics, but it is noteworthy that in theology he is celebrated as having laid the theological foundation for the doctrine that represents the zenith of the represssion of sexuality, the Immaculate Conception of the Virgin Mary.[11] According to tradition, Duns Scotus won the title of Doctor Subtilis by refuting more than two hundred objections to the doctrine of the Immaculate Conception in a single day.[12] It was during the twelfth century, with the ascetic movement, that, as Michelet put it, "God changed sex. The Virgin became the world's God." "Virginity in itself," as Feuerbach said, was the "highest moral idea" to the Catholic moralist, and it helped dictate the metaphysics of scholastic realism.[13]

The first revolt against scholastic realism is associated with the celebrated person of Abelard. He was not a priest, and did not join the Benedictine monks till after he had been sexually mutilated. The recovery of the sense of realities, and the dispersal of the vague projective fantasies of universals, were at their beginnings tied to a man famous in history for his love of Heloise. "Philosophers, not to say divines," wrote Abelard, "have excelled principally by the grace of continence." He, however, had departed "by the impurity of my life" from the philosophers' sexual asceticism. He recalled how "under the pretext of discipline," Heloise and he "abandoned ourselves utterly to love, and those secret retreats which love demands. . . . No stage of love was omitted by us in our cupidity, and, if love could elaborate anything new, that we took in addition." His love songs, "composed in amatory measure or rhythm," spread from person to person, captivating "even illiterates" with the sweetness of their melody. On this account, wrote Heloise, "women sighed for love of thee." [14] The same Abelard had with his arguments "shattered" his teacher's opinion concerning universals. He convinced William of Champeaux that a universal was not an object present in different things as their essence. Abelard did not deny that abstract terms function with a general significance, and as he characterized them, the pervasive medieval metaphor of desexual projection appeared:

> . . . the understanding of universals is rightly spoken of as alone and naked and pure, that is, alone from the senses, because it does not perceive the thing as sensual, and naked in regard to the abstraction of all and of any forms. . . .[15]

Latent in the hedonistic attitude and philosophical liberation of Abelard was a standpoint which, as the church feared, could be turned to the critique of itself and social institutions. Threatened with condemnation as a heretic, Abelard thought of St. Jerome fleeing to the Orient to escape the injustice of Rome. Under the impact of Abelard's criticism, noted Michelet, "all Christianity was at stake"; the dogmas of original sin and redemption were endangered:

> Thus, man ceased to be guilty; the flesh was justified and rehabilitated. The manifold sufferings by which men had sacrificed themselves, had been superfluous. To what end, the hosts of volun-

> tary martyrs, the fasts and macerations, the vigils of monks, the tribulations of hermits, the unnumbered tears, poured out in the sight of God—all this had been vanity and folly. This God was a kind and easy God, indifferent to every thing of the sort.

Perhaps the assault on Abelard's body prevented him from taking a leadership in this direction. But his pupil, Arnold of Brescia, undertook an indictment of the Pope and hierarchy. Arnold, said a contemporary, "seems to have been sane, manly and clear." He was "a popular tribune in the habit of a priest," and in libertarian fashion, he proposed that the church's prerogatives should be confined to spiritual matters.[16] Such men were the precursors in the Middle Ages of the philosophy of the scientific movement, but in their own time they were overwhelmed by the monolithic power of the church. A long, slow growth of the civilization of the towns and cities was required to make possible a reinforced basis for the scientific mode of thought.

In William of Occam, the great nominalist of the later Middle Ages, the emotional recovery of the reality of ordinary physical things reflected itself in philosophical argument and political outlook. To those who said that universals were entities that existed apart from individual objects, Occam queried: "But how could a singular thing exist in many things at once? If humanity were a thing different from the singular individuals, one and the same thing would be in many individuals. . . ."[17] A medieval realist could, of course, have accepted the latter consequence, but to Occam, who took the everyday world as a criterion of reality, the consistent adherence to a principle of fantasy construction seemed irrational, or, as we say today, neurotic. Occam approached every philosophical question, as Dean Rashdall said, with a standpoint which, from the view of "the modern non-metaphysical man of science," represents "the perfection of common sense."[18] The hedonist-libertarian ethic—the respect for human pleasure, the aversion to asceticism—seems to have been the emotional base for Occam's nominalism. He refused to grant the Holy Roman Emperor the authority to order fasting or to prohibit the drinking of wine; such commands, Occam maintained, were illicit, and could be disobeyed. Expelled from the Franciscan order in 1331, Occam maintained that the community, acting through a general council, had the right to depose the Pope if he acted illegally. Occam stood among the libertarians against the authoritarians. He did not try to ground human rights in Platonic entities but, as a nominalist, appealed to the observable *ius gentium*, the common customs of the human race. The emperor, according to Occam, was not an absolute ruler; if he violated the *ius gentium*, resistance against him was justified.[19] Occam became the principal ideological spokesman against papal authoritarianism. Accused of heresy, and a virtual prisoner in his convent for four years, Occam later placed his pen at the service of Louis of Bavaria, who was likewise embattled with the papal curia.

In Occam's philosophical writings, the pollution complex that characterized the scholastic realist tended to disappear. He could speak of the meaning of "healthy" in a way very much like Maimonides, without the loathing and abhorrence which the typical medieval realist experienced at the mention of the bodily functions. " 'Healthy,' " wrote Occam, "primarily signifies the health of an animal, and it also signifies a diet and urine, but in such a way that it always connotes the health of an animal." [20] Urine is mentioned often in this naturalistic spirit without the manifestations of repression that such a subject awoke in Plato, the forebear of realism. Occam liked homely illustrations. To indicate to "quibblers" what he meant by saying that a word is a sign, and an effect the sign at least of its cause, he remarked that "a barrel-hoop signifies the wine in the inn." [21] From Occam's teaching stemmed the logical principle of simplicity, central to all scientific thinking: "*Entia non sunt multiplicanda praeter necessitatem*" ("Entities are not to be multiplied except when necessary"). The hallmark of fantasy-thinking is that it invents all sorts of entities and beings in accordance with its longings, in complete disregard of bodily verification; it is the pleasure-principle operating to make its own wishes omnipotent in disregard of the reality principle.[22] Fantasy-thinking, born of the frustration of bodily drives and seeking some surrogate satisfaction in non-physical existence, dispensed with the principle of simplicity. The hedonistic-libertarian spirit expressed itself in the emphasis on the principle of simplicity; it was a principle of therapy for the medieval neurosis—a help in the recovery of the sense of reality.

To such profound students of the history of thought as Marx and Dewey, the source of medieval realism seemed to lie in the character of the economic institutions of the time. Marx, for instance, held that such false consciousness arose from the division between mental and material labor.[23] Consciousness, emancipated from the world, said Marx, began to flatter itself that it could conceive "something without conceiving something real." Scholars and aristocrats who did no work with their hands gradually defined "reality" in such a way as to divest it of material qualities. Dewey elaborated this technological explanation of philosophical realism. It reflected, he wrote, "the tragic division of theory and practice," the existence of a "class of 'thinkers' who are remote from practice and hence from testing their thought by application—a socially superior and irresponsible class." [24] The artisans and peasants, persons of low social status, were regarded by the philosophers of their time as having consort only with inferior realities, whereas the higher class had in its keeping the superior realities. The reality which philosophical realists from Plato to Duns Scotus believed to be given to their intuition was ideal, changeless, and eternal. Bukharin, the only and last Soviet sociological thinker of importance, thus similarly asserted that the philosophy of Thomas Aquinas "clearly reflects the feudal conditions" by dividing the world into its everyday segment and its underlying real forms.[25]

Now, at first sight the hypothesis that the nominalistic mode of thought reflects an involvement with technological activity, and realism a corresponding disinvolvement, seems to explain the historical facts. The hypostatizing tendency, for instance, was always conspicuously absent among Hebrew thinkers. Though their proverbs extolled wisdom, they never asked, as did the Greeks, whether wisdom was an entity in itself. Platonic wisdom was the wisdom of aristocrats, whereas Hebraic wisdom had the stamp of proletarians. The Talmudic sages were thus mostly artisans. Hillel was a woodcutter, Shammai a construction worker, Yehoshuah ben Chananya a charcoal worker, Akiba a wood-carrier, Yehuda a baker, Yochanon a shoemaker, Yose ben Chalafta a tanner, another Yehuda a tailor, Avuka a veil-maker, Huna a farmer, Yitzchak a blacksmith, Chanina a shoemaker, Hoshea also a shoemaker, Avin a carpenter, Abba ben Zimma a tailor.[26] The Talmud emphasized the obligation of the sages to work.

Nevertheless, a closer study of the comparative facts leads to an explanation of medieval realism that differs basically from that of Dewey and Marx. Medieval realism, in my view, stemmed directly from the emotional disfigurement that was imposed by the institution of sacerdotal celibacy. An intellectual class will develop this kind of metaphysics only when the social structure commits it to sexual repression. The Chinese literati who for many centuries constituted the civil service of their state were quite divorced from the processes of manual and agricultural labor. Yet they developed no considerable movement that made a central tenet of any doctrine resembling the Platonic universals; Confucius's philosophy, which suited their bureaucratic perspective, was earthy and matter-of-fact in its attitudes. The abhorrence of the material world, the desire to repress it and its essential manifestation of sexuality and pleasure, was lacking among the Chinese bureaucrats to whom a celibate life seemed grotesque, unnatural, and remiss in filial loyalty. Furthermore, the medieval Christian monks preached the dignity of labor —"*laborare est orare*,"—and often worked with their hands themselves. The Rule of St. Benedict, which set the organizational pattern for Christian monasticism, stipulated that a monastery "ought so to be arranged that everything necessary—that is, water, a mill, a garden, a bakery—may be made use of, and different arts be carried on, within the monastery; so that there shall be no need for the monks to wander about outside." [27] Their laboring activity, however, did not nullify the projective motive which sprang from their sacerdotal celibacy.

As for the Jewish sages, they were all advocates of marriage and, with only one exception, were all married themselves. Celibacy was regarded by the Jewish thinkers as a sin.[28] "Be fruitful and multiply," said the first chapter of Genesis, and Talmudical commentaries added:

> He who is without a wife is without joy, without blessing, without happiness, without protection, without peace; indeed he is no man. . . . He who is not married is, as it were, guilty of bloodshed and deserves death: he causes the image of God to be diminished. . . .

The asceticism of the Essenic communities was regarded as a deviation from the teachings of Judaism.[29]

Was it then dissociation from labor or the repression of sexuality that was the necessary condition for the belief in the reality of universals? The comparative circumstances of the Chinese scholar-gentry and the Jewish sages indicate that neither their association nor dissociation from labor was the decisive factor in determining metaphysical allegiance; rather, it was their adherence to or rejection of sexual asceticism. Neither the leisured Chinese civil servants nor the proletarian Jewish sages were drawn to "pure Ideas" because neither group was sexually ascetic.

To understand a philosophical movement, it is helpful to make use of the concept of a "modal personality structure"—that is, those traits of character which a particular social institution tends to instill and reinforce. Military institutions, for example, inculcate a military bearing, a military language, and eroticized attitudes toward the army; usually they promote an attitude toward women as indiscriminate objects for satisfying sexual needs, and there are typical attitudes as well toward the commander, superiors, inferiors, brothers-in-arms, and the outside world of civilians.

Likewise, monasticism reinforced certain personality traits upon its members, imposed a common denominator of outlook, and obliterated, as far as it could, non-monastic attitudes. Metaphors of "adoration" for heavenly non-physical entities filled their speech; noblemen's sons like Thomas Aquinas who joined the celibate orders took on a common mentality as they did a common attire. Thomas's family tried to sway him from his decision to join the Dominican Order by presenting him in his chamber, it is said, with an alluring young woman. He chased her from his room, and scorched the sign of the cross on the door.[30] Years later, he polemicized against the naturalistic Arab philosopher Averroes, and defended the regular clergy against their less ascetic secular colleagues. The monks were always embattled with their sexual drives, warring against their bodies. Jerome set the pattern for centuries to come with his horror of marriage as indecent, his imprecation against the anti-virginitarians who would enter "that blessed vase which the Lord has filled," his loathing for bearded priests (with their pubic suggestion), and his repulsion from sexual organs, the "nasty stain." Two, he held, was a bad number because it was linked to the uncleanness of matrimony. Jerome, as G. G. Coulton points out, was quoted all through the Middle Ages as "a decisive authority." The desire for beautiful dancing girls tormented Jerome as it did so many of those dedicated to holiness defined as asceticism.[31]

A typical psychological ailment called "accidie" (from a Greek word meaning "not caring") came to afflict monks and holy men from the third century on. Life then seemed an indifferent thing, without zest, without color, with the perpetual savor of defeat and self-frustration. There was a monotonous apathy, in which every desire was the hapless occasion for self-denial, and the pains of bodily mortification offered at least the excitement of intense masochistic experience.[32] "It is remarkable," writes Herbert B. Workman, "that every Father after the first three centuries, Basil, the two Gregories, Ambrose, Augustine, Jerome, Chryostom exhaust language in the effort to exalt virginity."

The masochist ascetic was thus the modal personality structure shaped by the formative influences of the sacerdotal celibacy imposed by the medieval church. As Harnack writes:

> The monastic ideal was at first identical in its essentials both in the East and in the West, and it remained so during a thousand years —absorption in God and stern asceticism, but especially virginity, which, in West as in East, ranked as the first condition of a consecrated life. To many, indeed, virginity was neither more nor less than the very essence of Christian morality.[33]

There were underlying social and economic causes for the rise of monasticism, the clerical orders, and the emphasis on celibacy. But a philosophy or ideology is never determined directly or fully by socio-economic institutions. What mediates between the latter and an ideology is the effect of the institutions on personality structure, on sexual emotion, on affections and aggressions, on modes of repression and formation of defense mechanisms. Between the economic stimulus and the ideological response, there is the intervening role of the modal personality structure, with its corresponding emotional sense of what is real and unreal, and its response to social happenings; the ideological response is shaped directly by the underlying emotional vectors. Apart from the pattern in which change in social institutions arises, the latter causal chain is then from the social and economic institutions to their shaping (at least in large part) of modes of emotional expression and repression, and then to the consequent intellectual formulation. Modes of thought must be understood through the underlying modes of emotion, with the mode of production only mediately, indirectly involved.

Now, there were several social and economic causes for the church's commitment to sacerdotal celibacy. It began early to receive large gifts of property whose usufruct would have been dissipated, if married churchmen had been allowed, among their respective families. Therefore, the popes toward the end of the fourth century promulgated a rule of perpetual celibacy for ministers of the altar. The people, too, however, wanted "holiness" in their priests. An unmarried priest can more easily take on the role of a surrogate father, for he is not the object of sexual animosity. A celibate priest, one might say metaphorically, is a father who has castrated himself, or, in the words of the New Testament, has made himself "an eunuch for the kingdom of heaven's sake." [34] Far from being the son's sexual rival, he represents, we might say, the castration complex deflected from the son and assumed by the father. Last, sacerdotal celibacy strengthened the intensity of the emotional ties among priests and monks themselves, and enhanced their own emotional identification with the church. Sacerdotal celibacy, as Hildebrand realized, helped make the church a theocracy.

The conflict within the church on the celibacy issue was severe. In the eleventh century, a formidable party arose, the so-called Nicolites, who opposed clerical celibacy. They were denounced by Pope Urban II in 1095, shortly before he proclaimed the First Crusade. Under Calixtus II, a general council finally, in 1123, forbade marriage to those who took vows or holy orders in the church. The party of masochist asceticism triumphed. As Henry C. Lea writes, the emphasis on mortification and self-denial then "exercised a most depressing influence in restraining the general advance of civilization." It weighed down "the efforts of almost every man," and those ardent minds who might have been leaders in progress were apt "to be foremost in maceration and self-denial" under the influence of the pervading ascetic ethos.[35]

The nominalist recovery of the sense of reality, by contrast, signified a more hedonistic answer with reference to the question of celibacy. Abelard, who, as R. L. Poole notes, was "certainly nearer nominalism than realism," married Héloise, and defended the right of the lower clergy to take wives so long as they were not in charge of parishes. Celibacy, he said, was simply a question of expediency, and was contravened by the custom of the Greek Church.[36] Thinkers of the fourteenth and fifteenth centuries, especially within the

Dominican order, says Harnack, feared the "Pelagian tendency of Nominalism, and strenuously resisted it in the spirit of Augustine." [37] Pelagius, far back in the fifth century, had rejected the gloomy doctrine of original sin, and averred that a life of holiness could be lived even without divine help; he stressed man's freedom, not his helplessness, to choose his own life. From the church's standpoint, such a doctrine stressed man's potential strength, natural health, and independence far too much; the church endorsed Augustine's condemnation of Pelagianism.[38] The horror Augustine felt for married life and sexuality generally became the church's orthodoxy, and provided the emotional culture that nurtured doctrines such as the reality of universals.

It was Thomas Hobbes, the hardheaded scientific philosopher of the seventeenth century, who first glimpsed, though in vague fashion, the connection between philosophical realism and clerical celibacy. The doctrine of "separated essences," he observed, arose in a church which held to the "vain and false philosophy" that marriage was repugnant to chastity; the church required of its functionaries "a continual abstinence from women under the name of continual Chastity, Continence, and Purity." To be "Spiritual" signified for churchmen, said Hobbes, to regard wives as an "incongruity." And the "separated essences," the realm "of these Terms, of Entity, Essence, Essential, Essentiality," were the language and metaphysic of those who repressed the sexual and physical as unclean.

The psychoanalytical Pastor Pfister, in our century, has written with clarity that "the scholastic philosophy of the Middle Ages, with its useless notional acrobatics, was the necessary consequence of the medieval ideal of life," with its self-abnegation in celibacy, obedience, and poverty.[39] What are the psychological mechanisms by means of which ascetic celibacy expressed itself in the metaphysical doctrine of the reality of universals? In the world of neurosis, as Freud wrote, the psychical reality of fantasies displaces material realities; sexual energies that are deflected from the avenues of real satisfaction are accumulated in the direction of fantasies.[40] Now, the ascetic celibate tries especially to repress the objects of sexuality, and whatever is physically associated with them. He aims to negate the reality of the sexual world, and to triumph at least metaphysically over that which he cannot annihilate in his unconscious. He sets out to purify the external world; he does so by arguments which try to show that its physical traits are unreal. He engages in a kind of metaphysical destructive distillation, and the residue left at the end he calls "universals" or "ideas." These residual ideas he then eroticizes with all the feeling that has survived the repression of his sexuality.

In the Middle Ages, the de-realization of the physical world took the form of scholastic realism rather than, let us say, absolute idealism, because of a special historical circumstance. The grammatical and logical writings of Aristotle were the first of his works to become known to medieval thinkers. The biological writings, for instance, as Charles Singer has pointed out, were little known to the Christian thinkers until as late as the sixteenth century.[41] Philosophical discussion therefore raged chiefly around the new categories of grammatical analysis which had been introduced. "Grammar is the cradle of all philosophy," said John of Salisbury. There was something like a grammatical madness, and an eroticization of words, that ensued. As John of Salisbury described it:

> . . . the word "argument" was on the lips of all. To mention "an ass," "a man," or any of the works of nature was considered a crime, or improper, crude, and alien to a philosopher. . . . Not even an argument was admitted unless it was prefaced by its name. . . . They would probably teach . . . that the carpenters cannot make a bench unless he is simultaneously forming on his lips the word "bench" or "wooden seat." The result is this hodgepodge of verbiage. . . .[42]

The doctrine of scholastic realism was a species of grammatical mysticism, the endowing of adjectives with a substantial reality all their own, apart from things. A passage from Porphyry leaving open the question whether "genera or species . . . subsist or whether they are placed in the naked understandings alone or whether subsisting they are corporeal or incorporeal, and whether they are separated from sensibles or placed in sensibles" became the departure for inquiries which were deemed "most exalted." The Gospel According to St. John had said, "In the beginning was the Word . . . And the Word was made flesh. . . ." What took place in medieval thought was quite the reverse. In the beginning there was the Flesh, and the Flesh repressed became the Word. To the medieval intellectual, physical objects, as Lynn White, Jr., observes, lost their concrete reality and became suffused with "spiritual meanings"; to the masochist ascetic, "red" signified the blood of Christ, and "wood" His cross.[43]

Philosophers, as Flügel noted, have tended to take matter as representing the female component in reality.[44] Plato, for instance, in the *Timaeus* had spoken of "the mother and receptacle" of all sensible things; while the source or spring was likened to a father, the receptacle was "the nurse of all generation." The *Timaeus* was the most influential of Plato's dialogues in the Middle Ages.[45] Maimonides thus remarked that Plato called substance the female and form the male.[46] Now, the purpose of the Platonic argument was to purify reality of the sexual, material dross. Plato therefore became much disturbed by the suggestion that perhaps his dialectic would not successfully achieve that purification. All seemed to go well as long as one was talking of Absolute Justice, Beauty, or Good, which were given to the person "who goes to each with the mind alone," without any intruding act of sense; access to Reality was to be the prerogative of him "who has got rid, as far as he can, of eyes and ears and, so to speak, of the whole body." Only the "polluted" soul is "in love with and fascinated by the body," wrote Plato, "and by the desires and pleasures of the body, until she is led to believe that the truth only exists in a bodily form, which a man may touch and see and taste. . . ." The empiricist philosophy, according to Plato, was founded on the dominion of sexuality.

But the very same arguments for the existence of an Absolute Truth could be used to prove that there was an Absolute Dirt, and at this point the Socratic neurotic repression was threatened by its own weapon against physical reality:

> "Socrates," said Parmenides, "about things of which the mention may provoke a smile? I mean such things as hair, mud, dirt, or anything else which is vile and paltry; would you suppose that each of them has an idea distinct from the actual objects with which we come into contact, or not?"
>
> "Certainly not," said Socrates. ". . . I am afraid that there would be an absurdity in assuming any idea of them, although I sometimes get disturbed, and begin to think that there is nothing without an idea; but then again, when I have taken up this position, I run away, because I am afraid that I may fall into a bottomless pit of nonsense, and perish; and so I return to the ideas of which I was just now speaking. . . ."

Parmenides in this dialogue forecasts to Socrates that as he will get older, he "will not despise even the meanest things." But meanwhile we have a classical statement of the motivation of the belief in ideas. The "vile and the paltry," the excremental and bodily and sexual, are to be repressed. As Edwyn Bevan indicated in his essay on the philosophical significance of dirt, the idea of dirt involves a feeling of pollution, a feeling of the uncleanness of excrements and secretions, digestive, sexual, and otherwise, which goes "far beyond any logically drawn conclusion from their dangerousness as breeders of disease."[47] This "pollution complex" was central, for instance, to Hindu thought and society, and made an uncongenial soil for the growth of experimental science.[48] The "bottomless pit" menaces Plato when he perceives that he may not be able to exclude the sexual-physical objects from their counterparts in the realm of ideas.

This anxiety lest lowly objects intrude into the realm of pure ideas always persisted among the medieval realists. As late as 1410, when Jerome of Prague was examined for heresy, a student witness testifying against him said, "We heard him say in a sermon that there is a universal ass."[49] Evidently, in the case of asses, there were to exist only individuals, and "asininity" was to be the name for an adjective, not a pure idea.

The Platonic repression of sexuality was transmitted to the medieval ethic through such thinkers as Philo Judaeus, who, though Jewish, adhered to an ascetic standpoint not typical of Jewish philosophers.[50] Philo, for instance, gave to the rite of circumcision an ascetic, castrational interpretation. It was, he said, a mutilation of the organ which was the source of physical pleasure, a cutting off of "superfluous and excessive desires"—a sign of the renunciation of fleshly desire. Philo, as Professor Erwin Goodenough tells us, wished to portray a universe "eternally virgin," in which we would seek immersion.[51] The simple earthly love of Isaac for Rebecca was transformed into a union with an eternal Virgin, "from whose love," Philo prayed, "may I never cease"; Rebecca comes to Isaac "veiled as are the inner secrets of the Mystery." The language of mystery depicted a world whose traits were to be as veiled and repressed as human sexuality. The worship of the Virgin, the exclusion of the father's defilement of the mother, made easier the mystic celebration of the pure union of son with mother. "The soul is reborn by union with its own mother," said Philo. The medieval ascetics were to deal with oedipal feelings by "purifying" themselves and their mothers of sexuality.

Arabic philosophy did not take the path of asceticism which its Christian counterpart followed, and was therefore not impelled to elevate the doctrine of universals into a central metaphysical tenet. The great scientific philosopher of the Middle Ages was Averroes, who with his three doctrines—the eternity of the material world, determinism, and the denial of individual immortality—spoke for an Arab intellectual class which was not prepared to inscribe panegyrics to masochist asceticism. Averroes enunciated a nominalist disbelief in the objective existence of pure ideas; ideas were events in the thinking of human organisms: "Being and Unity are not annexed to the Essence, but are given only in Thought, just like all universals. Thought produces everywhere the general in the particular. It is true that the universal as a disposition is operative in things, but the universal *qua* universal exists in the understanding alone." Forms, according to Averroes, could be separated from matter only by way of intellectual distinction; they did not enjoy an autonomous ghostlike existence. Underlying Averroes' refusal to project a surrogate realm of ideas was an emotional perspective very different from that of the Christians. The celibate churchmen tended to be misogynists, warning against women's wiles and urging their subordinate status. Averroes, on the contrary, was a medieval feminist; poverty and distress arose, he said, because women were treated like domestic animals; they should be allowed to serve society to the full extent of their capacities. "It is not impossible," wrote Averroes, that there may be among women "philosophers and rulers," and it is a mistake to confine them to "the business of procreation, rearing, and breast-feeding." We can understand why the Jews, co-religionists of the physician-philosopher Maimonides, found themselves in especial kinship with Averroes, and constituted the bulk of his admirers.[52] For Averroes' approach to ethical problems was likewise in a physician's spirit:

> In general, the problem is similar to those in Medicine. As the final part [of Medicine] sums up and makes known how the body grows up in health, how it should be preserved, and how disease should be removed from it when it departs from [the way of] health, so it is in the treatment of the soul.

R1087

The cosmopolitan spirit which was to be an intrinsic ingredient of the scientists' ethic in the seventeenth century was also present in the Arab scientists' outlook. Religion divided people into elect and damned, chosen and rejected, but Averroes, writing in reply to Plato's notion that only the Greeks were capable of philosophic wisdom, argued that persons "predisposed to philosophy are found, for example, in our own country Spain, and in Syria, Iraq and Egypt, even though such individuals may have existed much more frequently in Greece." The scientists, in Averroes' view, would constitute the ruling class in an ideal state; he deplored the rule of either the rich, the poor, or the priests, and believed, on the basis of his sociological analysis, that they all degenerate much too easily into tyrannies.[53]

Physician-philosophers, especially, were numerous throughout the Islamic world, and gave to its thinking a more naturalistic, undistorted sense of reality than obtained among the Christian celibate churchmen. Avicenna was perhaps the outstanding opponent of the naturalistic temper in medieval Arabic thought. He was not representative, however, of the philosophy of the Arab scientific world. There was an inner duality in his thinking which seemed to mirror some deep-seated, unresolved emotional conflict. Although Avicenna never married, he is said to have indulged in excessive sexual relations, as well as abundant medications. He was "hounded from town to town for reasons that he does not care to tell." He oscillated between nominalist tendencies and a Neo-Platonic mysticism. Avicenna's upbringing had been severely ascetic, and he remained hostile to the dominant physicalism of Arabic thought.[54] He especially attacked the hedonist philosophy of Rhazes as the lucubrations of a man who should have stuck "to testing stools and urine." Rhazes, regarded as the greatest clinical genius among Arabic physicians and called "the Voltaire of Islam," bluntly defined pleasure as "a return to the normal state." An admirer of the ancient materialist Democritus, Rhazes did not include universals among the substances. Much more than Avicenna, Rhazes and Averroes expressed the spirit of the scientists whose open, friendly interest in the physical world coincided with their own acceptance of their physical natures. The Averroist tradition, transmitted to the University of Padua, in the fortunate environs of Venice, helped make of it the greatest scientific center at the inception of the modern era. The nominalist critique of fantasy-entities and its recovery of the sense of physical reality were part of the movement against masochist asceticism which made possible the rise of experimental science.

The compulsion to detach reality from physical objects, to attach it to intellectual abstractions, and its linkage with asceticism are traits that have never been absent among philosophers. Several such typical cases have been narrated in psychoanalytical reports. There was the case of Julius (as described by Pfister), who became increasingly involved in "formalism and intellectualism," with a passion for "forms of language," in proportion to his decline in affection for people. "The desolation of the emotional life and the abandonment of the intellect to empty formalism" went hand in hand. The emotional energies withdrawn from human realities were redirected toward formal entities, which were endowed with a surrogate personified "reality." There was the case of the student of philosophy (as narrated by Stekel) who was a complete ascetic and fantastically devoted to "truth." Stekel found that this ascetic self-castigation was "the attitude of a masturbator who has kept from all the world one fact (his masturbation) and now overcompensates this lie with his fanaticism for truth." Thus, the replacement of ordinary truths by Truth as a goal was conjoined with the ascetic self-punishment of sexual longings and guilt. What the psychoanalysts call the "libidinization" of the thought process, the making of ideas into Entities, which one experiences with all the feeling usually evoked by persons and things, is characteristic of the ascetic, realistic tradition.[55]

Only rarely have philosophers set down in detail the emotional mainsprings of their thought. Augustine, whose immense influence gave to the Church its heritage of metaphysical realism, wrote a psychological autobiography which is always read because it exposes with such frankness the emotionale of his ideas. Asceticism for him was a metaphysical method for the experiencing of Pure Reality. "Thus doth the soul commit fornication, when she turns from thee, seeking without Thee, what she findeth not pure and untainted, till she returns to Thee." In the attractiveness of "beautiful bodies," in "bodily touch," in the theatre, in "human friendship" itself, and in the like, "is sin committed," said Augustine, for thereby "the better and higher are forsaken." In his youth, that which was not bodily did not seem to Augustine "to be anything," but as he submerged his human affections, overcame his "enthrallment" with "the love of woman," and enrolled himself among the "eunuchs for the kingdom of heaven's sake," he believed himself to have achieved contact with the Pure Substance for which his soul "panted," "Thee Thyself, the Truth, in whom is no variableness. . . ." Augustine's mother had wished him to put aside his pagan father, Patricius, with his free sexual ways, so "that Thou my God, rather than he, shouldest be my father. . . ."[56] The maternal fixation triumphed, and from its ascetic withdrawal from physical realities there issued a metaphysics consonant with that projected by Plato's homosexuality and the celibacy of the later medieval clerics. "The Realism of Augustine dominated the schools until the eleventh century," says Carré. Philosophy became the handmaiden of self-destruction, the sign of the masochist, so that to be "philosophical" came to signify to be submissive, resigned, acquiescent, feminine; philosophy became, as Plato said in the *Phaedo*, "the study of death." It was the great achievement of the scientists and philosophers of the seventeenth century, the men of the "new philosophy," that they made the word "philosophical" synonymous with courage, daring, pride, and vigor of self, that they made philosophy the study of life.

The Concept of Renaissance, Urban Hedonism, and the Thomist Compromise

THE RENAISSANCE IN EUROPE, says Wallace K. Ferguson, was "the age of transition from medieval to modern civilization"; during the years from approximately 1300 to 1600, it changed European civilization so radically that it amounted "to a change in kind rather than in degree." Medieval culture was founded on a society that was agrarian, feudal, and ecclesiastical. By the beginning of the fourteenth century, however, the Renaissance in Italy was arising in "an urban society, constructed upon an economic foundation of large-scale commerce and industry, and with rapidly developing capitalist institutions." The Renaissance, says Professor Ferguson, was founded on a "massing of population in cities" and "the growth of large private fortunes." Religion became laicized, anticlerical sentiment grew, the layman was placed on an even footing with the cleric, and revolts began "against the hierarchical authority of the church and the sacramental-sacerdotal aspects of medieval religion." With the new, unprecedented wealth, there began to flourish "an unprecedented variety of social types." The atmosphere was one of "intellectual excitement caused by the challenge of new conditions of life, of new potentialities in every field of culture, and, in general, of a sense of breaking new ground and of scanning ever-widening horizons." In this age there was "a growing awareness of personality and a keener sense of individual autonomy" than had been possible in medieval society.[57]

The historian of European civilization is concerned with dating the bounds of the Renaissance, with its "periodization." For the psychologist, however, what is important is the occurrence of renaissances, with this phenomenon of renaissance as recurrent. Within the Renaissance proper, there were a multitude of renaissances; the scientific renaissance, for instance, as George Sarton pointed out, came almost a century after the renaissance in art, and the scientific renaissance itself was a complex of renaissances—astronomical, medical, mathematical.[58] Several centuries after the Italian Renaissance, a renaissance burgeoned in Scotland; there was a scientific renaissance in Sweden in the late seventeenth century, and a Jewish renaissance in the nineteenth. Every renaissance is essentially a psychological phenomenon; the essence of this phenomenon of rebirth is a liberation of human energies, a disengagement from the past, a disenthrallment from self-aggression and asceticism; renaissance renews a delight in the human status, a friendliness to the senses, a diminution of the cultural burden of guilt. Every renaissance has been based on a revival of the hedonist-libertarian ethics.

Social changes in Europe slowly strengthened the towns with their hedonist-libertarian ethic, and most scholars would be inclined to see in these social and economic changes the dynamic of the European Renaissance. Behind the development of commerce and industry, however, there was a new psychological standpoint; the runaway serf, the rebellious scholar, the adventurous seaman were seeking a new world, seeking a new industry, a new commerce, a new science. The urban revolution and the scientific revolution both rested on a psychological revolution whose inner dynamic has not yet been explored.

Meanwhile, social changes in Europe were slowly strengthening the towns with their hedonist-libertarian ethic. Science made its first appearances in Western Europe at the time medieval asceticism and hatred for the body declined. The Middle Ages were characterized by Michelet: "*Mille ans d'histoire mais pas un seul bain*." ("A thousand years of history but not a single bath"). The historian Lecky has portrayed the era in which self-degradation was for some centuries regarded as the chief measure of human excellence: "The cleanliness of the body was regarded as a pollution of the soul, and the saints who were most admired had become one hideous mass of clotted filth." [59] St. Anthony was revered for his holiness because he never in his long life washed his feet, while St. Abraham was admired because, for fifty years after his conversion, he washed neither his face nor his feet. Cleanliness during the Middle Ages was the Devil's domain; meanwhile, body lice thrived and brought their bearers, it was believed, close to God.

The development of the medical sciences, the first harbinger of the scientific renaissance, was intimately tied to the awakening of the hedonistic spirit. The University of Salerno, the earliest medical school in Europe, had preserved a tenuous existence for several centuries. It flourished in the twelfth. Its students and teachers urged the value of bathing and diet; they taught a simple self-respect for the human body, and advocated proper exercise. The baths of Salerno became famous in verse. Medical studies were the first to find centers of instruction in the new universities. The town of Montpellier had long been a trading place for Christians, Jews, Arabs. One could meet within its walls Jewish merchants from Spain and merchants from Lombardy. Centuries later, Rabelais and Locke came there to study. In its atmosphere of tolerance, a famous medical school began to emerge from the twelfth century on. Medicine, furthermore, was the first branch of science to possess a commercial value.[60]

To the medieval churchmen, with their ideals of asceticism and poverty, the commercial revival, as Pirenne writes, seemed "a thing of shame and a cause of anxiety." [61] Had not St. Jerome said, "The merchant can please God only with difficulty"? For the merchants inevitably brought a hedonistic ethics to their market places. Like advertisers today, they became more prosperous the more they could stimulate wants. The merchant has always wished people to satisfy their desires. The ethics of commerce is intrinsically anti-ascetic. The Aristotelian philosophy which began to penetrate Western Europe was used to express the attitudes of the newly awakened urban hedonistic revolution.

The Aristotelian ethics was welcome to the towns because it was opposed to asceticism. The doctrine of the mean—that virtue lies between extremes—was congenial to the rising middle class; this was their moderate style of life elevated into a principle of medical therapy, and it accepted physical pleasures in just proportion. From Aristotle the townsman could learn that deficiency in pleasures is only less reprehensible than self-indulgence; the mean is temperance. From Aristotle he learned that happiness involves pleasure and that excess in the ascetic direction is not virtuous. From Aristotle he could learn, too, that the humility of the monks was one extreme and the vanity of the lords another; he, the bourgeois, had the proper pride of the virtuous mean. Aristotle was the guide to the practical wisdom of how to act for human goods. To the medieval martyrologist came Aristotle's therapeutic reply: "Those who say that the victim on the rack is happy if he is good, are, whether they mean to or not, talking nonsense." "The happy man," said the Stagirite, "needs the goods of the body and external goods." [62]

Aristotle's ethics meant a break with the excesses of monasticism, asceticism, and anti-bathing. It provided the first, incipient philosophy of a humanist bourgeoisie. At the court of the heterodox scientist-emperor, Frederick II of Sicily, the full text of Aristotle's *Ethics* was known and appreciated.[63] Frederick himself appealed to its argument when he wrote a preface to a translation of an Arab book on falconry. The different human activities have their respective appropriate pleasures, said Frederick.

Above all, a new student class was coming into existence, unclerical in its attitudes and with something of the revolutionary. For "the professions were soon overstocked, and living by the wits became common." The Goliards, the wandering students in the universities of the later Middle Ages, betokened a new era. Vagabond poets, songsters who delighted in love, the spring, and the tavern—these hedonist intellectuals of the lower echelon were in their full vigor around 1160. They sang such songs as "The Confession of Golias":

Much too hard it is, I find,
So to change my essence
As to keep a virgin mind
In a virgin's presence.
Rigid laws can never bind
Youth to acquiescence;
Light o' loves must seek their kind
Bodies take their pleasance.[64]

The poems of the oft-recited *Carmina Burana* were "invariably carnal":

Love controls the gods alone
Jove takes Juno's orders;

While I still wore Wisdom's colors
I was fain with Venus' scholars.

The love lyrics that Abelard, analytic philosopher of the twelfth century, wrote for his Heloise were sung among the common people. Composed in vernacular French, not in pedantic Latin, these poems of love were related in a curious way to the liberating power of Abelard's questioning, which fired a new generation of students, and made Abelard's classes centers for challenge, doubt, and faith in human reason. In Abelard's refusal to people hell with the pagan philosophers, and in his recognition that their lives were exemplary despite their ignorance of Christ, we have the entry of the urban liberal spirit into theology.

All observers testified to the hedonistic spirit which diffused from the universities. "I saw at Paris," wrote John of Salisbury in 1167, "abundance of life, popular joy, life respected, a crowd of philosophers absorbed in various occupations." Petrarch, in the fourteenth century, recalled the university city of Montpellier:

> On passing out of my childhood, I spent four years at Montpellier, at that time a very flourishing city. What tranquillity reigned there! What peace! What riches were possessed by the merchants! What a crowd of students. What an abundance of masters.

The first release of aggressive energies in the new academic channels took the form of a passion for disputation. Hitherto men had jousted with arms, but now the tourneys of knights were supplanted by the verbal bouts of scholars. Men could be impaled on the horns of dilemmas as effectively, though less irrevocably, as on lances. "I preferred the conflicts of discussion," said Abelard, "to the trophies of war." A chancellor of the University of Paris said, "What are the contests of our savants if not real cock-fights? . . . One cock struts up to another, and bristles his feathers." The tradition of submission and asceticism was being broken. The Catholic Church was perturbed by the novel Aristotelian ideas, the questioning, the challenge to vested ideas and interests latent in the nominalist disputationists and the urban hedonistic spirit. Aristotle came to Christian Europe in the garb of Averroist commentaries; heterodox principles such as the eternity of matter and the denial of personal immortality were expounded in the Arab's texts. There were rumors that in the towns and country, materialist philosophers were appealing to the authority of Epicurus and Lucretius. Aristotelianism was, in Van Steenberghen's words, "fraught with *very real danger* for Christianity"; it posed the threat "of a philosophical movement in the Arts Faculty becoming increasingly independent, 'rationalistic,' and daring." The church tried to stem the menace by edicts of prohibition. At Paris in 1210, the public or private teaching of Aristotle's natural philosophy and the Arab commentators was forbidden. There were varying interdictions in 1210, 1215, 1231, 1245, 1263, and 1277.[65] Gradually, however, the church came to terms with Aristotle, and transformed his doctrine to suit apologetic and bureaucratic needs. At the same time, it effected a compromise with the rising national states and towns. When modern science arose in the seventeenth century, it contested an Aristotelianism which had become the ideology of clerical restraint and censorship. Scholastic Aristotelianism put a curb on the test of the senses—their claims to validate knowledge.

Every philosophical movement has tended to evolve into wings, a left, right, and center. The philosophy of Thomas Aquinas represented what has been called the "Thomist compromise" because it enabled the church to come to terms in the thirteenth century with the standpoint of the growing urban centers. On the one hand, there were the left Aristotelians—the Averroist Aristotelians—who actually taught at Paris that the physical world was eternal, and that there was no personal immortality; on the other, there were the right Aristotelians, persons such as Duns Scotus and Bonaventura, who infused Aristotelian forms with Platonic Ideas.[66] The left Aristotelians were hedonist-libertarians who verged on theological and political heresy. The right Aristotelians were the party of asceticism and theological and political austerity. Thomas devised the centrist theological formula, which condemned the leftist hedonist-libertarians but which at the same time rebuked the ascetic right in a measure sufficient for the church to maintain a precarious hold upon the loyalties of the more worldly burghers. To the townsmen came Thomas's assurance, as against the ascetics, that "integral happiness requires a perfect disposition of body," and that the flesh, though corruptible, would be turned to glory by the heaven-directed mind.[67] To the new middle class, he brought the Aristotelian word that virtue resides in the middle, the "mean": "Evil comes from tilting the balance when there should be an equilibrium, the bad being overweight or underweight. . . . The mean between excess and defect is an equality or conformity." "The middle and Aristotelian way is to be preferred," said Thomas. With the Averroist intellectuals, Aquinas agreed that the notion of Pure Ideas, the "bodiless forms" of Plato and Avicenna, ran contrary to the evidence that we derive our ideas through the bodily senses. "The forms of sensible things," said Thomas with Aristotle, "can neither exist nor be understood apart from sensible things." To believe in such pure forms as in themselves substances, said Thomas finally, "smacked of heterodoxy."

The Thomist compromise abrogated philosophical realism, but it still retained the ultimate primacy of ascetic values. With Augustine, Thomas paid tribute to the state of innocence where the "heat of lust" would be gone, and where there would be "fruitfulness without lechery." "The law of concupiscence" was the Devil's work. And Thomas demanded a more thoroughgoing conformity to Scriptural theology than the pantheistic Parisian Averroists were prepared to give. The latter had devised the twofold theory of truth as a way of mollifying the church—the theory that what can be true from the theological standpoint can be false philosophically. This was a transparent ideological device, a ritualistic formula for philosophic heretics to use to evade the Inquisition. The Left Aristotelians, precursors of the scientific intellectuals, were the bearers of the scientific spirit and hedonist-libertarian ethic during the era when the church held to an organizational hegemony over the intellect.

GORDON COLLEGE

NOTES

1. Etienne Gilson, *The Unity of Philosophical Experience* (New York, 1937), p. 3.

2. Maurice de Wulf, *Scholasticism Old and New*, trans. P. Coffey (New York, 1907), pp. 13, 32, 105, 106. Cf. Vilfredo Pareto, *The Mind and Society*, trans. Andrew Bongiorno and Arthur Livingston (New York, 1935), Vol. IV, pp. 1710-14.

3. Dr. A. Wolf, "Aristotle and Medieval Jewish Thought," in Leon Simon, *Aspects of the Hebrew Genius* (London, 1910), p. 131.

4. Moses Maimonides, *Guide for the Perplexed*, ed. M. Friedlander (2nd ed., reprinted, New York, 1956), p. 289. Cf. Harry Austryn Wolfson, *Crescas' Critique of Aristotle* (Cambridge, 1929), p. 107.

5. Edward Gibbon, *Memoirs of My Life and Writings*, ed. George Birkbeck Hill (London, 1900), p. 57. Edward Gibbon, *History of the Decline and Fall of the Roman Empire*, ed. J. B. Bury (London, 1897), Vol. IV, p. 67.

6. *The Eight Chapters of Maimonides on Ethics*, trans. Joseph I. Gorfinkle (New York, 1912), pp. 62, 63, 70, 72. Rev. A. Cohen, *The Teachings of Maimonides* (London, 1927), pp. 275-80.

7. Rev. A. Cohen, *op. cit.*, p. 263. *The Eight Chapters of Maimonides on Ethics*, p. 76. Salo W. Baron, "The Economic Views of Maimonides," in *Essays on Maimonides*, ed. S. W. Baron (New York, 1941), p. 239.

8. Nima H. Adlerblum, *A Study of Gersonides in his Proper Perspective* (New York, 1926), pp. 14, 26. Isaac Husik, *A History of Jewish Mediaeval Philosophy* (Philadelphia, 1916), p. 338. Jehuda Halevi, *Kuzari*, ed. Isaak Heinemann (Oxford, 1947), pp. 77, 86.

9. Max Meyerhof, "Mediaeval Jewish Physicians in the Near East from Arabic Sources," *Isis*, XXVIII (1938), 448. Solomon ibn Gabirol, *The Improvement of the Moral Qualities*, trans. Stephen S. Wise (New York, 1901), pp. 13, 17. Gabirol's naturalistic ethics entered into the stream of Jewish philosophic thought; his Neo-Platonic metaphysics, on the other hand, was completely ignored. Cf. Isaac Husik, *op. cit.*, pp. 62, 71.

10. *The Metalogicon of John of Salisbury: A Twelfth-Century Defense of the Verbal and Logical Arts of the Trivium*, translated by Daniel D. McGarry, Berkeley, 1955, pp. 151-2.

11. Cf. Frederick G. Holweck, "Immaculate Conception," *Catholic*

Encyclopaedia (New York, 1910), Vol. VII, pp. 676, 679. Parthenius Minges, "Duns Scotus," *Catholic Encyclopaedia*, Vol. V, (1909), pp. 197-8.

12. Béraud de Saint-Maurice, *John Duns Scotus*, trans. Columban Duffy (St. Bonaventura, 1955), pp. 85, 44, 92-3, 142, 212 ff., 221 ff., 236. C. R. S. Harris, *Duns Scotus* (Oxford, 1927), Vol. I, p. 206.

13. Ludwig Feuerbach, *The Essence of Christianity*, trans. George Eliot (reprinted, New York, 1957), pp. 137-9. Insofar as it concerned the Holy Virgin Mary, said St. Augustine, "I will have no question whatever where sin is concerned."

14. *The Letters of Abelard and Heloise*, trans. C. K. Scott Moncrieff (New York, 1933), pp. 5-6, 10-11, 13, 58-9. Cf. M. Michelet, *History of France*, trans. G. H. Smith (London, 1845), Vol. I, pp. 180-5.

15. *Selections from the Medieval Philosophers*, trans. Richard McKeon (New York, 1929), Vol. I, p. 250. Abelard's theological works were principally written after his sexual mutilation, and most of his writing evidently did not receive its final form until his last years. Cf. Charles de Rémusat, *Abélard* (Paris, 1845), Tome I, pp. 169-70; Tome II, pp. 93-4. Also, Tome I, p. 121.

16. George William Greenaway, *Arnold of Brescia* (Cambridge, 1931), pp. 37, 44-5, 123-4.

17. Ockham, *Studies and Selections*, ed. Stephen Chak Tornay (La Salle, 1938), p. 5.

18. Hastings Rashdall, *The Universities of Europe in the Middle Ages* (new ed., F. M. Powicke and A. B. Emden, Oxford, 1936), Vol. III, p. 263.

19. Max A. Shepard, "William of Occam and the Higher Law," *American Political Science Review*, XXVI (1932), 1009, 1014, 1021-3; XXVII (1933), 33-7. Léon Baudry, *Guillaume d'Occam* (Paris, 1956), Tome I, pp. 15-22, 96 ff.

20. Ockham, *Philosophical Writings*, ed. Philotheus Boehner (Edinburgh, 1957), p. 109.

21. *Ibid.*, p. 49.

22. Lewis S. Feuer, "The Principle of Simplicity," *Philosophy of Science*, XXIV (1957), 109-22.

23. Karl Marx and Friedrich Engels, *The German Ideology*, ed. R. Pascal (New York, 1939), p. 20.

24. John Dewey, *Reconstruction in Philosophy* (New York, 1920), pp. 106-7, 140.

25. Nikolai Bukharin, *Historical Materialism: A System of Sociology* (New York, 1925), p. 186.

26. Simon Federbush, *The Jewish Concept of Labor* (New York, 1956), p. 27. W. A. L. Elmslie, *Studies in Life from Jewish Proverbs* (London, 1917), p. 174.

27. Ian C. Hannah, *Christian Monasticism* (New York, 1925), pp. 82-3. Thomas Merton, *The Silent Life* (New York, 1957), pp. 30-2.

28. Max L. Margolis, "Celibacy," *Jewish Encyclopedia*, (New York, 1902), Vol. III, p. 636.

29. Norman Bentwich, *Hellenism* (Philadelphia, 1919), p. 106.

30. M. C. D'Arcy, *Thomas Aquinas* (Boston, 1930), p. 35, 43-6.

31. *Select Letters of St. Jerome*, "The Virgin's Profession," trans. F. A. Wright (London, 1932), p. 67. Edward Kennard Rand, *Founders of the Middle Ages* (Cambridge, 1928), p. 107. G. G. Coulton, *Five Centuries of Religion* (Cambridge, 1923), Vol. I, pp. 444, 527.

32. Graham Wallas, *The Art of Thought* (New York, 1926), pp. 221-3. Herbert B. Workman, *The Evolution of the Monastic Ideal*, 1st ed. (London, 1913), pp. 56-57, 326-330.

33. Adolf Harnack, *Monasticism: Its Ideals and History*, trans. E. E. Kellett and F. H. Marseille (New York, 1901), p. 67.

34. *Select Letters of St. Jerome*, p. 41.

35. Henry Charles Lea, *History of Sacerdotal Celibacy in the Christian Church* (3rd ed., revised, New York, 1907), Vol. I, p. 448. Cf. M. Michelet, *op. cit.*, Vol. I, pp. 152-3.

36. Reginald Lane Poole, *Medieval Thought and Learning* (New York, 1920), pp. 120, 125.

37. Adolph Harnack, *History of Dogma*, trans. William M'Gilchrist (London, 1899), Vol. VI, p. 169.

38. Arthur Cushman McGiffert, *A History of Christian Thought* (New York, 1933), Vol. II, pp. 125-35.

39. Thomas Hobbes, *Leviathan* (Everyman's Library, London, 1914), pp. 368-369, 372-3. *Behemoth*, in *The English Works of Thomas Hobbes*, ed. Sir William Molesworth (London, 1840), Vol. VI, pp. 216, 218. Oskar Pfister, *Some Applications of Psycho-Analysis* (London, 1923), p. 314.

40. Cf. C. G. Jung, *Psychological Types*, trans. H. Godwin Baynes (reprinted, New York, 1953), p. 55.

41. Charles H. Haskins, *Studies in the History of Mediaeval Science* (Cambridge, 1924), pp. 233-5. Meyrick H. Carré, *Realists and Nominalists* (London, 1946), p. 65. Charles Singer, "Science and Scholasticism," *Nature*, CV (1920), p. 548.

42. *The Metalogicon of John of Salisbury*, p. 16.

43. Richard McKeon, ed., *Selections from the Medieval Philosophers*,

Vol. I, p. 91. Lynn White, Jr., "Natural Science and Naturalistic Art in the Middle Ages," *American Historical Review*, III (1947), 424.

44. J. C. Flügel, *The Psycho-analytic Study of the Family* (London, 1921), p. 145.

45. Charles Singer, *From Magic to Science* (New York, 1928), p. 67.

46. A. Cohen, *op. cit.*, p. 22. Moses Maimonides, *Guide for the Perplexed*, p. 27.

47. Edwyn Bevan, "Dirt," *Hellenism and Christianity* (London, 1921), Chapter VIII. For a brilliant psychoanalytical study of Plato's thought, cf. Hans Kelsen, "Platonic Love," *The American Imago*, III (1942), 28, 50-1, 57. Ronald B. Levinson, in his criticism of Kelsen's argument, still acknowledges that "paederastic, untouched by indulgence, is the proper meaning of 'Platonic love.'" Ronald B. Levinson, *In Defense of Plato* (Cambridge, 1953), pp. 106-7. Cf. Sigmund Freud, *Group Psychology and the Analysis of the Ego*, trans. James Strachey (New York, 1922), pp. 41-51. Jung does not like to see Plato's metaphor of the cave regarded as a symbol for the uterus, and as an indication that Plato was arrested at a level of infantile sexuality. His own argument, however, is rhetorical: "What becomes of beauty, greatness, and holiness?" To which we answer that authentic beauty, greatness, and holiness are reinforced by the psychoanalytical method. C. G. Jung, *Contributions to Analytical Psychology*, trans. H. G. and Cary F. Baynes (London, 1928), pp. 151, 232. On the linkage between Pythagorean asceticism and realism, cf. Diogenes Laertius, *Lives of Eminent Philosophers*, trans. R. D. Hicks (New York, 1925), Vol. II, pp. 329, 349. The correlation between nominalism and hedonism is vivid in the cynics. The asceticism of the cynics was strictly of a utilitarian kind. *Ibid.*, pp. 55, 75, 99-101. Donald R. Dudley, *A History of Cynicism from Diogenes to the 6th Century* A.D. (London, 1937), pp. 48-52.

48. Owen Berkeley-Hill, "The Anal-Erotic Factor in the Religion, Philosophy and Character of the Hindus," *International Journal of Psycho-analysis*, II (1921), 308.

49. R. W. Betts, "The Great Debate about Universals in the Universities of the Fourteenth Century," *Prague Essays*, ed. R. W. Seton-Watson (Oxford, 1949), p. 69.

50. Nima Adlerblum does not even reckon Philo among the Jewish philosophers; *op. cit.*, p. 103.

51. Erwin R. Goodenough, *An Introduction to Philo Judaeus* (New Haven, 1940), pp. 190-2, 206-7. Philo, *Questions and Answers on Genesis*, Supp. I, trans. Ralph Marcus (Cambridge, 1953), pp. 245, 382, 424.

52. *Averroes' Commentary on Plato's Republic*, trans. E. I. J. Rosen-

thal (Cambridge, 1956), pp. 165-6. T. J. De Boer, *The History of Philosophy in Islam*, trans. Edward R. Jones (London, 1905), pp. 191-7. De Lacy O'Leary, *Arabic Thought and Its Place in History* (London, 1922), p. 253. Ernest A. Moody, *The Logic of William of Ockham* (London, 1935), p. 85. Isaac Husik, "Averroes on the Metaphysics of Aristotle," in *Philosophical Essays*, ed. Milton C. Nahm and Leo Strauss (Oxford, 1952), pp. 164, 167.

53. *Averroes' Commentary on Plato's Republic*, pp. 116, 120, 214. Also, pp. 129, 228-9, 212, 216-7.

54. Soheil M. Afran, *Avicenna: His Life and Works* (London, 1958), pp. 54, 76, 188, 267-9, 77, 203, 33, 75, 61-2, 58. Cf. V. Courtois, ed., *Avicenna Commemorative Volume* (Calcutta, 1956), p. xii. *The Spiritual Physick of Rhazes*, trans. Arthur J. Arberry (London, 1950), pp. 10-12, 25-6. A. J. Arberry, "Rhazes on the Philosophic Life," *The Asiatic Review*, XLV (1949), 703-4, 708.

55. Oskar Pfister, *op. cit.*, pp. 310-311. Wilhelm Stekel, *Compulsion and Doubt*, trans. Emil A. Gutheil (New York, 1949), Vol. I, p. 205. W. Ronald D. Fairbairn, *Psychoanalytic Studies of the Personality* (London, 1952), pp. 20-1.

56. *The Confessions of Saint Augustine*, trans. Edward B. Pusey (Pocket Library, New York, 1957), pp. 11, 25, 27, 31, 35, 77, 128. Cf. Charles Kligerman, "A Psychoanalytic Study of the Confessions of St. Augustine," *Journal of the American Psycho-Analytic Association*, (1957), 469-84. Meyrick H. Carré, *op. cit.*, p. 37.

57. Wallace K. Ferguson, "The Interpretation of the Renaissance: Suggestions for a Synthesis," *Journal of the History of Ideas*, XII (1951), 483-95.

58. George Sarton, *The Appreciation of Ancient and Medieval Science During the Renaissance (1450-1600)* (Philadelphia, 1955), pp. 1-3.

59. Cf. Ronald Hare, *Pomp and Pestilence* (New York, 1955), p. 139. William Edward Hartpole Lecky, *History of European Morals from Augustus to Charlemagne* (New York, 1929), Vol. II, pp. 109-10.

60. Charles Homer Haskins, *The Renaissance of the Twelfth Century* (Cambridge, 1927), pp. 24, 62, 64, 285, 303. Gabriel Compayré, *Abelard and the Origin and Early History of Universities* (New York, 1893), pp. 243-47. "We cannot be wrong," says Rashdall, "in connecting the prominence of medicine at Montpellier with the comparatively advanced state of material civilization in the rich and prosperous commercial cities in the countries bordering upon the Mediterranean. The study of medicine prospered at Montpellier from the same causes which ensured its prosperity in Italy. Before the days of mechanism, medicine

was the one branch of speculative knowledge which had a distinct commercial value." Cf. Hastings Rashdall, *op. cit.*, Vol. II, p. 121.

61. Henri Pirenne, *Medieval Cities: Their Origins and the Revival of Trade*, trans. Frank D. Halsey (Princeton, 1948), p. 124.

62. *Introduction to Aristotle*, ed. Richard McKeon (New York, 1947), p. 467, from *Nicomachean Ethics*, Bk. VII, Ch. 13.

63. Charles Homer Haskins, *Studies in the History of Mediaeval Science* (Cambridge, 1924), pp. 149, 223, 247-8, 255, 261, 284, 318.

64. *The Goliard Poets: Medieval Latin Songs and Satires*, trans. George F. Whicher (Norfolk, 1949), pp. 3, 109.

65. Cf. Gabriel Compayré, *op. cit.*, pp. 189-90, 264-5. *The Letters of Abelard and Heloise*, pp. 3-4. Fernand Van Steenberghen, *The Philosophical Movement in the Thirteenth Century* (London, 1955), p. 79. Maurice de Wulf, *History of Mediaeval Philosophy*, trans. Ernest C. Messenger (London, 1926), Vol. I, pp. 189, 248. Van Steenberghen, *op. cit.*, pp. 45-6. Etienne Gilson, *The Christian Philosophy of St. Thomas Aquinas*, trans. L. K. Shook (New York, 1956), p. 279. Bernard Landry, *Duns Scot* (Paris, 1922), pp. 1-2, 33, 38.

66. Etienne Gilson, *The Philosophy of St. Thomas Aquinas*, trans. Edward Bullough (Cambridge, 1929), p. 16. Ernest Renan, *Averroès et l'Averroïsme*, troisième ed. (Paris, 1866), pp. 268-73.

67. G. G. Coulton, *The Inquisition* (London, 1929), pp. 69-71, 6, 18. St. Thomas Aquinas, *Philosophical Texts*, ed. Thomas Gilby (London, 1951), pp. 277, 309, 378, 233, 232, 30, 16, 17, 61, 276, 326. Etienne Gilson, *The Philosophy of St. Thomas Aquinas*, p. 22.

IV

The Ethic of the Copernican Revolution

THE COPERNICAN REVOLUTION WAS THE ACHIEVEMENT OF A small group of scientific intellectuals in Western Europe who gave their allegiance to the hedonist-libertarian ethic. It set the stage for the scientific movement of the seventeenth century.

When Copernicus on May 24, 1543, lay dying on his bed, a copy of his newly printed *De Revolutionibus Orbium Caelestium* was placed in his hands. The dying man's testament was a new world in birth. The European order was reeling under the impact of the Protestant Reformation and the rise of new national states. The ancient Ptolemaic cosmology departed with the feudal system and Catholic hegemony. Copernicus proposed two principal hypotheses: that the earth, together with the planets, move around the sun in concentric circular orbits, and also that, in addition to its annual revolution around the sun, the earth rotates daily around its axis. Although Copernicus still required the assistance of a variety of auxiliary hypotheses, he provided a conception of the universe which accounted for the astronomical observations in a remarkably simpler fashion than Ptolemy's. The work of three other men helped complete the Copernican Revolution—Tycho Brahe, Kepler, and Galileo. The four men were forerunners of the new international community of scientists which was superseding the clerical order: Copernicus was a Pole, Tycho a Dane, Kepler a German, and Galileo an Italian. All four men were representatives, in the circumstances of their time, of the hedonist-libertarian ethic. Let us discuss briefly the salient facts in each of their lives that bear on their common underlying ethic.

Copernicus

MOST PERSONS THINK of Copernicus as a Roman Catholic priest, and as given therefore to ascetic fasts and vigils. But as the distinguished scholar Edward Rosen has said, "The simple truth of the matter is that Copernicus was neither a monk nor a friar nor a priest." [1] Copernicus was one of the sixteen canons of Frauenburg; they did not usually take priestly vows, and in Copernicus's time "could barely muster one priest for the service of the altar." How shall we describe this chapter of canons and their duties? They are most accurately characterized as a collective of managerial administrators; they were contented members of the clerical managerial class. They lived in the Cathedral in fine style, each with his own apartment, two servants, and three horses. The canons helped the Bishop of Ermland to administer his Cathedral and diocese. The Bishop, indeed, was the biggest landowner in the domain, for he held one-third of Ermland; in turn, one-third of his land was used to maintain the canons. Copernicus was known as an able manager. In 1516, he took over the management of two of the Chapter's estates, and by 1523 rose to become Administrator-General of Ermland.

Copernicus's values were those of a Renaissance humanist, not of a Christian ascetic. The University of Cracow, where he first studied, was a stronghold of nominalism.[2] The only book he published up until the last year of his life was his Latin translation of the poems of a seventh-century Byzantine, Theophylactus Simocatta. The verses were moral, pastoral, and amorous, but not theological. Among the amorous epistles was a hymn to the pleasures of love:

> Well deserving of praise are the eyes that turn in love to a beautiful maiden. Do not complain that thou hast been conquered by love; for greater is the delight that will reward thy labor of love. Though

> tears pertain to grief, those of love are sweet, for they are mixed with joy and pleasure. The gods of love bring delight at the same time as sadness; with manifold passions is Venus girded.[3]

There were critics, Copernicus said, who might find love poems "lighthearted and frivolous." But, Copernicus added in his preface, such poems are like "the admixture of sweet ingredients" that the physician uses to soften bitter medicines. Moreover, people's moods alternate; "the public takes pleasure in such different things" that it is wise to provide them with a pleasing variety of themes.

Copernicus was studying canon law at Bologna when his uncle, Bishop Waczenrode, helped secure his election as a canon at Frauenburg. No impulse of religious vocation seems to have moved Copernicus. The canonry guaranteed him a good livelihood and leisure for his scientific and literary pursuits. At Bologna, Copernicus felt the stimulation of the Neo-Platonic philosophy which was stirring northern Italy; his professor of astronomy, Domenico Maria da Novara, was a leading participant in the Platonic revival.[4]

There is a tendency to see in Italian Neo-Platonism a kind of bizarre Pythagorean mysticism. Such an element was undoubtedly present, but the primary signification of Neo-Platonism, in the Renaissance context, was not toward any cult of ascetic practices in the manner of the ancient Pythagorean order. Rather, it expressed a hedonistic liberation of the emotions, a cult almost of the joys of love. This Neo-Platonic movement did not belittle man, or inculcate humility or feelings of guilt. Rather, it joined with Pico della Mirandola in saying, "Man is the most fortunate of creatures and consequently worthy of all admiration." It called for a fresh contact with living fact, for a departure from bookishness; the ascetic abstention from living fact produced a sterility of the intellect which was like sexual sterility. Pico straightforwardly compared intellectual to sexual fecundity:

> It is surely an ignoble part to be wise only from a notebook (as Seneca says) and, as if the discoveries of our predecessors had closed the way to our own industry and the power of nature were exhausted in us, to produce from ourselves nothing. . . . For if a tiller of the soil hates sterility in his field, and a husband in his wife,

> surely the Divine mind joined to and associated with an infertile soul will hate it the more that a far nobler offspring is desired.[5]

For Pico, the real dignity of man consisted, as Cassirer observes, in the fact that man is not simply the creation of a force beyond himself, but that he can be his own free maker and master.

Platonism, as a philosophy of Renaissance humanism, did not propose the repression of the natural desires. It would be contrary to the order of nature, said Marsilio Ficino, for a natural desire not to be endowed with the power to achieve its proper end. The figure of Prometheus did not for the humanist exemplify the sin of pride; rather, he stood for man's reason, which makes him more perfect. True, as Platonists they spoke of the ascent from Vulgar Love to Divine Love, but the divine was already latent in "Venus, Beauty, which kindles the fire of Love in Mankinde," and Plotinus's authority was invoked for the proposition "that there was never any beautiful Person wicked." [6] Eros and beauty, says Cassirer, "stand as the nucleus of the philosophy of the Florentine Circle." Under the Neo-Platonic influence, as Erwin Panofsky points out, the significance of human nudity was transformed. It came to be understood as the symbol of both truth and virtue; medieval theology had taken it to stand for humility and vice.

The Neo-Platonic ideas which Copernicus encountered during the near ten years which he spent at Bologna, Rome, Ferrara, and Padua were not then such as would have made for an ascetic mortification of the flesh. Copernicus evidently retained a sense of thankfulness for his Italian years, for he and his uncle, Bishop Waczenrode, wished to found a humanist university for students too poor to go to Italy. Copernicus's joy in science was that of the humanist. At the outset of his *De Revolutionibus Orbium Caelestium*, he wrote of "the unbelievable pleasure of mind" which the study of the sciences gives, and spoke of astronomy as most deserving of study because of the sheer beauty of its objects. "For what could be more beautiful than the heavens which contain all beautiful things? . . . Many philosophers have called the world a visible god on account of its extraordinary excellence." [7]

Copernicus's mind was a secular one. If his nights were spent gazing at the skies and trying to find a simpler order in the planetary movements, his days were spent seeking a simpler economic system which would introduce order into the movements of prices. He wrote in 1526 a little treatise on money, *De Monetae Cudendae Ratio* (*Concerning the Principle of Coining Money*), in which he urged the Prussian Landtag to establish a monetary union with Poland which would end the debasement of coinage, curb inflation, and promote foreign trade. To replace the multiplicity of coinages of different cities and districts, as numerous as the epicycles and auxiliary hypotheses of the Ptolemaic cosmology, Copernicus proposed a single state monopoly for the minting of coins.

> Innumerable though the evils are with which kingdoms, principalities and republics are troubled, there are four which in my opinion outweigh all others—war, death, famine, and debasement of money. The first three are so evident that no one denies them, but it is not thus with the fourth.[8]

He explained the relative prosperity and poverty of states not by their adherence to theological dogma but to sound monetary policy:

> We see flourish the countries that possess a good currency, while those that have only a depreciated one, fall into decadence and decline. . . . It is uncontestable that the countries that make use of good currency shine in all the arts, have better workmen, and have of everything in abundance. On the contrary, in the States which make use of degraded money, reigns cowardice, laziness and indolence.

Copernicus's treatise on money was written at the request of Sigismund I, King of Poland. Copernicus advised the King to seek above all a stable currency:

> Money is therefore in some sort a common measure of estimating values; but this measure must always be fixed and must conform to the established rule. Otherwise, there would be, necessarily, disorder in the State: buyers and sellers would at all times be misled. . . .

Copernicus's mode of thought, his basic categories—simplicity, stability, and uniformity—were applicable equally to the economic order and the heavenly. Copernicus was no "sleepwalker," as Arthur Koestler claims; he was a rational thinker, an adherent to the reality principle, a true son of a father who had made his living as a merchant from the trade that sailed along the Vistula to and from the ports of Northern Europe.

The libertarian standpoint remained with Copernicus all through his life; in an age when religious agitation and hatred divided Europeans, Copernicus stood steadfast with the party of tolerance. He urged his friend, Canon Tiedemann Giese, to publish a book in 1525 which pleaded for mutual tolerance between Catholics and Lutherans. Copernicus's name was cited in the preface of this book, in evident agreement with the author's affirmation *au dessus de la mêlée*, "I reject the battle." "The wild animals," said Giese, "behave more gently to their kind than do Christians to theirs." Copernicus worked closely and intimately with Lutheran scientists. Lonely in his last years, he was cheered by a new disciple, Rheticus, professor of mathematics at the University of Wittenburg, a Lutheran center. Darwin had his Huxley, Newton his Halley, and Copernicus his Rheticus. But for Rheticus's cajoling, Copernicus might never have sent his great book to press. It was Rheticus who, in 1540, published the *Narratio Prima*, the first account of the Copernican system. He included a short character sketch of Copernicus as a free spirit, loyal to the requirements of fact and uncoerced by the authority of the past:

> However, when he became aware that the phenomena, which control the astronomer, and mathematics compelled him to make certain assumptions even against his wishes, it was enough, he thought, if he aimed his arrows by the same method to the same target as Ptolemy, even though he employed a bow and arrow of far different type of material from Ptolemy's. At this point we shall recall the saying "Free in mind must he be who desires to have understanding."

Rheticus confided the supervision of the final stages of the publication of the *De Revolutionibus Orbium Caelestium* to a prominent Lutheran clergyman, Andrew Osiander. Copernicus had already been in correspondence with Osiander, who can claim to be regarded as a founder of the positivist theory of knowledge. For Osiander hoped to placate the critics of Copernicus, "the peripatetics and theologians," with the assurance that his "hypotheses are brought forward, not because they are in reality true, but because they regulate the computation of the apparent and combined motion as conveniently as may be." The notion that scientific hypotheses are neither true nor false but only convenient or inconvenient formulae of computation was thus conceived as a defense mechanism against theologians' polemics. Copernicus himself would have none of this device; he intended his hypothesis to be a more truthful account than Ptolemy's, in the plain sense of truthfulness as fidelity to actual fact. As Kepler wrote, "Strengthened by a stoical firmness of mind, Copernicus believed that he should publish his convictions openly. . . ." [9] Nevertheless, Osiander saw fit to suppress Copernicus's introduction to the *De revolutionibus*, and to replace it with one he had written himself. Apart from their epistemological disagreements, what stands out is the collaboration of Protestant and Catholic in a common scientific enterprise against the theologians. The latter, moreover, included in the sixteenth century both Luther and Calvin. Luther decried Copernicus as

> . . . a new astronomer who wished to prove that the earth moved and went around, not the sky or the firmament or the sun or the moon. . . . The fool wants to change the whole science of astronomy. But the Holy Scripture clearly shows us that Joshua commanded the sun, not the earth, to stand still.

And Calvin spoke magisterially, in the same vein, of the earth "placed in the center of the universe," "unmoved, while the heavens above are in constant rapid motion." [10]

What is striking in Rheticus's *Narratio Prima* is how much the language and imagery of neo-pagan hedonism predominate over the conventionalities of Christian theology. He launches into a paean, "In Praise of Prussia," because Prussia, he declares, is of all regions most worthy to succeed to the mantle of Minerva once held by Rhodes, famed for its "wisdom and education." Indeed, "by an act of the god Prussia passed into the hands of Apollo, who cherishes it now, as once he cherished Rhodes, his spouse." Prussia is "this most beautiful, most fertile, and most fortunate area," and this modern spouse of Apollo has given him progeny: Konigsberg, seat of the prince who is patron of all the learned men of our time; "Thorn, once famous for its market, but now its foster-son, my teacher"; Danzig, metropolis of Prussia, eminent "for the wealth and splendor of its renascent literature"; Frauenburg, where dwell "a large body of learned and pious men." Prussia had all the delights of mercantile hedonism: "Prussia is the daughter of Venus and the sea." It feeds Holland, England, and Portugal with the crops and quantities of fish of every sort which it exports. "But Venus is interested in the things that promote culture, dignity, and the good and humane life." And these she "successfully imported into Prussia from abroad." Thus, Venus was the mother of science in Prussia and of the efflorescence of Copernicus' ideas. Science had been nurtured by mercantile prosperity and the joys of the good life. This was no ascetic devotion with which Rheticus closed the *Narratio Prima*, but an ode to Minerva and Jupiter, who had blessed the people of Prussia.

> Moreover, they worship Minerva with every type of art and for this reason receive the kindness of Jupiter. For, not to speak of the lesser arts attributed to Minerva, like architecture and its allied disciplines, the revival of literature in the world is everywhere welcomed with keenest interest. . . . Therefore Jupiter forms a yellow cloud and rains much gold . . . because Jupiter is said to preside over kingdoms and states, when the mighty undertake to support studies, learning, and the muses. . . .[11]

The prosperity and happiness of Prussia, said Rheticus, made them hospitable to science. He could not "enter the home of any distinguished man in his region . . . without immediately seeing geometrical diagrams at the very threshold or finding geometry present in their minds." As men of good will, they "bestow upon the students of these arts every possible benefit and service, since true knowledge and learning are never separated from goodness and kindness."

Was Copernicus, as Arthur Koestler states, a timid man, infatuated with a Pythagorean cult of secrecy which answered the neurotic needs of his personality? Rather, if anything, what stands out is the immense courage of this lonely scientist who dared challenge single-handed a cosmology that had prevailed for two millennia. When Luther nailed his Theses to the door of the Wittenberg Church on October 31, 1517, it was as if he were doing what millions of Europeans were awaiting. The surging restlessness of countless peasants, the discontent of townsmen and bourgeois, the ambitions of princes all identified themselves with his document of revolt. Copernicus, however, could look to the support of no underlying socio-economic movement. The Protestant Reformation, although it articulated profound social discontents, did so at its inception with a complete loyalty to Biblical authority. Even Philip Melanchton, "the sweetest-natured of all the Reformation champions," quoted Biblical passages in Luther's fashion to adjudge Copernicus's hypothesis as absurd.[12] The Protestant Reformation was a mass movement that embraced the lower classes in a revolutionary situation, and at such revolutionary transitional critical points, an authoritarian, anti-intellectual mood has often prevailed. The one recorded reaction of the lower classes themselves to Copernicus's ideas in his own lifetime came in the form of a satirical burlesque that was given at a local carnival near Frauenburg about 1531. Copernicus, in the guise of a star-gazing cleric, was held up to mockery. The lower classes, at this time, had no appreciation for the love of knowledge as a motive for scientific research; it was "of all passions the least explicable to the vulgar," who had from an early time taken it "as a motive for supposed compacts with the Powers of Darkness." [13] Faustus was the prototype of the scientist who bartered his soul to the Devil in exchange for knowledge and the delights of the body.

Thus, the emerging scientist represented a kind of third force amidst the religious divisions of the sixteenth century. On the one hand, his ideas portended conflict with the scheme of thought promulgated authoritatively by the Catholic Church; on the other hand, his ideas were out of keeping with the authoritarian anti-intellectualism characteristic of the Protestant Reformers. The scientific revolution was begun by a small group of intellectuals who could look for friendship only to the community of non-dogmatic, tolerant, enlightened men who might be found scattered among the middle and upper classes in the towns, and among the student intellectuals in the universities.

We can understand therefore that Copernicus hesitated for a long time before allowing his book to be published. His friends urged him frequently and sometimes reproachfully, wrote Copernicus, "that I should publish and finally permit the book which, hidden by me, had lain concealed not merely nine years but already four times that period." The generality of people, he felt, would regard him as absurd, and he would need all the agreement and help of the small community of mathematicians. At first, he wondered whether it might not be enough to publish his useful new astronomical tables without the accompanying theoretical analysis and innovations. Thereby, tells Rheticus, "the Pythagorean principle would be observed that philosophy must be pursued in such a way that its inner secrets are reserved for learned men, trained in mathematics, etc." Copernicus, however, withdrew from this Pythagorean ideology of a privileged truth for an elite. He was persuaded by Tiedemann Giese's argument that a truncated publication of the tables "would be an incomplete gift to the world," and that the Pythagorean ideology led to an authoritarianism which men of science could not accept, "since we were compelled to assume and to approve their ideas on the principle that, as the Pythagoreans used to say, 'The Master said so'—a principle which has absolutely no place in mathematics." "I hesitated long," wrote Copernicus, "whether it would indeed be more satisfactory to follow the example of the Pythagoreans and various others who were wont to pass down the mysteries of philosophy not by books, but from hand to hand only to friends and relations. . . ." It seemed to Copernicus that the real motive for such secrecy had been principally a fear on the part of thinkers that they would be "despised by those to whom spending good work on any book is a trouble unless they make profit by it."

Finally, in his supreme libertarian act, Copernicus agreed to publish his book. He dedicated it to the Pope, he wrote, "in order that learned and unlearned may alike see that in no way whatsoever I evade judgment." He hoped that "even in this very remote corner of the earth in which I live" he might hope for the Church's support of "all letters and of mathematics." [14] The old man's hopes were not fulfilled. For the Counter Reformation was soon to bring a heightened authoritarian hostility toward free thought on the part of the Church. Meanwhile, Copernicus's act of publication initiated a chain of reactions that gradually made the scientific movement more potent perhaps than the ethico-religious systems of either Roman Catholicism or ascetic Protestantism. "A fog has now lifted," wrote Rheticus.

◆ Tycho Brahe

THE WORK OF TYCHO BRAHE, the greatest observer of the skies, can be regarded as part of the Danish Renaissance of the second half of the sixteenth century. Denmark became a leading maritime and trading power; foreign ships sailing into the Baltic Sea had to strike their topsails to Danish men of war. The son of the governor of Helsingborg, Tycho was born in 1546, in a castle in Scania. The hedonistic ethic was part of his heritage; he came from a noble family known as "the jolly Brahes," and throughout his life Tycho remained faithful to this heritage. At the age of thirteen, Tycho entered the University of Copenhagen. Its most distinguished professor, the theologian Niels Hemmingsen, preached a philosophy of life noteworthy for its simple naturalism:

> The devil knows there is no peace outside wedlock; he has thus made bishops, monks and priests miserable writhing creatures, helpless in the face of women's lures. It is true that Abraham, Isaac and David had all the joys of several wives, but we must not envy them. As for Solomon, the less we think of his good fortune the better.

Monogamy was thus regarded as a renunciation of joy which the conditions of social existence imposed. The Copenhagen philosophy did not extol asceticism for its own sake; Solomon's polygamous state was regarded as a piece of good fortune that we unfortunately could not enjoy. Professor Hemmingsen's son Hans, who was also on the faculty, had difficulty coming to terms with even the minimal requirements of decorum; he ran around Copenhagen during the night intoxicated, and menaced the town's cook.

A passion for science filled Tycho from his youth. He neglected his studies in jurisprudence, spent his money on instruments and his nights observing the constellations. His most wonderful experience while later a student at Leipzig came when he witnessed in 1563 the conjunction of Jupiter and Saturn. Tycho expressed his scientist's creed of the joy and beauty of the world in his first book, *De Nova Stella,* published in 1573: "I want to see what is beautiful in this wide world, what human industry here and there has invented, and to learn the customs of all kinds of people. The rush of youth and an inborn craving bids me see much more and learn much about the glorious arts. . . ." The sight of a new, very bright start in the constellation of Cassiopeia on the night of November 11, 1572, tremendously excited Tycho. He stopped all and sundry in the streets of the village Herrevad—"Do you see it? What does it look like to you?"—as he trembled with excitement, then rushed away to secure his sextant to make the locational measurements of the star, and finally hurried to his uncle as if to announce the arrival of a beautiful betrothed from another land. He gazed for seventeen months at that star, his biographer tells us, "as a lover would at his sweetheart." [15]

From his earliest years, Tycho's singlehearted devotion to science took him from town to town, from one country to another. His instruments were built to enable him to transport them easily to different places. "For an astronomer must be cosmopolitan," said Tycho, because few statesmen encouraged studies, and the astronomer must go where his science found its best welcome. His twenty years at Uraniborg, on the little Danish coastal island of Hveen, were the happiest in his life, but when he lost the royal favor of King Christian IV, he left his beloved Denmark, in 1597, and two years later became astronomer at the court of the Holy Roman Emperor, Rudolph II, in Prague.

King Christian IV was never himself an adherent to the ascetic ethics. As C. V. Wedgwood writes, "Monogamy never suited his exuberant nature, and the number of his bastards grew in time to be a Danish problem and a European joke. . . ." Nevertheless, the King found Tycho's easy attitude toward the Protestant religion and ethic even more than he could condone. Christian plaintively accused Tycho of having allowed the local church to go to ruin, diverted its funds for his own scientific use, starved the local parson, and discontinued the baptismal rite. The island of Hveen, we might say, was the first locality in the world that ever lived under the dictatorship of a scientist, and religion, even in that religious age, fared very poorly under it indeed. It was in 1576 that King Frederick II, wishing to keep Tycho in Denmark, had graciously assigned the island to him:

> Our land of Hveen, with all Our and the Crown's tenants and servants who live thereon, with all rents and duties which come therefrom, and We and the Crown give it to him to have, enjoy, use and hold, quiet and free, without any rent, all the days of his life, and so long as he lives and likes to continue and follow his *studia mathematices*, but he shall keep the tenants who live there under law and right. . . .

Around himself, Tycho gathered a corps of students, apprentices, and assistants who came from all parts of Europe, even from distant Iceland, to work with him and learn his science and craft and enjoy copious quantities of fish and beer. It was the first scientific collective and research organization of modern times. Although he was a grueling taskmaster in his assignment of observational duties, Tycho inspired many of his assistants with an enthusiasm for their science. A group of some twenty skilled artisans also lived with Tycho; they constructed his astronomical instruments, which were astonishing for their beauty. Tycho also built for himself a paper mill and printing press. To maintain his research institute and scientific elite, he required a lot of work from his tenants; the peasants had to contribute two days' labor per week for the benefit of their scientific oligarchy. Tycho called his island kingdom Insula Venusia, after the goddess of beauty. But in 1597 this little scientific oasis came to an end. King Christian's letter to Tycho stated the case against the scientific dictatorship:

> You remember well what complaints our poor subjects and peasants of Hveen have brought against you, your behavior in regard to the church there, from which you for some years took the income and titles and appointed no churchwarden, letting the church fall into ruin. You also remember that you took the land belonging to the parsonage and partly pulled down its houses. And as for the parson . . . you gave him a few pennies weekly and fed him in the company of the laborers. During a series of years, moreover, there was one parson after another, who had received no call from the congregation in accordance with the law. . . . Everybody is well acquainted with the manner in which the baptismal rite was omitted for a long time and with your cognizance.

Tycho's conflict with clericalism and the Protestant ethic was evidently of long standing. An old diocesan record tells us that a minister of Hveen was dismissed in disgrace "for not having punished and admonished Tycho Brahe of Hveen, who for eighteen years had not been to the Sacrament, but lived in an evil manner with a concubine." Tycho had indeed taken to himself as his permanent companion a woman of lowly birth; his disregard of class status enraged his relatives and Danish noblemen generally. His wife was called "Tycho's harlot," and their children were considered illegitimate. Tycho, however, in this respect as in others, ignored the feelings of his class. He had his own conception of what made life worthwhile, and it diverged from that of his peers. When he published his first book on the new star of 1572, he had had to liberate himself from the prejudice that "it was not proper for a nobleman to write books." As a youth in Copenhagen, his scientific dedication had been ridiculed by drinking, duelling young noblemen. On one unhappy occasion, Tycho, while arguing a mathematical point with a countryman at the University of Rostock, had yielded to the excitement and the wine, and fought a duel; part of his nose was cut off, and afterward he had to wear an artificial nose. His joy in science separated him from the Danish aristocracy. He wrote to a friend:

> Neither my country nor my friends keep me back. One who has courage finds a home in every place and lives a happy life everywhere. Friends, too, one can find in all countries. There will always be time enough to return to the cold North to follow the general example, and, like the rest, to play in pride and luxury for the rest of one's years with wine, dogs, and horses. May God, as I trust He will, grant me a better lot.

Thus Tycho rejected the aristocratic ethic of "pride and luxury." "My mind is set on much greater things," he said, "in which there is real work." He was a rebel and as his biographer tells us, "He protested against most contemporaneous opinions, by his marriage, by disbelief in the devil worship of the time, by favoring the introduction of the Gregorian calendar, by condemnation of the life of his social equals." He was not an ascetic; rather, he felt the joys of science transcended by far the self-destructive activities of the aristocrats. He had seen the beauty of knowledge, and it entranced him all his life.[16]

Tycho's name became famous in Europe. He went to many of

its leading towns as his scientific interests required—to Leipzig, to Rostock, to Wittenberg, and to Augsburg, a free city that was a trading center between Germany and Italy, and where the most skilled instrument-makers could be found to design for him his quadrant, sextant, and globe. On the day his quadrant was completed, twenty proud artisans, followed by a cheering crowd, brought it through the streets to him; it had been paid for in large part by the burgomaster. The wealthy burghers of Protestant Augsburg were friendly to science, but so, likewise, was the Catholic Emperor Rudolph II, who was frankly indifferent to confessional fealties; despite the Spanish Jesuits, he succeeded in making Prague the intellectual heart of Central Europe. "The astronomer must be cosmopolitan, for every country is a fatherland of the mind." The hedonist-libertarian ethic was the simple common denominator of all scientists and their friends, no matter what their formal religious professions. And conversely, we might add, an ascetic-authoritarian ethic tended to be the common platform of the anti-scientists, whether they were Catholic, Lutheran, or Calvinist in their formal avowals.

"Tycho's explosive, enthusiastic, uncontrolled character belonged entirely to the sixteenth century. He was a child of nature as well as a child of genius," writes Professor Gade. With part of this judgment one might perhaps dissent, for Tycho's explosive qualities were largely personal. His naturalistic outlook, however, linked him to the scientists of the seventeenth century and, indeed, to the hedonist-libertarian ethic which has been shared by scientific movements in their beginnings in whatever century and place. Tycho, as Professor Gade writes, was a "Greek in his conception of life," a "sensitive artist. . . . Everything he touched, whatever he surrounded himself with, must be finished and beautiful. . . ." At Tycho's funeral, the orator said, "Science was his passion, his sufficiency and his riches." Tycho's love for science was a lover's quest to know his beloved; he took a direct pleasure in the world—an expressive and cosmological hedonist.

Tycho's own theory of the universe was from the logical standpoint a retreat from Copernicus's. It was a kind of compromise of standpoints. Tycho still proposed to hold to the Ptolemaic conception that the earth was the center of the universe, with the sun, planets, and fixed stars revolving around in it; but in addition, he maintained, the five planets also move in orbits around the sun. Toward the end of his life, lonely in his scientist's exile, Tycho secured the appointment at Prague for a new co-worker, Kepler. The two men were worlds removed in background and temperament. There were trying episodes between them, but their common scientific ethic proved finally a stronger bond than class, cultural, and individual differences. Kepler found no merit in Tycho's theoretical structure, but the many years' wealth of Tycho's patient, loving observations was the foundation for his profound reconstruction of the Copernican cosmology.

Johannes Kepler

THE TRANSCENDENT PERSONALITY OF KEPLER has in recent years justly commanded the attention of gifted writers. The contradictions in his nature; his mystical metaphysics; his casting of horoscopes; his tremendous scientific labor; his tortuous route through alternative theories to the three encompassing laws of planetary motion; his guileless simplicity of character in a time when peoples, princes, and prelates plotted against each other; the agony of his mother's trial for witchcraft all blend into an epic of a man.[17]

Like Newton, Kepler was born prematurely in the seventh month of his mother's pregnancy. Was the yearning to find unity and harmony in the universe which filled their lives somehow related to the traumatic sundering of a premature child from its mother?

No scientist's personality is known to us so well as Kepler's. He was the most autobiographical of scientific writers; he narrated each research with its entire drama of failures, misgivings, and success. Kepler's spirit triumphed over tremendous personal obstacles. His father a roving, unsuccessful soldier of fortune who abandoned his family; the mother, Katharina, restless, talkative, neurotic, gifted with flashes of insight, prescribing herbs for her neighbors' ailments, living in a world she populated with magical beings and forces, giving her son Johannes to the care of grandparents who treated him cruelly; and Johannes himself, almost dying in childhood of smallpox, his eyesight impaired, but filled with an unconquerable zest for existence. He recalled, from the tawdriness of his childhood days, that when he was six years old, in the year 1577, his mother had led him up a hill to show him a great comet in the sky.

At school, at the age of ten, and reading the Biblical stories, Kepler took the love of Jacob and Rachel as his model for what marriage should be. A violent sermon against the Calvinists which he heard at the age of twelve from his Lutheran deacon upset him greatly. From the first, Kepler revolted against religious dogmatism and intolerance. Experiencing doubts at the age of thirteen, he could not assent to the doctrine of predestination. "Freshman," a schoolmate teased him, "hast thou also doubts about predestination?" [18] He wanted peace between the warring creeds and factions, and wondered why the rival adherents destroyed each other. He spent his spare time as a schoolboy writing comedies and lyric poems.

At the University of Tübingen, as a student of theology, Kepler continued to struggle with his religious doubts. The writings of a Professor Hunnius, he said, helped him to "a healthy condition." He came to hate and be repelled by the entire controversy about predestination. Since he both agreed and disagreed on various points with Catholics, Lutherans, and Calvinists, all groups in later years grew suspicious of him. Some said he was giving up his Lutheran birth for a Catholic conversion; many others called him an atheist. To his friend Georg von Schallenberg, who admired his freedom of mind, Kepler wrote:

> It is indeed an annoying and, for the common uninformed man, a very strange notion that someone should be so bold, proud and puffed up as not to agree with any party. . . . It hurts my heart that the three great factions have torn the truth so miserably that I must collect it piece by piece, wherever I find a piece.

His religion was of the simplest: "I tie myself to all simple Christians, whatever they are called, with the Christian bonds of love." "My conscience tells me that one should not wrong the enemy, but love him. . . ." "My argument in matters of religion is only that the preachers in the pulpit are too haughty and do not abide by the old simplicity; that they arouse much dispute . . . interpret many actions of the Papists too maliciously. . . ." In 1600,

Kepler was banished from the city of Graz and lost his professorship, because he would not become a Catholic. In its turn, the Lutheran University of Württemberg, in 1611, would not have him as a professor of mathematics because he was "an opinionist in philosophy," and did not think Calvinists must go to hell. In 1612, the consistory at Linz refused him communion.

The spirit of theological dogmatism was simply foreign to Kepler's nature. He condemned it for the hatred and wars it brought upon men. In his *Harmonies of the World*, published in 1619, he pleaded that "we should keep at a distance all the discords of enmity, all contentions, rivalries, anger, quarrels, dissensions, sects, envy, provocations, and irritations arising through mocking speech and the other works of the flesh." He deplored the outbreak of "a very destructive war" upon science and the universities. Writing in 1621, when the Thirty Years' War was in its career, Kepler, in his *Epitome of Copernican Astronomy*, described how the war had dispersed "the assemblages of students for whom these things are written," and how he had worked for its publication "in the midst of the Bavarian armies and the frequent sicknesses and deaths both of soldiers and of civilians." He looked forward to the time when "this horrible tempest" would be calmed, "the clouds dispersed," and the sun shone again upon "these peaceful arts" in Austria. Above all, Kepler wrote the eloquent words of a scientist's advocacy of freedom of thought: "For the boundary posts of investigation should not be set up in the narrow minds of a few men. 'The world is a petty thing, unless everyone finds the whole world in that which he is seeking,' as Seneca says." The early Christians, in Kepler's view, had set an ignoble example with their persecution of scientists. They had vainly set up boundary posts to inquiry where God has not done so: "How severely all the astronomers were blamed by the first Christians." The Christian Fathers were not to be emulated: Eusebius had ignominiously assailed an excommunicated astronomer who honestly "preferred to desert Christianity" rather than his science. Tertullian and Augustine had regarded those scientists presumptuous "who taught that there was an antipodes." Kepler hoped the modern Christians would not repeat the mistakes of their forerunners. He said that his worst crucifixion was to suppress what he thought: "Whatever I profess outwardly, that I believe inwardly: nothing is a worse cross for me than—I do not say, to speak what is contrary to my thought—to be unable to utter my inmost sentiments." [19]

Wherever Kepler went, there was his work, the philosophical drive, the "*cupiditas speculandi*, his "sacred madness." The pleasure he felt in scientific research was indescribable. When, in 1595, he believed that he had discovered that the orbits of the planets conformed to the analogy of the five circumscribed regular solids, he was moved to tears by what seemed to him the final unveiling of ultimate truth:

> It will never be possible for me to describe with words the enjoyment which I have drawn from my discovery. Now I no longer bemoaned the lost time; I no longer became weary at work; I shunned no calculation no matter how difficult. Days and nights I passed in calculating until I saw if the sentences formulated in words agreed with the orbits of Copernicus, or if the winds carried away my joy.

Kepler's theory of knowledge was cast in a theological idiom. But he reconstructed God into a benevolent being who actively assisted man to know the truths of things. According to both Luther and Calvin, man's depravity had basically impaired his capacity even for mundane truths. Kepler, however, declared that since man is made in the image of God, he could share God's thoughts and know the nature of things. The mathematical laws of the cosmos were open to man's discovery.

> For man is an image of God, and it is quite possible that he thinks the same way as God in matters which concern the adornment of the world. For the world partakes of quantity and the mind of man grasps nothing better than quantities for the recognition of which he was obviously created.[20]

"Geometry is one and eternal, a reflection out of the mind of God. That mankind shares in it is one of the reasons to call man an image of God." God has created the world's forms in accordance with geometrical beauty. "The mind seizes upon these forms, and whether by instinct or by astronomical or harmonic ratiocination, discerns the concordant from the discordant." Luther and Calvin were epistemological pessimists; Kepler was an epistemological optimist. Each of them constructed a theology to satisfy his respective emotional requirements. The Bible was a repository of alternative metaphors from which one could choose in order to fashion a God with alternative attitudes toward human beings. Calvin was drawn to the Fall, Kepler to man's dignity as God's image.

Science for Kepler was ultimately justified as a joy in itself, as man's highest pleasure. In 1596, at the age of twenty-five, he wrote in a letter an astronomer's ode of joy:

> Must one measure the value of the heavenly object with dimes as one does food? But, pray, one will ask, what is the good of the knowledge of nature, of all astronomy, to a hungry stomach? . . . Painters are allowed to go on with their work because they give joy to the eyes, musicians because they bring joy to the ears, though they are of no other use to us. . . . What insensibility, what stupidity, to deny the spirit an honest pleasure but permit it to the eyes and ears! He who fights against that joy fights against nature.[21]

The God whom Kepler worshiped was a "kind creator" who would not "deprive the spirit of man, the master of creation and the Lord's own image of every heavenly delight." "Do we ask what profit the little bird hopes for in singing?" Kepler continued. "We know that singing in itself is a joy to him because he was created for singing." The scientist's research into "the secrets of the skies" was validated by its own delight. Science as a human pleasure—an outpouring of the human spirit, not a pursuit of asceticism—was Kepler's creed.

Kepler's theological idiom and metaphors, if taken on their manifest level, naturally suggest that his scientific thinking was shaped to religious requirements. The eminent physicist W. Pauli, following the lines of Jung's psychological ideas, has argued that Kepler's archetypal concept was the Trinitarian Christian Godhead, arranged hierarchically. Kepler did indeed find in the three-dimensional sphere the image of the triune God, with the Father in the center, the Son in the outer surface, and the Holy Ghost in the equality of relation between point and circumference. But the imagery with which Kepler suffuses the Trinitoid sphere is filled with what we have called "cosmological hedonism"; indeed, his language suggests a kind of universalized sexual energy and joy pervading the nature of all things, and emanating from God. When God "created playfully the image of his venerable Trinity," writes Kepler, the center point spread itself out "by an infinite expansion" to the outer surface, so that between point and surface there exists the "closest unity, the most beautiful harmony (literally: breathing together!), connection, relation, proportion, and commensurability. And, although Centre, Surface, and Distance are manifestly Three, yet are they One. . . ." Such is the "principle of all beauty in the world," "this primary principle and this most beautiful thing in the whole corporeal world, the matrix of all animal faculties, and the bond between the physical and the intellectual world. . . ."[22] The striving of all things for the spherical shape of beauty, seeking to "imitate the sun," the Father, is redolent with the suggestion of seeking an all-diffused unity of the primary sexual source. This is indeed an optimistic cosmological hedonism, in which the Trinity has ceased to be the symbolic bearer of the austere severities of masochistic asceticism.

The various criteria of reality, the guiding postulates of method, which Kepler used in his work all reflected the new hedonist liberation. In a letter to Fabricius in 1607, Kepler set forth what Professor Holton calls "the great new *leitmotif* of astronomy": ". . . you use circles, I use bodily forces." Those who insisted that the planets must move in circles, that their orbits could not possibly be elliptical, had to superpose imaginary circles on each other to approximate the planets' real motions. For Kepler, however, the human body provided the source for the final criterion of reality; the imaginary circles, he said, were "something existing in thought; i.e., something that is not there in reality." The ascetic epistemologists had always denigrated sensation as an avenue to truth, and had regarded physical properties as indexes of relative unreality. The methodological revolution was founded on an emotional revolution. The hands assumed an epistemological importance that they had been denied by philosophers; the tactual had long been repressed in favor of the visual, and ascetic philosophers would yield only to metaphors of light. Kepler, however, even dared to seek a God whom, he said, "I can grasp, as it were, with my very hands."[23]

Kepler furthermore undertook to find a universal law for all bodies, both celestial and terrestrial. Even Copernicus had still believed that the laws of celestial phenomena were not those of the earth; the heavens, the medieval metaphysics had taught, were of a higher order of reality. Kepler, however, placed the physics of the earth on an equal level with the planets; the earth's physical phenomena provided a representative sample for those of the universe. When he tried to understand the solar system as "a clockwork . . . carried out by means of a single, quite simple magnetic force," he was guided by the experiments with magnets that Gilbert had performed in England.

The conception of mathematical laws of nature was, however, Kepler's deepest methodological conviction, and it reflected what we have called "cosmological hedonism," the notion that the objective structure of the universe is inherently based on patterns that are pleasure-giving to human beings. This is the significance of Kepler's devotion to the notion of the "harmony" of the universe. Harmonies, says Kepler, are given in two ways; first, there are those given in sense phenomena, as when we listen to music; and, second, there are the harmonies constructed of mathematical concepts. The common significance of "harmony" is hedonistic, for it is found whenever a person, or God himself, enjoys the mathematical configuration of things. "The bodies would not be beautiful," says Kepler, "if they did not move," and the world must be beautiful. He concluded his *Harmonice Mundi*, his last great work, with a prayer to the God who had filled him with pleasure in his works: ". . . to Thee I offer thanks, Creator, God, because Thou has given me pleasure in what Thou has created. . . ."

Various writers have spoken of the Neo-Platonic, Pythagorean source of Kepler's quest for harmonies. Again, however, we must look for the emotional drive behind the literary garment. The Platonic and Pythagorean tradition was multi-potential in its uses; it could provide ascetics with their ideologies and emphases, and it could, as in Kepler's case, assist in the literary expression of the hedonistic liberation. Philosophical texts mean very different things under different emotional perspectives, and it is the emotional perspective which is the controlling factor in the history of ideas. Harmonies never, however, became an all-sufficient principle for Kepler. "Harmonies," he said, "must accommodate experience." The sensory criterion of reality would provide the determination from among different hypotheses, and Kepler was prepared to abandon his favored harmonies when they failed to fit the observed facts.[24]

Kepler's optimist epistemology expressed itself, remarkably, in the creation of a new genre of literature; he was the author of what has been called "the first modern scientific moon-voyage." This moon-voyage is a document that projects Kepler's underlying emotions; it was Kepler's voyage into his unconscious. The characters in this tale, as Marjorie Nicolson observes, were "clearly based upon Kepler's own life, the allusions so thinly veiled that they were readily recognizable, as Kepler learned to his sorrow." The *Somnium* was "a dream with nightmare touches." The first draft of the manuscript *Somnium seu Astronomia Lunari* (*Dream or Astronomy of the Moon*) began to circulate in 1611, and evidently, as Kepler wrote sadly, became the theme for gossip in "barbers' shops." Abetted by "lying tittle-tattle . . . harbored by stupid minds, and fanned by ignorance and superstition" against himself and his mother, it finally contributed to the ordeal of Kepler's mother's trial for witchcraft.

Kepler had wanted to bring home the standpoint of the new astronomy by the device of an imaginary journey to the moon. The earth, for instance, as seen from the moon, would simply be perceived as one planet among several, moving in its orbit. The observer on the moon would be a natural Copernican; he would see no paradox in the heliocentric hypotheses. In the guise of the young Duracotus, helped by his mother's sorcery, Kepler undertook in his dream a journey to the moon. Fioxhilda, the mother, was depicted as a collaborator of demons who, at her behest, would provide her with magical transport.

From his mother evidently, Kepler had derived his libertarian standpoint, the independence of mind. He tells us in the dream:

> My mother was Fioxhilda, who having lately died, furnished to me freedom for writing, for which I had been yearning. . . . She often said that there were many ruinous haters of the arts who accuse what they fail to understand because of dullness of mind, and hence make laws injurious to the human race. . . .

Kepler's mother was portrayed in a strange Oedipal fantasy. She was a "wise woman" who supported herself by selling little bags of herbs with mysterious charms to sailors. Once, her young son chanced to examine curiously the contents of one of the bags. The mother flew into a great rage, and pledged the boy to belong to a sea captain, so that she might keep the money for the spoiled bag. The symbolism of this story is classical—the son drawn with curiosity to examine the bag, the mother's genital organ; the mother's rage and neurotic response, evidently combatting her own desire for her son; her pledging the son to voyages elsewhere, including a sojourn with Tycho Brahe, as a substitute for the spoiled bag. Kepler's consuming scientific curiosity is portrayed as a kind of sublimation of tremendous Oedipal drives. The sailors to whom the mother sells her bags of charms probably reflect the anxiety Kepler experienced as a boy, observing his mother compelled, because of her husband's desertion, to fend for herself. Yet evidently there was bitterness in him that he had been rejected by his mother, for in the atmosphere of the year 1610 it was almost predictable that a narrative of this sort would be bound to make trouble for a poor, neurotic old woman who was described as having intercourse with devils. In a later note, Kepler indicated that he had been aware of the tragedy potential in his allowing the manuscript to be circulated:

> . . . you will understand that that little book, that those happenings, were of evil omen to me and mine. I think so, too. There is indeed a deep foreboding of death in the infliction of a deadly wound, in the drinking of poison; and there seems to have been no less of private tragedy in the circulation of this work. It was really a spark dropped on kindling wood—by which I mean those reports, caught by hearts black to the core, filled with dark suspicion.[25]

Especially was persecution to be apprehended because of the political and religious suspicion surrounding Kepler himself. The year 1609 had been one of political crisis. Emperor Rudolph, a patron of the sciences, was deposed from the throne by the Lutheran party, which was described as intending "everything for the destruction of the Catholic Church." [26] Kepler, Imperial Mathematician to Rudolph II, the caster of the Emperor's horoscopes and purveyor of political prognostications, was especially suspect to the Lutheran folk. Anxiety was the people's permanent state of mind; within the town of Leonberg, where Kepler's mother lived, six women were punished as witches during a few months of the year 1615-16. That year, too, was the beginning of Katharina Kepler's ordeal; it lasted for six years, through trials, the testimony of forty witnesses, imprisonment for fourteen months, and subjection to "territion," the procedure of interrogating the accused under the threat of torture. Throughout all this, Kepler labored indefatigably to show how the alleged incidents of bewitchment were either lies or based on occurrences that could be explained with naturalistic simplicity.

What, however, is the relationship between Kepler's Oedipal dream and the hedonist-libertarian ethic of the foundation of science? Such Oedipal experiences occur with great frequency, whereas a curiosity such as Kepler's is uncommon. The significant fact is, however, that toward the end of the sixteenth century such an Oedipal frustration was resolved through a redirection of energies into curiosity concerning the physical world. An ascetic society inflicts an intense guilt upon its young intellects for such Oedipal desires; they then turn in horror from all things physical, and direct their energies inward in self-reproach and dedication to higher, purified impulses. What stands out in Kepler's experience is that his dream does not condemn him to guilt; rather, it is the source of the "freedom for writing" which he had been yearning for, and which is his mother's gift to him. An Oedipal complex can be resolved through masochistic asceticism or libertarian hedonism; the latter resolution was conducive to the rise of the scientific spirit. The masochist ascetic is hostile to curiosity; it partakes of evil to him, and his abhorrence of curiosity is reflected in fables and legends. The hedonist-libertarian praises curiosity.

The hedonist-libertarian emotion basically reconstructed man's conception of himself in relation to Cosmic Fate. Man ceased to see himself as an impotent creature. Astrological forecasts until the sixteenth century were cosmic decrees upon human guilt. However, they took on a less awesome status in the outlook of Tycho Brahe and Kepler. Both of them had to provide monarchs with astrological forecasts. But they both became exceedingly diffident about astrology and tried to discourage it, though much of their livelihood and presumable usefulness to their monarchs was based on their providing astrological advice. Tycho wrote that he "did not care to mix in astrological matters and for some years had endeavored to put astronomy in its proper place." Kepler likewise protested against political prophesying based on celestial events. When a bright new star appeared in 1604, there was a plethora of prophecies—the overthrow of the Ottoman Empire, a European revolution, the Day of Judgment. Kepler, however, said:

> . . . we are looking for too much art in these things. We should grasp the ox by the horns, the buck by the beard, and so on. Moreover, to speak about these signs, one should value them for what they are worth and in accordance with their effects. If they signify nothing we are acting foolishly when we investigate them. If they signify something, well then, the significance must be so constituted that even the common man can understand it.

Both Tycho and Kepler remained nonetheless committed to astrological ideas. Kepler thus believed that a person's character was shaped by the constellation of heavenly bodies and heavenly forces transmitted through the mother's imagination and rearing of the child. There was a plausibility to this hypothesis, especially if one believed in the interrelation of physical forces. Neither Kepler nor Tycho, however, were astrological determinists; they did not believe that men were impotent against the determinations of the heavenly bodies. They were astrological interventionists—that is, they maintained that the heavenly prognostications could be used to guide action which would prevent them from being fulfilled. An astrological prediction was one subject to a refutational condition. Kepler was frank about his "predictions:"

> We make use of the disordered and corruptible desires of the masses, in order to instill in them [as cure] proper warnings, disguised as prognostications, warnings which contribute to the removal of illness and which we can scarcely introduce in another manner.

People were superstitious; superstition was a "universal idea of all people," so that when the heavens were wild, people became wild. The Imperial Mathematician, as a member of the scientific intellectual elite, used this principle for political wisdom: "And it is permissible to let a ruler of the vulgar crowd once in a while take advantage of such influences." Kepler had to draw his prophecies loosely enough so that it would not be easy to call them wrong, for: "Each one wants me to prophesy what he desires, and inversely from what I prophesy draws conclusions about my party leanings." So Kepler vacillated in his astrological professions, as he submitted them to realistic sociological and physical analysis.[27] The astrological forecast took on the character of a public-relations statement adapted to the mass-medium needs of the seventeenth century.

NOTES

1. Edward Rosen, "Galileo's Misstatements About Copernicus," *Isis,* XLIX (1958), 320.

2. Stanislaw Kot, *Five Centuries of Polish Learning* (Oxford, 1941), p. 4.

3. Translated in Arthur Koestler, *The Sleepwalkers* (London, 1959), p. 15.

4. Copernicus, wrote Rheticus, "was not so much the pupil as the assistant and witness of observations of the learned Dominicus Maria." Edward Rosen, *Three Copernican Treatises* (New York, 1939), p. 111. Angus Armitage, *Copernicus: The Founder of Modern Astronomy* (London, 1938), pp. 47-8. Dorothy Stimson, *The Gradual Acceptance of the Copernican Theory of the Universe* (Hanover, 1917), p. 25. Leopold Prowe, *Nicolaus Coppernicus,* Erster Band, 1 Theil (Berlin, 1883), pp. 235-46.

5. Giovanni Pico della Mirandola, "Oration on the Dignity of Man," in *The Renaissance Philosophy of Man,* ed. Ernest Cassirer, Paul Oskar Kristeller, and John Herman Randall, Jr. (Chicago, 1948), pp. 223, 244. Ernst Cassirer, *The Platonic Renaissance in England,* trans. James P. Pettegrove (Edinburgh, 1953), pp. 102-3.

6. G. Pico della Mirandola, *A Platonic Discourse upon Love,* ed. Edmund G. Gardner (Boston, 1914), pp. xviii, xix, 72-3. Giovanni Francesco Pico, *Giovanni Pico della Mirandola: His Life,* trans. Sir Thomas More, ed. J. M. Rigg (London, 1890), pp. xxxi, 22. Erwin Panofsky, "The Neo-platonic Movement in Florence and North Italy," *Studies in Iconology* (New York, 1939), pp. 156-159.

7. Nicolaus Copernicus, *On the Revolutions of the Heavenly Spheres,* trans. Charles Glenn Wallis, in *Ptolemy, Copernicus, Kepler,* in *Great Books of the Western World,* ed. Robert Maynard Hutchins (Chicago, 1952), Vol. XVI, p. 510.

8. Leopold Prowe, *Nicolaus Coppernicus* (Berlin, 1884), Vol. II, p. 33, cited and translated in Simon Newcomb, *The Reminiscences of an Astronomer* (Boston, 1903), pp. 399-400. J. Taylor, "Copernicus on the Evils of Inflation and the Establishment of a Sound Currency," *Journal of the History of Ideas,* XVI (1955), 540-547. Cf. Angus Armitage, *The World of Copernicus* (New York, 1956). Thomas Willing Belch, *The*

Law of Oresme, Copernicus, and Gresham (Philadelphia, 1908), pp. 13-18.

9. Edward Rosen, *Three Copernican Treatises*, pp. 22-5.

10. John Calvin, *Commentaries on the First Book of Moses called Genesis*, trans. Rev. John King (Grand Rapids, 1948), Vol. I, p. 61. *Conversations with Luther*, trans. Preserved Smith and Herbert Percival Gallinger (New York, 1915), p. 104. Thomas Campanella, "The Defense of Galileo," trans. Grant McColley, *Smith College Studies in History*, XXII (1937), xxi. Also, Dorothy Stimson, *op. cit.*, p. 41. Many scholars have cited Calvin as saying: "Who will venture to place the authority of Copernicus above that of the Holy Spirit?" Edward Rosen has shown in a painstaking research that it is doubtful Calvin ever said this. Calvin held to a pre-Copernican cosmology, disliked the allegorical tampering with Scripture, and accepted literally the Biblical version of Joshua's miracle. But, asks Professor Rosen, was Calvin's cosmology "anti-Copernican"? He answers, "Never having heard of him, Calvin had no attitude toward Copernicus." Professor Rosen's conclusion that Calvin never heard of Copernicus seems to leap far beyond what the evidence supports. Calvin, one can be sure, heard of lots of people whom he chose not to discuss in his sermons. Moreover, to hold to pre-Copernican views in Calvin's time was equivalent to aligning oneself with the anti-Copernican standpoint. We can speculate as to why Calvin did not explicitly refer to Copernicus. Authoritarian leaders do not like to create a vogue for persons, ideas, and books they dislike. They wish to avoid suggesting avenues of dissent that the rebellious may explore. As an authoritarian chief, Calvin may well have been following authoritarian prudence in not mentioning Copernicus's name. Cf. Edward Rosen, "Calvin's Attitude Toward Copernicus," *Journal of the History of Ideas*, XXI (1960), pp. 438-41. Also John Dillenberger, *Protestant Thought and Natural Science* (New York, 1960), p. 38.

11. Edward Rosen, *Three Copernican Treatises*, pp. 190-1. On the practical significance of Copernicus's work for the reform of the calendar, cf. the translation of the *Praefatio* of Copernicus, in Dorothy Stimson, *op. cit.*, App. B, p. 115. Tiedemann Giese, Bishop of Kulm, had urged Copernicus "that it would be of no small importance to the glory of Christ if there existed a proper calendar of events in the Church and a correct theory and explanation of the motions." Copernicus "promised that he would draw up astronomical tables with new rules and that if his work had any value he would not keep it from the world. . . ." Edward Rosen, *Three Copernican Treatises*, p. 192.

12. Arthur Koestler, *op. cit.* p. 149. Ephraim Emerton, *Desiderius Erasmus of Rotterdam* (New York, 1899), p. 324. Dorothy Stimson, *op. cit.*, p. 40.

13. Christopher Marlowe, *Tragical History of Dr. Faustus*, ed. Adolphus William Ward (Oxford, 1901), p. xxxiii. Ernest Belfort Bax, "Dr. Faustus and his Contemporaries," in *The Ethics of Socialism* (London, 1902), p. 177.

14. Edward Rosen, *Three Copernican Treatises*, pp. 27, 167-8, 193. Dorothy Stimson, *op. cit.*, pp. 109, 110, 114-15.

15. John Allyne Gade, *The Life and Times of Tycho Brahe* (Princeton, 1947), pp. 13, 41.

16. J. L. E. Dreyer, *Tycho Brahe: A Picture of Scientific Life and Work in the Sixteenth Century* (Edinburgh, 1890), pp. 13, 43, 261. John Allyn Gade, *op. cit.*, pp. 43, 59, 60-1, 156, 171, 187, 189.

17. Max Brod, *The Redemption of Tycho Brahe*, trans. Felix Warren Crosse (London, 1928).

18. Max Caspar, *Kepler*, trans. C. Doris Hellman (New York, 1959), pp. 41, 217-18.

19. Johannes Kepler, *Epitome of Copernican Astronomy:* IV and V; *The Harmonies of the World:* V, trans. Charles Glenn Wallis, in *Ptolemy, Copernicus, Kepler* ("Great Books," Vol. XVI), pp. 849-50, 961-3, 1050.

20. Max Caspar, *op. cit.*, pp. 57, 63, 93, 96. Also, Charles S. Peirce, "Kepler," in *Values in a Universe of Chance*, ed. Philip P. Wiener (New York, 1958), pp. 255-6. Johannes Kepler, *The Harmonies of the World* ("Great Books," Vol. XVI), pp. 849-50, 961-3, 1030, 1050.

21. Carola Baumgardt, *Johannes Kepler: Life and Letters* (New York, 1951), pp. 34-5, 101, 113, 121-2.

22. W. Pauli, *The Influence of Archetypal Ideas on the Scientific Theories of Kepler*, trans. Priscilla Sitz, in C. G. Jung and W. Pauli, *The Interpretation of Nature and the Psyche* (New York, 1955), pp. 159, 168-70.

23. Gerald Holton, "Johannes Kepler's Universe: Its Physics and Metaphysics," *American Journal of Physics*, XXIV (1956), 342, 345, 351.

24. Max Caspar, *op. cit.*, pp. 375, 382. Gerald Holton, *op. cit.*, p. 347.

25. Marjorie Hope Nicolson, "Kepler, the *Somnium*, and John Donne," *Journal of the History of Ideas*, I (1940), 259, 265, 267. Marjorie Hope Nicolson, *Voyages to the Moon* (New York, 1948), pp. 43, 47.

26. C. V. Wedgwood, *The Thirty Years War* (Penguin ed., Harmondsworth, 1957), p. 67.

27. John Allyn Gade, *op. cit.*, pp. 18, 80, 107. Max Caspar, *op. cit.*, pp. 38, 43, 59, 152, 156, 184, 302, 303.

V

Scientific Revolution and Counterrevolution in Italy

THE COPERNICAN REVOLUTION PRODUCED A CRISIS OF THEOLOGY in the Roman Catholic Church. In the person of Galileo Galilei, the church was confronted with all the potential consequences of the scientific movement for its organization and ethic. The scientific movement in Italy was especially associated with the University of Padua, which for many years gave to Galileo the support of its free atmosphere.

☙ The University of Padua

THE MERCANTILE REPUBLICS OF ITALY—Venice, Florence, Genoa, Milan—were, during the Renaissance, Catholic in their religion but hedonist in their ethics. The Italian upper and middle classes came to have a great contempt for the church and its professed asceticism and otherworldliness. Especially in Venice, the great commercial center, from the later Middle Ages on, "the supreme objects," as Burckhardt said, "were the enjoyment of life and power. . . ." Venice became the center of Italian anticlericalism. It amazed Protestant Northern Europe by its daring. It taxed its priests, prevented them from receiving bequests of land, placed them under civil law, and received the heretical English Ambassador despite the papal objection. In the year 1606, Pope Paul V finally put the entire city under interdict. The Republic of Venice defied him, and warned its clergy to continue their usual functions. The Interdict was rescinded after a year. Venice yielded on no basic issues; its victory resounded through Europe. Venice went on to ally itself during the seventeenth century as its commercial interest indicated—with the Protestant powers.

Although Venice lagged behind the other Italian cities with respect to original creations in art and poetry, it was supreme in science. A few miles away was the town of Padua, which in 1405 was incorporated into the Republic of Venice. There stood the University of Padua, a fortress of intellectual freedom; already in the forefront of science in the fourteenth century, it became the scientific center of Europe in the fifteenth and sixteenth centuries, and was especially renowned for having the most distinguished medical school on the Continent. The University of Padua was alma mater to Copernicus and Vesalius, to Harvey and Gilbert. At Padua, Galileo spent many fruitful years, untroubled by the Inquisition so long as he lived under Venice's protective arm. Reaction had set in at all the Italian universities with the exception of Padua. All non-Catholic students were excluded by the Pope from Italian universities; a sort of papal curtain over Catholic Italy was part of the response to the Protestant Reformation. Padua, however, secure within the borders of republican Venice, circumvented the papal order by creating for administrative purposes a separate university for non-Catholics. Shakespeare hailed Padua as the "nursery of the arts"; it was indeed the cradle of the European scientific movement.[1]

The Italian Scientific Renaissance, as Arturo Castiglioni writes, assumed at once "an international character"; it marked "the beginning of a universal scientific movement." Venice, aware that its prosperity rested on free trade, opened its doors to foreigners and safeguarded free thought as well as free trade. When academic freedom later collapsed in German universities under the impact of religious wars, Padua maintained its tradition of freedom, and welcomed the diverse "Nationes." "In the second half of the sixteenth century, the German nation alone had 977 students enrolled in the Medical Faculty." In 1616 the Church protested vigorously the granting of medical degrees without a religious oath. The

Council of the Venetian Republic replied with Paolo Sarpi's words: "It is not necessary for a physician also to be a theologian." [2]

To Padua came bedecked sons of English noblemen, austere sons of Scandinavian pastors, and pale, turbaned Polish Jews, fresh from Talmudical academies. An Englishman, William Thomas, wrote in 1549 that at the University of Padua there was an

> . . . infinite resorte of all nations. . . . And I thinke verilie, that in one region of all the worlde again, are not half so many straungers as in Italie; specially of gentilmen, whose resorte thither is principallie under pretence of studie . . . all kyndes of vertue maie there be learned: not of such students alone, as moste commonly are brought up in our universities (meane mens children set to schole in hope to live upon hyred learnyng) but for the most parte of noble mens sonnes, and of the best gentilmen: that studie more for knowledge and pleasure than for curiositee or luker. . . .[3]

Of the fifteen hundred scholars at Padua that winter, "knowledge and pleasure" had evidently brought among them at least a thousand gentlemen.

When Europe's universities in the sixteenth and seventeenth centuries rigorously refused to admit Jews as students, Padua was the shining exception. From 1517 to 1721, two hundred twenty-nine Jews were among its graduates, and it is estimated that in any given year an average of ten Jews would have been found in its student body. Though they were obliged to pay special fees and tributes which made their tuition costs almost twice those of the Christian student, still they could wear the same black hat that the other students wore, rather than the otherwise compulsory Jewish headgear. Polish Jewish students especially came to Padua in the second half of the sixteenth century to pursue medical studies. Jewish graduates of Padua served as physicians to kings of Poland. The Christian Poles at Padua, lacking the Italian liberalism, refused to admit their Jewish countrymen into their national register. Consequently, the Jewish students were enrolled on the university's rolls as "Hebraei Poloni"; these were perhaps the first student fraternities divided along religious lines.[4]

At Padua, the scholars between studies engaged in jousts of arms and took excursions to Venice on boats whose principal other passengers were courtesans and monks. Venice was evidently the English hedonists' proving ground; the proverb arose: "An Englishman Italianate is a devil incarnate," and the scholars in turn were warned of the charms of Italian women, "*Inter faeminas, formae conspicuae, sed lasciviae et provaces,*" ("Among women, of striking figure, but wanton and provocative"). The Italianate Englishmen were reputed to be freethinkers, atheists who mocked at both Protestants and Papists. This was the wind, as Shakespeare said, which "scatters young men through the world," sending

> Some to discover islands far away;
> Some to the studious universities.[5]

Roger Ascham said that they went to Italy to serve Circes, but at Padua Circes blended with Athena.

A hedonistic naturalism was for several centuries the philosophical orthodoxy at the University of Padua. The doctrines of the Moslem philosopher Averroes were made the vehicles of religious unbelief. Petrarch complained that these Averroists assailed Christ and supernaturalism. When he quoted St. Paul to one of them, the Averroist replied that he followed a better master. "Remain a Christian," he said. "As for me, I don't believe a word of any of your fables." Pope Leo V, therefore, for all his humanist sympathies, felt constrained to issue in 1513 a bull against Averroism as a heresy that denied the soul's immortality. The Renaissance naturalists were confident in the powers of human beings. They agreed with Lucretius that the human race must be liberated from fear, and they expelled asceticism from their way of life.[6]

Galileo, as Professor Randall has pointed out, was a "typical Paduan Aristotelian." He was indeed an inheritor of the whole tradition of Averroism, which, with its secular and anticlerical tone, had flourished in Padua since the fourteenth century:

> At Padua, Bologna and Pavia there reigned an Aristotelianism that made little attempt to accommodate itself to theological interests. And it is no accident that while the Church-controlled science of the North drove all those who felt the new currents into open rebellion against science itself, the anti-clerical science of the Italian universities could progress steadily in self-criticism to the achievement of a Galileo.[7]

Galileo's achievement was rooted in the soil of what I have called the Left Aristotelian mode of thought in Padua.

The philosophy of liberty of the Italian scientific intellectuals was most eloquently set forth by an alumnus of Padua, Thomas Campanella. Born in 1568, Campanella joined the Dominican Order in his boyhood, but concluded his education at Padua in 1595. His intellectual forays against Aristotle led to his "detention" by the Holy Office of the Inquisition, and his political activities against the Spanish kingdom in Naples led to his trial, torture, and imprisonment on the charge of conspiring to establish a communist commonwealth. For twenty-seven years, until 1626, Campanella languished in the prisons of the Inquisition. In the Neapolitan dungeons, he wrote his vision of a scientific society, *The City of the Sun*, and in 1616 his *Defense of Galileo*. He stated the significance of liberty of thought:

> I have shown that liberty of thought is more vigorous in Christian than in other nations. Should this be true, whosoever prescribes at his own pleasure bounds and laws for human thought, as if this action were in harmony with the decrees of Holy Scripture, he not only is irrational and harmful, but also is irreligious and impious.[8]

Where liberty of thought flourished, there science could prevail. Liberty could transfuse Catholic, Mohammedan, or Protestant milieus. Campanella spoke for an Italian liberalism which was soon to be enfeebled by the hegemony of the Holy Inquisition. Liberty of thought, however, had long been regnant at Padua.

Campanella's *Civitas Solis—The City of the Sun*—was the first of the scientific utopian visions. Thomas More's *Utopia* was principally inspired by the social crisis of his time, and represented the hopes of a statesman whose ideas blended tradition with reform. But Campanella's *City of the Sun* projected the vision for the first time in the modern era of the rule of the scientific intellectuals. His wandering sea captain described the scientific society he had seen. Its intellectual-in-chief, the Hoh, was not a man who "has contemplated nothing but the words of books." One who "has gathered his knowledge from books, is unlearned and unskilled." The chief official was, rather, a master of "all the mechanical arts, the physical sciences, astrology and mathematics."

"Nearly every two days they teach our mechanical art." The Hoh knows "the laws and the history of the earth and heavenly bodies." In this scientific society, people worked only about four hours a day. "The remaining hours are spent in learning joyously, in debating, in reading, in reciting, in writing, in walking, in exercising the mind and body, and with play." In their schools, the "boys are accustomed to learn all the sciences, without toil and as if for pleasure." Their priests "write very learned treatises and search into the sciences." Their thinkers admire Copernicus, but "disbelieve in Aristotle," whom they consider a logician but not a scientist.

The City of the Sun was also a land of sexual freedom. Campanella's libertarian hedonism reached an extreme point with his description of the sexual communism practiced by the inhabitants of the Civitas Solis. "And they defend themselves by the opinion of Socrates, of Cato, of Plato, and of St. Clement," though, added Campanella, by way of prudent precaution, "they misunderstand the opinions of these thinkers." The scientific society aimed to reduce human frustration, and to make affection and joy the law of human life.

> Forsooth, no one is envious of another. They sing a hymn to Love, one to Wisdom, and one each to all the other virtues. . . . Each one takes the woman he loves most, and they dance for exercise with propriety and stateliness under the peristyles.

The women were described as athletic, "strong of limb, tall and agile," the equals of men. Campanella contrasted the image of the scientific society with the actualities of Neapolitan life. Every man had honorable work in the City of the Sun, and there was no slavery. But: "In Naples there exist seventy thousand souls, and out of these scarcely ten or fifteen thousand do any work, and they are always lean from overwork and are getting weaker every day." [9] The City of the Sun, the society imbued with a scientific philosophy and social affection, governed by men of science, was the hope of the world. *Civitas Solis* was the dream in which all the motifs in the unconscious of the Italian scientific intellectuals were combined, and their hedonist-libertarian values fully realized.

Bruno

Every movement generally has at least one participant who tends to speak out without restraint or inhibition its underlying creed. Such a person can embarrass the movement itself with his excess of zeal and lack of judgment as to the place and time to say things. The scientific movement had its evolving unconscious grand strategy; the tragically poorest of its tacticians was Giordano Bruno. His life was a series of flights and excommunications. Not a scientist but, rather, a literary spokesman for science, he was a bitter, sardonic critic of the ascetic ethics and a propagandist for love and scientific knowledge. He found no home in any European creed, no sanctuary in any town. But, in his extreme manner, he gave a poetic expression to the scientific moment of the Italian Renaissance. He wore and discarded the habit of a Dominican friar; he fled from Rome to Geneva; he was denounced by Calvinists and excommunicated by Lutherans. He outraged Oxford by telling it it needed an "awakener"; he described his Oxonian opponent in disputation:

> . . . a wretched doctor got stuck, like a chicken in stubble, fifteen times in the fifteen syllogisms he propounded as Coryphaeus of the University. Hear how vulgar and violent the pig was. . . .

He left England after saying it was a country ruled by "pedants who exhibit obstinacy, ignorance and presumption. . . ." He left Paris after its students demonstrated violently against his critique of Aristotelian metaphysics; they indulged in "turning up their noses, gibing, blowing out their cheeks and banging at the desks." He was betrayed in Venice, and endured imprisonment in Rome for seven years; condemned as a heretic, he died bravely at the stake in 1600. People were reluctant to mention Bruno's name; he was of the underworld of the scientific movement, errant, stormy, combative.

Apart from his cosmological speculations, Bruno is outstanding as a most forthright exponent of the hedonist-libertarian ethic. That was why he was as out of place in Calvinist Geneva as in a Dominican cloister. Like almost all Italian scientists and intellectuals, he wrote a play; *Il Candelajo* (*The Candle*) it was called, composed in "a few burning days," and Rabelaisian in spirit. Its lines filled with spontaneity, buffoonery, and obscenity, it lit the candle which was to "clarify certain shadows of ideas." Bruno felt that Christianity was far inferior to the pagan religions; it was, in his eyes, a cult of ascetic saints which multilated human joy. He looked back regretfully to the tolerance practiced among the pagans and to their Bacchic rites. He told Germans they were wasting their time on theological nonsense; when they would become saner, they would be "not men, but Gods." He admired Luther for having heard "the awakening spirit of the Lord," but it was the awakening he admired, not the theology.

Behind the daring of the cosmological speculator, expansive with a vision of the universe's infinitude, was a liberation of emotion, of bodily feeling, which was the perennial theme of Bruno's writing:

> What do I hold? Am I perchance a foe to generation? Do I hate the sun? Do I regret having come into the world? Shall I keep men from the delicious fruits of our earthly paradise? Is it for me to bar the holy law of nature? . . . Am I to persuade myself and others that we are not born to carry on the life we have received? Methinks I am not cold. I doubt if the snows of Caucasus would put out my fires. . . . What do I conclude? . . . That women, being women, should be honored and loved as such.[10]

This reveling in the delights of existence was also, in Bruno's view, tied to scientific empiricism. "All love proceeds from seeing: . . . in the sense and the intellect there is one desire and one impulse to the sensuous in general. . . ." He was bored with the theological subtleties of transubstantiation, and preferred the mysteries of Ceres and Bacchus: "A woman is worthy of being loved in the flower of her beauty and ability to produce children of Nature and God." Intellectual pursuit seemed to him plainly akin to sexual drive. And in the midst of his tribute to women's beauty he suddenly speaks the language of science: "All things which exist have solidity and consistency only insofar as they have weight, number, order, and measure. . . ." Though the Platonic theme of the uplift to spiritual love is always present, there is a still more distinctive description of sexual love as "that sweetest apple which the garden of our earthly paradise can produce." "However great the realms and beatitudes which might have been offered me," says Bruno, naught would have made him wish "to castrate myself or make me into a eunuch." [11]

Such, then, was Bruno; the censors, as he said, tried to restrain him from that "towards which he was naturally inclined, sought to enslave his genius, and from being free in virtue they would have rendered him contemptible under a most vile and stupid hypocrisy." He rejected a professorship at Paris because he did not think it worth a Mass. He found no sanctuary even in Venice, where the love of lucre was said to have happily prevailed over the love of God. His name whispered softly among Italian intellectuals suggested the deepest emotional striving, sometimes subdued into the unconscious, of the scientific revolution.

Galileo

GALILEO WAS THE MOST ILLUSTRIOUS of Padua's men of science. There was no semblance of asceticism or frugality in his personality. In 1590, Galileo, then at Pisa, wrote a fragment of a play, a licentious burlesque ridiculing a university ordinance that compelled professors to wear their gowns even while they were not lecturing. Galileo offended the academic body; "the author was set down as a man of easy morals, and little mindful of the professorial dignity." Galileo, as musician, painter, and lover of the arts, was typical of the devotion of Renaissance men to the senses.[12] His unmarried life with Marina Gamba, with whom he had three children, was outside the Christian code.

The judgment against Galileo in 1633 by the Inquisitors-General of the Holy Office was a turning point in the struggle between the scientific intellectuals, committed to the libertarian ethic, and the managerial religious intellectuals, who stood by the principle of authority. When Galileo's spirit was broken in 1633, it was also the future of science in Italy which was darkened for the next two centuries. As Giorgio de Santillana writes in his remarkable book *The Crime of Galileo*, "this was the end of the whole scientific movement in Italy. . . ." John Milton saw the depression of emotion and intellect which the Inquisition's triumph over Galileo produced among Italians:

> I have sat among their learned men, and been counted happy to be born in such a place of philosophic freedom as they supposed England was, while they themselves did nothing but bemoan the servile condition into which learning amongst them was brought; that this was it which had damped the glory of Italian wits, that nothing had been there written now these many years but flattery and fustian.

The clerical managerialists fashioned the "servile condition" of the Italian intellect. Italian science, which had been the envy and glory of Europe, had previously "reached the point," says Professor de Santillana, "where it was ready to burst into flower." [13]

There was among the Italians of the sixteenth century, writes von Ranke, an earnest devotion to scientific truth, a zeal for progress. "The whole system of ideas as previously accepted was called in question. . . . Who shall say to what glorious results this might have led?" [14] The Inquisition's repression and terror destroyed the Italian scientific supremacy, which, within a generation, passed to England. One should not jump therefore to facile generalizations about the greater proclivity of Protestant asceticism for science as compared with Catholic indulgence. For the striking fact is that the termination of Italian scientific leadership was due, as the contemporary John Milton saw, to the power of authoritarianism. It was not the Catholic ethic but the authoritarian principle which stifled the scientific spirit; it could make Protestantism, too, inimical to science, just as the hedonist-libertarian ethic could make both Catholics and Protestants into friends of scientific inquiry. Science cannot coexist with the spirit of servility.

The authoritarian principle in science was not intrinsic to Catholic doctrine or practice. The Renaissance popes were often secular men, well-inclined toward the arts and sciences. But an organization under attack tends to tighten its organizational discipline. Every intellectual difference then becomes a suspect ideological deviation, for deviation is simply an intellectual difference which may threaten the rule of the dominant elite. The authoritarian principle is a defense mechanism against the anxiety of deviation. During the latter part of the sixteenth century, it grew stronger in the Catholic hierarchy. When Pope Paul III decided on an active persecution of heretics through the Inquisition, directed by the newly established

Society of Jesus, there was a "panicky migration" from the towns of northern Italy. Many were arrested and tried, and some were executed. The outcome of the conflict between Catholic liberals and authoritarians was by no means, however, foreclosed. There were liberal scientific intellectuals to be found throughout Italy, in the lower echelons of the church hierarchy and in the Roman Curia itself. The party of Galileisti was numerous and growing in numbers, as gentlemen and scholars everywhere felt the delight of the new philosophy.[15] Venice under the inspiring guidance of Don Paolo Sarpi, mathematician and advocate of freedom, had defied a papal interdict. At any moment, a hundred, a thousand more Paolo Sarpis might spring up. The clerical managerialists lived in uneasy fear. Campanella had warned them that suppressing Galileo would bring mockery down upon the Roman theology. "Particularly is this true," he wrote, "since both his hypothesis and the telescope have been accepted with avidity by many men in Germany, France, England, Poland, Denmark and Sweden. . . . The new philosophy will be embraced eagerly by heretics and we shall be ridiculed."

The new science had within it a latent threat that far exceeded the Protestant heresies, for it brought forward the prestige of a new group, the scientific intellectuals, as against all theocrats, Catholic or Protestant. The Jesuit could feel himself a brother-under-the-cassock of Luther or Calvin, but he could never feel at home with a Galileo or a Vesalius, no matter how much they professed their Catholic loyalty. So Galileo wrote to his friend Diodati in 1633, shortly after he was summoned to appear before the Inquisition, ". . . the Jesuit Fathers have insinuated in the highest quarters that my book is more execrable and injurious to the Church than the writings of Luther and Calvin." [16] The Inquisition, for its part, saw in Galileo's friendship for such men as Diodati evidence of the waywardness of the scientific intellectual. Diodati, a Protestant, an émigré from his native Tuscany, living in Paris, had done an admirable translation of the Scriptures into Italian which circulated extensively in Venice. Moreover, Paolo Sarpi, the arch-enemy of the Jesuits, was still another good friend of Galileo's. Sarpi had foreseen misfortune when Galileo allowed himself in 1616 to try to come to an understanding with Rome as to the domain of his scientific research.

> I fear [wrote Paolo] that if in such circumstances he brings forward the learned considerations which have induced him to prefer the theory of Canon Copernicus of our solar system, he will incur the ill will of the Jesuits and of the other monks, that the physical and astronomical questions will be changed by them into a matter of theology and I foresee with sorrow that he will have to recant his opinions upon it, if he would live in peace without being regarded as a heretic.

The categories of the new science were indeed linked with the embryonic philosophy of political liberalism. Paolo Sarpi, the theoretician of Venetian liberties, was, for instance, a forerunner of Galileo and Locke in making the distinction between primary and secondary qualities. And Paolo, too, fought against the adoration of the Virgin, which seemed especially to unfit men for scientific work. He managed to effect the removal of the prayer "Salve Regina" in Venice, and also warned against promulgating dogmas such as the Immaculate Conception of Mary.[17]

It was one thing, furthermore, for learned men to dispute within the confines of the church, keeping their quarrels to themselves by writing their views only in Latin, and never appealing to the judgment of the outside lay public. But to invite the "masses" to take sides in a dispute among managerial intellectuals was to threaten to undermine the entire principle of authority and oracular respect which the managerial elite required. Diodati and Luther had translated the Scriptures into the common tongue, and now here was Galileo translating the Copernican arguments into Italian so that all readers of the *Dialogues on the Great World Systems* might judge for themselves, and see with their plain common sense how pitifully tenuous was the church's official view. So long as the clerical intellectuals could set the rules for disputation and maintain their supremacy as intellectual arbiters, it had not been difficult to find formulae that safeguarded Scriptural "truth" while allowing Galileo, with appropriate verbal fictions, to pursue his scientific truth. For the church oscillated between two attitudes toward the new science, involving respectively a "strict" and a "liberal" construction of Scripture.

In its strict mood, it simply asserted outright, as Galileo's judges did, that the Copernican hypotheses was "a most grievous error, as an opinion can in no wise be probable which has been declared and defined to be contrary to the divine Scripture." In its liberal mood, however, the church leaders could avail themselves of various formulae that would preserve the formal impeccability of revealed "truth" while giving material recognition to scientific truth. It could admonish Galileo, as Cardinal Bellarmine did in 1616, that the Copernican hypothesis "cannot be defended or held." But this admonition was compatible with proposing the Copernican theory as a "mathematical hypothesis"—a set of hypothetical propositions rather than declarative, categorical ones; as a conjecture. Or there was the escape clause proposed by Pope Urban VIII himself, for the Pope was no enemy of the sciences. When still Cardinal Maffeo Barberini, he had befriended Galileo, whose work he admired greatly, and his election to the Papacy had been hailed as a victory for the scientific intellectuals. "This is going to be the Papacy of the *virtuosi*," wrote one of Galileo's friends. Pope Urban VIII himself suggested the title of the *Dialogues;* he asked only for a saving clause, that Galileo should not interpret his system as a "necessitating" proof, that Galileo should recognize that "God is all-powerful, and if He is, why should we try to necessitate him?" God, in His infinite power, could have done things differently, in ways we cannot divine, and it would be the sin of what we call today "scientism" to presume that His mind is necessarily bound by the conveniences of ours.[18]

Such saving clauses were used and invoked by Galileo, but to no avail. For Galileo had dared to move the forum of the circle of discussion from the managerial-clerical intellectuals to the educated public at large, with its common sense relatively uncontaminated by theology or vested interest. Paolo Sarpi had said the Jesuits' learning was "only built on the ignorance of the people." [19] Galileo was taking his scientific case to the people, as Luther had done with his religious theses. Galileo's tactics had not lacked adroitness; he had almost been what we would call today a successful Fabian in his methods. He made use of his personal friendships and associations with Catholic functionaries to obtain from them a papal license for his book. Then, however, in the eyes of the church, he betrayed good faith by allowing its ideological formula to be ridiculed in his *Dialogues* in the person of Simplicio, who repeats in reply to scientific reasoning, "it would be an extravagant boldness for anyone to go about and limit the Divine power to some one particular conjecture of its own." [20] All the world was beckoned to laugh at the philosophy of the managerial Catholic intellectuals.

Galileo had come into conflict with reasons of state, indeed with the "theological superstate" (in Santillana's words), with the "modern state"—that is, with a state with managerial ideology and practice. Then, suddenly feeling very old, Galileo was strangely bewildered by the forces that arose against him. With a scientist's naïve puzzlement at the ways of religious ideologies, he wrote, ". . . why, in our search for knowledge of the various parts of the universe, should we begin rather with the words than with the works of God? Is the work less noble or less excellent than the word?" [21] As Galileo's friends saw the clerical engines of repression bearing down relentlessly against the old man, they pleaded with him to take sanctuary in Venice, which was generously offering him refuge from the Inquisitors. But Galileo, in an ill-advised and self-destructive decision, chose to remain. When he stayed in Rome to abjure his scientific beliefs, to accept the imprisonment of the Inquisition, he allowed the clerical managerialists to destroy his spirit and that of Italian science. If he had fled to the safety of Venice and Padua, he would have become the beacon of resistance for all Europe's scientific intellectuals, and especially of the younger Italian generation. And the Pope, who had never dared actually to affirm with a bull the falsity of the Copernican hypothesis but had left such judgments to the Holy Congregation, would probably not have been willful or stupid enough to stake Catholic "truth" against science. But Galileo, leader of the Scientific Revolution, was also a loyal son of the Church; he could gaily put to flight the Aristotelians, but the thought of pitting himself against the might of such an institution overwhelmed him. His scientific revolution, he perhaps vaguely surmised, required the political revolution for which his friend Paolo Sarpi had almost given his life. To become the symbolic leader of such a revolution was something the old man could not undertake.

There have been philosophers of science who have tended to belittle Galileo's stand against the authoritarian principle. Morris R. Cohen, for instance, was inclined to scold Galileo and to make of the Inquisitors-General the spokesmen for scientific logic:

> Galileo's difficulties with the church had nothing to do with his experiments. They developed, apart from personal causes, out of his refusal to treat the Copernican hypothesis as an hypothesis, which in the light of modern relativity was not an unreasonable request. There seem to be as many myths about Galileo as about any of the saints.[22]

But in this instance the myth concerning Galileo is closer to the truth than the relativistic revisionists grant. For what was at issue in the Galilean controversy was the whole question of the meaning of "hypothesis." The Inquisitors-General did not use the term "hypothesis" in its scientific sense; according to their usage, no accumulation of evidence could in any way increase the probability of the Copernican hypothesis. A hypothesis, in the Church's usage, was to remain a fancy which experiment could in no way confirm or invalidate. The Copernican hypothesis, they told Galileo, is "an opinion" which "can in no wise be probable," for it "has been declared and defined to be contrary to divine Scripture."[23] Of course the Copernican theory was a hypothesis, and Galileo treated it as such, and adduced observational evidence in its favor. When Galileo in 1611 announced his discovery of the phases of Venus, he had observational facts that confirmed the Copernican hypothesis; the absence of such observed phases had long been used as an argument against the truth of the Copernican theory. The Inquisitors condemned Galileo precisely because he took his "hypothesis" in the scientific sense: "You have nevertheless dared to discuss and defend it and to argue its probability," they declared in their decision. The church's injunction concerning hypotheses had nothing to do with Einstein's theory of relativity. They were appalled by Galileo's argument that his mathematical method could enable him to read Nature's truth. As their preliminary commission charged, "He perniciously asserts and sets forth that, in the appreciation of geometrical matters, there is some equality between the divine and the human mind." Galileo, said the Inquisition's counselor, gives to his hypothesis "physical reality." This was, in Pope Urban's words, "to impose necessity upon the Lord Almighty," submitting God to mathematical laws, when God's governance of natural phenomena might truly transcend the human intellect. The Tuscan Ambassador replied to the Pope that "I had heard Galileo saying that he was willing not to believe in the motion of the Earth, but that as God could make the world in a thousand ways, so it could not be denied that He could have made it in this way too." [24] The Pope grew very angry. The point was that no matter how much evidence one might adduce for the heliocentric theory, one must still disbelieve it as "absurd and false philosophically and formally heretical, because it is expressly contrary to the Holy Scripture."

In the church's usage, a "hypothesis" was a statement that was false no matter how much evidence there was in its favor. This has always been the ultimate logical retreat of the authoritarian ethic. Protestant authoritarians have also availed themselves of the church's conception of hypothesis. William Jennings Bryan, in demanding that the theory of evolution not be taught in American classrooms, said that evolution was being taught as a fact instead of as a theory, thereby causing students to lose their faith in the Bible.[25] Bryan and the Inquisitors-General agreed in their meaning of "hypothesis" and "theory."

Every departure from scientific logic is motivated by an anxiety. In this case, the managerial authority was compelled by its fears to abandon that adherence to the reality principle which is the essence of scientific thought. Corresponding to the managerial superego, which sought to repress the claims of perception and scientific reasoning, there was the arbitrarily superimposed criterion of that which is "philosophically and theologically true" as against lowly animal observations and reasonings. Philosophical theology became the tyrant of the sciences. The dualism between the "philosophically true" and the "mathematically convenient" expressed the unresolved anxiety of the clerical managerialists. The "logic" which condemned Galileo could—and would—also be used in later centuries to reinforce such doctrines as the existence of phlogiston and an ether, compounded to unverifiability with auxiliary hypotheses, as against the verifiable theories of Lavoisier and Einstein.

The managerial clericalists saw clearly now the menace of the scientific intellectuals, forging a new cosmopolitan community. They resented this new catholicism of science, which dispensed with dogma, sacred texts, congregations, holy offices, and popes, and which was not afraid to address the common people in their own tongue. The judgment against Galileo went out of its way to rebuke him "for holding correspondence with certain mathematicians of Germany" concerning his ideas, while the Counselors of the Inquisition contrasted Galileo's praise for the English scientist "William Gilbert, a perverse heretic," with his contempt for the "mental pygmies" who were not Copernicans.[26]

The scientific intellectuals of Italy, Galileo's friends, were typical men of the Renaissance, filled with the gaiety and adventures of life. Salviati, whom Galileo made the protagonist of his *Dialogues,* was indeed a young friend who not only collaborated in observations on Jupiter's satellites but shared with Galileo "an enthusiasm for burlesque poetry and low comedy." Galileo would visit him often at his hillside house. Sagredo, the interlocutor, a Venetian nobleman with a respect for science, was a "*bon vivant,*" a characteristic Galileo prized. It was Sagredo who wrote to Galileo in sorrow to protest against his friend's decision to leave the University of Padua for Florence, the tribute of a hedonist-libertarian patriot to his beloved Venice:

> To my great pleasure I have seen so many cities. . . . And truly it seems to me that God hath much favored me to be born in this place so beautiful and so different from all others. . . . Here the freedom and the way of life of every class of persons seem to me an admirable thing, perhaps unique in this world. . . . Where will you find freedom and self-determination as you did in Venice?

Sagredo pleaded with Galileo the advantages of teaching in a free republic. At Venice, he said, "you had command over those who govern and command others; you had to serve no one but yourself; you were as monarch of the universe." The crux of the matter, as Sagredo put it, was "the freedom and the way of life" which were the necessary milieu for the scientific spirit, what we have called the hedonist-libertarian ethic. It broke through class barriers, and enabled Galileo to share his epicurean pleasures and delight in science with Venetian noblemen as well as workingmen at the arsenal. "There was still too much Renaissance in the air to have people condemn him for his lack of Puritanism." [27]

Where a mode of life emphasizes the repression of sexuality, there likewise will generally be found a fear of fresh fact. The emphasis will be on authority. Truth will then be sought in the existing books and texts, and their interpretation will be the principal exercise of scholars. The general assault against sexual existence seems to undermine the zest of intellectual adventure and vigor. The scholastic philosophers who posed their texts against Galileo's telescope and observations were precisely men of this character: "What is to be done?" wrote Galileo to Kepler in 1610:

> What do you say of the leading philosophers here to whom I have offered a thousand times of my own accord to show my studies, but who with the lazy obstinacy of a serpent who had eaten his fill, have never consented to look at the planets, or moon, or telescope? Verily, just as serpents close their ears, so do men close their eyes to the light of truth. To such people philosophy is a kind of book, like the Aeneid or the Odyssey, where the truth is to be sought, not in the universe or in nature, but (I use their own words) by comparing texts! How you would laugh if you heard what things the first philosopher of the faculty at Pisa brought against me in the presence of the Grand Duke. He tried hard with logical arguments, as if with magical incantations, to tear down and argue the new planets out of heaven! [28]

Galileo, speaking of his opponents as "lazy serpents," employs one of the most classical of the unconscious's symbols for male sexuality. The scholastic philosophers were, indeed, he seems to say, men whose male vigor was spent, who had lost the zest for probing into the freshness of concrete fact, and who contented themselves with the pale, distorted record of other men's observations.

Galileo was aware that the very existence of free inquiry was at stake in the church's authoritarian principle. The psychological revolution had produced a respect for the body, its senses and reason, as the means toward knowledge. The clerical authoritarian ethic wished to promote a counterrevolution, and to denigrate once more the human senses. In the *Letter to the Grand Duchess Christina* (1615), Galileo's powerful plea for freedom of thought, he told the world that astronomers could not be asked to subvert their own integrity, and to deny their "own observations and proofs as mere fallacies and sophisms. . . ." Galileo's words had the elemental accents of the core of a scientist's commitment:

> For this would amount to commanding that they must not see what they see and must not understand what they know, and that in searching they must find the opposite of what they actually

> encounter. Before this could be done they would have to be taught how to make one mental faculty command another. . . .

Why, asked Galileo in *The Assayer* (1623), should I be asked to "subject the freedom of my intellect to someone else who is just as liable to error as I am?" [29]

One thing is clear. One cannot speak of Galileo as beset by the "collective obsessions" that Koestler attributes to the founders of modern science. With immense courage and clearness of mind, he was opening a path through the "dark and confused labyrinths" in which the "crowd" was "ever more entangled." He formulated categories in which natural phenomena could be measured—lengths, durations, speeds; he urged that such anthropomorphic categories as "sympathy," "antipathy," "hatred," and "enmity" would not help in understanding the nature of physical things. He was devoid of the masochist's false humility, and said he plainly knew that the mind of man was one of the most excellent of God's works. At the same time, however, he had the honesty of the man who truly seeks knowledge, the candor to say the words which no Jesuit dogmatist could utter, "that wise, ingenious, and modest sentence, 'I do not know.' " [30]

The distinguished author of *Darkness at Noon* has written:

> . . . the intellectual giants of the scientific revolution were moral dwarfs. They were, of course, neither better nor worse than the average of their contemporaries. They were moral dwarfs only in proportion to their intellectual greatness.

Arthur Koestler's masterly and sympathetic portrayal of the human mind under all the strains of totalitarian terror helped prepare the way for Giorgio de Santillana's unforgettable narration of Galileo's ordeal. It is perhaps a sign of a new irrationalism that Koestler belittles the moral stature of the greatest of the scientific revolutionists. I should hesitate to say that Rubashov in *Darkness at Noon* was a moral dwarf, for the tragedy of his crimes is that they were done in obedience to what he took to be the highest demands of morality. He was indeed a revolutionary ascetic, a blend of Leninist and Calvinist, denying his self as ascetics always have. He rose to heights of asceticism within a hopelessly askew moral universe. But Copernicus, Tycho, Kepler, Galileo, were men who were not divided against themselves. For the birth of modern science was not only a triumph of intelligence, it was a triumph of character and integrity. These were solitary men, with small handfuls of friends in Europe, conceiving a new philosophy which cut boldly across all traditional religious loyalties. They were the small third camp in a Europe where fanatical Catholics and Protestants destroyed each other and aped each other's authoritarian ways. They were revolutionists not for love of revolution but for love of truth and human happiness. "The real antagonist of theology," wrote George Lincoln Burr, the eminent historian of the Middle Ages, was the "impulse of human kindliness." [31] The ethic of the scientific intellectuals sought to liberate people from forms of thought and feeling which misshaped their lives.

NOTES

1. Jacob Burckhardt, *The Civilization of the Renaissance in Italy*, trans. S. G. C. Middlemore (London, 1950), pp. 45-6, 281. Richard Ehrenberg, *Capital and Finance in the Age of the Renaissance*, trans. H. M. Lucas (London, 1928), pp. 193, 234-5. William Roscoe Thayer, *A Short History of Venice* (New York, 1905), pp. 270-84. J. C. L. de Sismondi, *A History of the Italian Republics* (Everyman's Library, London, 1907), p. 326. *The Embryological Treatises of Hieronymus Fabricus of Aquapendente*, ed. Howard B. Adelmann (Ithaca, 1942), p. 49.

2. Arturo Castiglioni, *The Renaissance of Medicine in Italy* (Baltimore, 1934), pp. 37-8.

3. Clare Howard, *English Travellers of the Renaissance* (New York, 1913), p. 53.

4. Cecil Roth, *History of Jews in Venice* (Philadelphia, 1930), p. 291. S. M. Dubnow, *History of the Jews in Russia and Poland*, trans. I. Friedlaender (Philadelphia, 1916), Vol. I, p. 132.

5. *Taming of the Shrew*, Act I, Scene 2; *Two Gentlemen of Verona*, Act I, Scene 3. Clare Howard, *op. cit.*, pp. 134-6.

6. Ernest Renan, *Averroès et L'Averroisme* (Paris, 1852), p. 264. J. Roger Charbonnel, *La Pensée Italienne au XVIe Siècle et le Courant Libertin* (Paris, 1919), pp. 613, 711, 716-18. Alfred Halliday Douglas, *The Philosophy and Psychology of Pietro Pomponazzi* (Cambridge, 1910), pp. 261-3. John Addington Symonds, *Renaissance in Italy: The Age of the Despots* (3rd ed., London, 1926), p. 56.

7. John Herman Randall, Jr., "Scientific Method in the School of Padua," *Journal of the History of Ideas,* I (1940), 183.

8. Thomas Campanella, "The Defense of Galileo," trans. Grant McColley, *Smith College Studies in History,* XXII (1937), 36-7.

9. Thomas Campanella, *City of the Sun,* trans. Thomas W. Halliday, in *Ideal Commonwealths,* ed. Henry Morley (London, 1885), pp. 224, 228-30, 236-9, 259, 261.

10. William Boulting, *Giordano Bruno* (London, 1914), pp. 87, 97, 101-2, 284.

11. Giordano Bruno, *The Heroic Enthusiasts,* trans. I. Williams (London, 1887), Pt. I, pp. 36, 102-4. Giordano Bruno, *Des Fureurs Héroïques,* trans. Paul-Henri Michel (Paris, 1954), pp. 92-5. John Charles Nelson, *Renaissance Theory of Love: The Context of Giordano Bruno's Eroici furori* (New York, 1958), p. 171.

12. J. J. Fahie, *Galileo: His Life and Work* (London, 1903), pp. 6, 28, 48, 73. Cf. Erwin Panofsky, "Galileo as Critic of the Arts: Aesthetic Attitude and Scientific Thought," *Isis,* XLVII (1956), 3 ff.

13. John Milton, *Areopagitica,* in *Milton's Prose,* ed. Malcolm W. Wallace (London, 1947), p. 305. Giorgio de Santillana, *The Crime of Galileo* (Chicago, 1955), pp. 141, 149, 305.

14. Leopold von Ranke, *The History of the Popes,* trans. E. Foster (London, 1896), pp. 372-4.

15. Harvey Cushing, *A Bio-bibliography of Andreas Vesalius* (New York, 1943), pp. 74-5. Giorgio de Santillana, *op. cit.,* pp. 38, 92.

16. Thomas Campanella, "The Defense of Galileo," pp. 36-7, 216.

17. Alexander Robertson, *Fra Paolo Sarpi* (London, 1894), p. 96. Arabella Georgina Campbell, *The Life of Fra Paolo Sarpi* (London, 1869), pp. 41-4, 70, 132-4, 201-2.

18. Giorgio de Santillana, *op. cit.,* pp. 134, 155-7, 166-8, 183, 205, 222, 238, 308.

19. Arabella Georgina Campbell, *op. cit.,* pp. 67, 183-6.

20. Galileo Galilei, *Dialogue on the Great World Systems,* trans. Salusbury, ed. Giorgio de Santillana (Chicago, 1953), p. 146.

21. *Ibid.,* pp. 85, 215, 254.

22. Morris R. Cohen, *The Faith of a Liberal* (New York, 1946), p. 147. Such diverse writers as Philipp Frank and A. N. Whitehead find (in Frank's words) "in the standpoint of the Inquisition something corresponding to the modern relativistic conception." Cf. Philipp Frank, *Between Physics and Philosophy* (Cambridge, 1941), p. 56. Alfred North Whitehead, *Science and the Modern World* (Pelican reprint, London, 1938), p. 213.

23. Giorgio de Santillana, *op. cit.,* p. 308.

24. J. J. Fahie, "The Scientific Works of Galileo," in *Studies in the History and Method of Science*, ed. Charles Singer (Oxford, 1921), Vol. II, p. 234. Giorgio de Santillana, *op. cit.*, pp. 211, 222, 246, 309.

25. Wayne C. Williams, *William Jennings Bryan* (New York, 1936), pp. 448, 451.

26. Giorgio de Santillana, *op. cit.*, pp. 247, 307.

27. *Discoveries and Opinions of Galileo*, trans. Stillman Drake (New York, 1957), pp. 66-7. Giorgio de Santillana, *op. cit.*, p. 20.

28. J. J. Fahie, *op. cit.*, p. 102.

29. *Discoveries and Opinions of Galileo*, pp. 193, 272.

30. *Ibid.*, pp. 240-1. Galileo Galilei, *Dialogue on the Great World Systems*, pp. 116, 419, 452.

31. Arthur Koestler, *op. cit.*, p. 352. Giorgio de Santillana, *op. cit.*, p. 251. Roland H. Bainton, *George Lincoln Burr: His Life* (Ithaca, 1943), p. 56.

VI

Vesalius and the Psychological Sources of the Anatomical Revolution

ANDREAS VESALIUS, APPOINTED AT THE AGE OF TWENTY-TWO AS a professor of surgery and anatomy, arrived at the University of Padua in December, 1537. Thus began what Vesalius in later years called "that glorious period of undisturbed labor among the gifted scholars of divine Italy." In 1543, Vesalius published his monumental work, *De Humani Corporis Fabrica*, which inaugurated a revolution in the study of human anatomy. Scholars speak of "the Vesalian problem." It takes one to the heart of the psychological revolution on which modern science was founded. What is "the Vesalian problem"?

> The basic mystery [write Charles Singer and C. Rabin] is the abrupt intrusion into a non-scientific renaissance society, the intellectual interests of which were centered on the ancient classics, of an immense and highly finished monograph in a quite new manner. Nothing of the sort had been printed before. . . . The *Fabrica* introduced a new method of representation to the printed book. Who drew and cut these remarkable figures? . . .

To answer this problem, we must inquire how the psychological revolution, with its hedonist-libertarian standpoint, transformed the emotional attitudes toward the human body.

Christian asceticism had made the whole study of anatomy into an ungodly pursuit.

> The body being contemptible, was unworthy of study and Anatomy was the most vain of all those empty pagan sciences that did but concern themselves with the external temporary and perishable world. In that day of wrath, that dreadful day, when Heaven and Earth shall pass away, when shrivelling like a parched scroll, the flaming heavens together roll, what then can or will avail these pitiful details of Anatomy? [1]

The Christian masochist philosophy held that disease is a punishment of guilt; a holy man would have none of medicines. Under the influences of the psychological revolution, disease came to be regarded as "a disturbed harmony which Nature must heal." [2] As Arturo Castiglioni eloquently writes:

> . . . no more is the study of a corpse considered a profanation and a sacrilege, as unclean and abominable; the new yet old thought asserts itself that only through the direct study and understanding of the body may we know and attain perfect beauty. No one can be either a physician or an artist who has not studied the human body from the corpse. Thus fall the mysterious veils with which the functions of life had been covered by dogmatic scholasticism.

To lift the veil on the nakedness of life required the immense courage to confront all the resistances which the sexual self-aggression of Christian existence had reinforced. Joy in life was the source of this new courage, and Vesalius was its chief protagonist in anatomy. The psychological revolution first made itself felt in the arts, and then spread to the sciences. The naturalistic movement in art, after its beginnings in the thirteenth century, reached its full development in the fifteenth. Painters and sculpters took a keen interest in the accurate representation of the human body. Andrea Verrochio, Andrea Mantegna, Luca Signorelli, Leonardo da Vinci, Albrecht Dürer, Michelangelo, and Raphael all dissected human bodies. Vesalius partook of their spirit. "For him," as Charles Singer says, "Man is a work of art, God is an artist." [3]

Vesalius, born in Brussels in 1514, came from a family which had long produced eminent physicians. His forebears were aware that medical science knew no religious affiliation. His great-great-grandfather Peter had edited a treatise of Avicenna's; his grandfather Eberhard wrote commentaries on the writings of another great Arab doctor, Rhazes. Vesalius's great-grandfather Johannes had taught medicine at Louvain and had written on calendar reform; his father, also Andreas by name, had served the Emperor Charles V as apothecary. The heritage of his familial enclave of physician-scientists helped sustain Vesalius in his revolt against the weight of tradition in the universities.[4] As a boy, he pursued his passion for dissection, and anatomized rats, moles, dormice, dogs, and cats. Soon he was to move on to the human body.

At Louvain, Vesalius became in his adolescent years a *trilinguis homo*, a man of three languages—Latin, Greek and Hebrew. He used them to help recover a lost scientific legacy. In 1533, however, Vesalius went to the University of Paris to study medicine, and there encountered all the forces of traditionalism in thought. There had been no dissection at the university until 1493; now dissections were still rare, no department was assigned their responsibility, and they were held, like underground ceremonies, in a cellar of the hospital Hôtel-Dieu. The professor, however, never himself deigned to dissect a human body; dressed in academic gown, he read from his podium a Galenic text while a menial performed the dissection, directed by a demonstrator in cap and gown. Vesalius in the preface to his *De Humani Corporis Fabrica* described the academic repression of contact with the body:

> When the whole conduct of manual operation was entrusted to barbers, not only did doctors lose true knowledge of the viscera but the practice of dissection soon died out. . . . And equally inevitably this deplorable dismemberment of the art of healing has introduced into our schools the detestable procedure now in vogue, that one man should carry out the dissection of the human body and another give the description of the parts. The latter is perched up aloft in a pulpit like a jackdaw and with a notable air of disdain he drones out information about facts which he has never approached at first hand but which he has committed to memory from the books of others, or of which he has a description before his eyes. The dissector, who is ignorant of languages, is unable to explain the dissection to the class and botches the demonstration which ought to follow the instruction of the physician, while the physician never applies his hand to the task but contemptuously steers the ship out of the manual, as the saying goes. Thus everything is wrongly taught, days are wasted in absurd questions, and in the confusion less is shown to the class than a butcher in his stall could teach a doctor.

The abandonment of direct dissection by European anatomists from Roman almost until modern times has been usually explained as an outcome of the rise of a leisure class in society, based on slave or serf labor. Under such social conditions, writes Benjamin Farrington, the head became independent of the hand; the contempt for manual labor brought anatomical dissection, like manipulative experiment, into social disrepute.[5] But Professor Farrington has himself directed attention to a set of facts which calls this theory into question.

> I can find no clear proof [he writes] that the prejudice against manual labor did, in fact, operate in Greek society to check the progress of the science of anatomy. From Alcmaeon in the fifth century B.C. to Galen in the second century A.D., the names of great anatomists are too numerous and the progress, if spasmodic, still too remarkable to warrant the assertion that the science of anatomy, before the time of Galen, suffered from the prejudice engendered by the social structure of ancient society.

Clearly, something more than the institution of a leisure class was responsible for the suppression of human dissection. And the very date of the suppression's beginning, the second century A.D., coeval with the rise of Christian asceticism and hatred for the body, suggests that the intense aversion to dissection was related to the underlying emotions associated with the ascetic ethics. What might have been this emotional substratum which made up the deep antipathy to dissection?

Remarkably, there is documentation among Freud's papers of one case that involved a physician's experience of a resistance to dissection. An American physician wrote Freud of an experience he had in his last year at the university:

> One afternoon while I was passing through to the dissecting-room my attention was attracted to a sweet-faced dear old woman who was being carried to a dissecting-table. This sweet-faced woman made such an impression on me that a thought flashed up in my mind, "There is no God: if there were a God he would not have allowed this dear old woman to be brought into the dissecting room."
>
> When I got home that afternoon the feeling I had had at the sight of the dissecting-room had determined me to discontinue

going to church. The doctrine of Christianity had before this been the subject of doubts in my mind.

Subsequently, however, as the physician reported, a voice spoke to his soul and convinced him that the Bible was the Word of God.

Freud proposed a psychoanalytical interpretation of the American physician's experience:

> The sight of a woman's dead body, naked or on the point of being stripped, reminded the young man of his mother. It roused in him a longing for his mother which sprang from his Oedipus complex, and this was immediately completed by a feeling of indignation against his father. His ideas of "father" and of "God" had not yet become widely separated; so that his desire to destroy his father could become conscious as doubt in the existence of God. . . .[6]

This revived Oedipal situation was finally resolved, however, by a complete submission to the will of God the Father.

For more than a thousand years under the sway of Catholic Christendom, human dissections were unknown. The people at large were evidently as hostile to the notion as the ruling church. Central to Catholic doctrine was a repression of sexuality, a cult of virginity, a horror of the body's natural functioning as unclean. Every child was born in the guilt of its parents' concupiscence; only Jesus, born of the Virgin Mary, and Mary, immaculately conceived, were exempt from the evil taint of sexuality. The conviction about the sexual guilt of both one's mother and father, added to the Oedipal feelings, must have imposed a terrible strain. The monks who turned their backs on their parents were punishing them for their guilt; the familial bond, a guilty one, was not highly esteemed, for it was a partnership of sin. One can imagine what horrible associations the dissection of dead men and women would awaken. Wild rumors swept among people at the very mention of dissection. When the populace heard that Michelangelo was engaged in the dissection of cadavers, the word spread that Michelangelo was prepared to crucify a living man in order to paint Christ on the cross. Informers and intriguers charged Leonardo da Vinci with sacrilegious intent when he dissected human bodies. Pope Leo X closed Rome's hospitals to him, and Leonardo therefore left Rome forever in 1515.[7]

A melange of feelings—guilt for one's own sexual curiosity, guilt for hatred against a father or mother, one's own castration-complex—all jostling each other in the tormented feelings of people in the Middle Ages, probably accounted for the horror with which dissection was regarded. Theological concepts were invoked against dissection. It was felt, for instance, that dissection of the brain did violence to the seat of the soul; it therefore became customary to remove the subject's head prior to the actual dissection in order to placate the objectors. The papal decree of Pope Boniface VIII in the year 1300, entitled *De Sepulturis*, was widely interpreted to be a ban on dissections. It began with the words "Persons cutting up the bodies of the dead," and closed with the words "are by the very fact excommunicated." Evidently the bull's intervening text indicated clearly that it was not intended to prohibit dissections; nevertheless, the decree was thus interpreted in influential circles.[8] As late as 1668, Joseph Glanvill wrote that "one of the Popes (I take it 'twas Boniface VIII.) threatens to Excommunicate those who should do anything of this then-abominable nature."

With the onset of the Renaissance, the performance of a public dissection licensed by papal writ became something of a festive occasion, attended by students, clerics, townsfolk, and officials—a kind of communal partition of a human totem. At Bologna in 1315, when Mondino, the "Restorer of Anatomy," directed the public dissection of an executed criminal, there was almost a vicarious cannibalism; dogs barking around the table awaited the pieces of human flesh that would be thrown them when the professor concluded his lecture. It was Mondino who established the custom of reading the text while the barber anatomized. The dissociation of functions fulfilled a certain psychological purpose. All the traumatic effects of the dissection were inflicted on the person of the lower class.

The medical traditionalists, the Galenists, when they allowed dissections, were still opposed to anatomical drawings. Pictorial representations, said Sylvius, Vesalius's teacher at Paris, "at best, only serve to gratify the eyes of silly women"; to see only the surface of things, he argued, "must always be a hindrance" to the true physician. Evidently pictorial representations could also stir unconscious anxieties and resistances. Sylvius indeed was a coarse, brutal man who was having trouble with his emotions. His friends found him unwontedly hilarious one day. They asked him why. Sylvius replied he was happy because he had dismissed his "three beasts, his mule, his cat and his maid." [9]

At Padua, the anatomical revolution took on the aspect of a public demonstration. The citizenry was shedding superstitious fears. Fabricius of Aquapendente dissected, as it were, before the whole city. "The gaping mouths of the small-fry" ("*biantia huisus-modi homuncionusa ora*") were there—tailors, cobblers, butchers, fish-sellers, who may have outnumbered the students.[10]

To fulfill his anatomical revolution, Vesalius experienced the anxieties of social rejection and inner guilt. He was a courageous solitary revolutionist, cast in the mold of his older contemporary Copernicus; both men published their era-creating books in the same year, 1543. Vesalius's character, notes Charles Singer, was that of a researcher in the modern scientific sense. "He took little interest in great general ideas, none of which was he pledged to refute." For this reason, he never evoked the violent response Galileo called forth, and he managed to accomplish his work "relatively free from authoritarian interference." He conceived of anatomy as making a practical contribution to the healing art. The religious disputations of his time meant nothing to Vesalius. "He never exhibits any but conventional sentiments on religious themes in his books. He disliked priests and monks," and he chose his companions as he liked "from Catholics, Protestants and Jews." If he was a Catholic, notes Harvey Cushing, "he was a liberal Catholic to say the least, if we may judge from his Paris friends." [11] The translation of the Ninth Book of the Arab Rhazes, which Vesalius published in 1537, was prefaced with an ode by his Dutch Protestant friend Velsius, which testified to the cosmopolitan outlook of Vesalius's group of scientific intellectuals:

> The dusty crowd of Arabs declare that learning aids us,
> While in olden times things barbaric were in favor
> Among the Arabs, Rhazes, the medical writer, is pre-eminent,
> An excellent man because of his service to mankind.

As a medical student at Paris, Vesalius revolted strongly against a mode of teaching in which the Galenic text held supremacy over the anatomical facts as revealed to dissection. He could never have succeeded when he was a student, wrote Vesalius, if "I had not myself applied my hand to this business, but had acquiesced in the casual and superficial display to me and my fellow-students by certain barbers of a few organs at one or two public dissections." His own professor, Sylvius, who later led the opposition to Vesalius, calling him Vesarus (Madman), was not himself averse to his students taking direct part in the dissections. But he was aware that "many do not like at first to view the dissection of man and cannot endure it without great disturbance of mind," and he put his advice to the students to accustom themselves to dissection gently. Vesalius, however, required no advice on this matter. In 1535 he persuaded his other teacher, Johannes Guenther, and his students, to ask him to help in the actual dissections, and by the following year was doing them almost all himself. Guenther, who at this time became converted to Lutheranism, paid tribute in his manual *Institutiones Anatomicae* to the help of "Andreas Vesalius, son of the Emperor's pharmacist—a young man, by Jove, of great promise, possessing a singular knowledge of medicine, erudite in both languages and most skilled in dissecting bodies . . . ." The young Vesalius was also helping his teacher in other ways. At the risk of his life, he made expeditions to the gallows of Montfaucon and the graves of the Cemetery of the Innocents to seek bodies and bones for the anatomical theater; fierce dogs attacked him. The young scientist was prepared to turn body-snatcher and violate the criminal law for the sake of his science.[12] Then, in 1536, Charles V, the Holy Roman Emperor, invaded France, and the medical school suspended sessions. Vesalius and Guenther parted; the Protestant went to Wittenberg, the Lutheran center, and Vesalius went home to Louvain.

At Louvain, a momentous event took place in Vesalius's life. A young girl of eighteen had died, and poisoning was suspected. The physician asked Vesalius to make an autopsy. It was his first independent post-mortem examination, and the first woman he had ever opened. "It made a strong impression on his mind, for he described it in detail twenty years later." The young girl, wrote Vesalius, had shown the symptoms of those who are desperately in love; she had become pale, and her menstruation had ceased. She died from the suffocation of the uterus, wrote Vesalius; when he dissected her, he found the "great whiteness and softness" of her lungs, but there was "nothing vicious, not even around the uterus," except that the "yellow tubercules of her testicles had a very peculiar odor."[13] The poor, evidently pregnant girl affected Vesalius's emotions. Did the dissection of this Belgian girl stir feelings in Vesalius for his own mother akin to those Freud surmised in the case he described? Andreas's mother, Isabella Crabbe, had influenced her son greatly, and impressed it upon him that a great destiny awaited him.[14] The sexuality of women as uncovered in dissection in any case awoke some trauma in Vesalius, for many years later it operated to distort his perception of the female anatomy.

Vesalius was a physician at the court of the Spanish king, in Madrid, when Gabriele Falloppio in 1561 published his *Observationes Anatomicae.* Falloppio, always remembered for his discovery of the tubes that bear his name, was then the incumbent of Vesalius's old chair of anatomy and surgery at Padua. He was a diligent teacher, an honest man, and a great researcher; though he disagreed on some points with Vesalius, and found him too contentious, he generally sided with him in the controversy with the Galenists: "I came to concur in the opinion of the divine Vesalius in regard to the greatest part of their contrary ideas, and I now persist in this conviction." Falloppio added greatly to the knowledge of sexual anatomy. He described accurately for the first time the structure of the female genital organs, including the clitoris, and its analogy to the penis; he corrected the account Vesalius had given of the vessels of the penis. As Professor Castiglioni notes: " . . . in thus correcting Vesalius it is clear that Fallopius was right." One would have expected Vesalius, the peerless observer and dissector, to have either welcomed or awaited verification on the dissecting table of the accuracy of his admirer's work. Some strange resistances, however, moved in Vesalius when the anatomy of sexuality was now raised for discussion. "Vesalius was at a disadvantage, and his reply came from the armchair." He failed to follow his own precept of exact observation.

> He denied the existence of the arteries of the penis, and what seems unbelievable, rejected the existence of the clitoris and its homology with the penis, preferring to accept the mistaken description of Galen rather than recognize his error.[15]

Vesalius's chapter on the reproductive organs, observed Lind, was the least adequate of the *Epitome*.[16] Were perhaps the same Oedipal feelings which may have been aroused by his first postmortem examination now moving him to deny the evidences of female sexual desire? Such feelings had once made human dissection a horror to Europe, and perhaps were now reviving in Vesalius, who for twenty years had been living far from the Paduan scientific community, in the stifling, priest-ridden atmosphere of Madrid, where the Inquisition had succeeded in destroying the roots of independent, scientific thought, and where it was impossible for Vesalius to secure a single body as a dissectional subject. The repression of Oedipal feelings, with their concomitant guilt, may have warped the powers of this great observer. To Falloppio he replied:

> I willingly confess that in dissections of healthy women I have observed nothing corresponding to what you have found outside the peritoneum, although I have dissected the abdominal muscles in several women, and especially in the one which first fell to my lot for anatomy at Paris. She was hanged by a noose, and had a most attractive figure. Her body exhibited (as I learned at the time) a notably fleshy likeness to the vessels carying semen from the testes (ovaries) into the uterus. . . .[17]

The phraseology of this passage is astonishing. The dead woman is spoken of as having "a most attractive figure," a warmth of utterance which suggests the involvement of Vesalius's unconscious sexual feelings in the performance of dissection, and in the report on the structure of women's sexuality. And Vesalius's memories as to the first woman he had ever dissected were evidently under an emotional strain which led to a confusion between the bodies of the woman in Paris and the one in Louvain.

When Vesalius's *Fabrica* was published in 1543 in Basel, a Protestant center, a storm of abuse descended upon him from the Galenists. To be called the "Luther of Anatomy," as Cushing observes, was by no means a joke. Six years earlier, Vesalius had experienced similar attacks in Louvain, where his public dissection evoked the resentment of theologians. They took umbrage at his remarks concerning the seat of the soul, and saw a propensity toward heresy in his friendship with such Protestants as Guenther. But now Padua itself, the cradle of European science, whose freedom he had sought when Louvain grew oppressive, Padua—which had received him to its bosom, where hundreds of students hung upon his every word and flocked around his dissecting-table, students from all parts of the world as one of them wrote, "Germans, English, Spaniards, Italians, and others of all nations who all agreed that the like of this admirable and almost divine man was not to be found in the whole of Europe"—Padua was reproaching him like an angry mother for his work.[18]

Vesalius grew despondent. Late in 1543 he held a public anatomy on a female subject—his last dissection before Paduan students. Shortly afterward, "he made a sacrificial pyre of his accumulated documents." He burned all his medical manuscripts, trying to destroy his past, punishing himself for his acts of independent thought and observation, for all those dissections he himself had practiced, which had given him the wherewithal to challenge Galenic authority. He was burning himself at the stake as a heretic and a defiler of the sexual mysteries of the human body:

> As to my notes, which had grown into a huge volume, they were all destroyed by me; and on the same day there similarly perished the whole of my paraphrase of the ten books of Rhazes to King Almansor, composed by me with far more care than the *Paraphrasis* which I published on the ninth book.

In retrospect, he said, he hoped that this act of destruction would help his prospects for appointment at the Emperor's Court in Madrid:

> I was on the point of leaving Italy and going to Court; those physicians of whom you know had given the Emperor and the nobles a most unfavorable report of my books and of all that is published nowadays for the promotion of study; I therefore burnt all these works mentioned thinking at the same time it would be an easy matter to abstain from writing for the future. I have since repented more than once of my impatience, and regretted that I did not take the advice of the friends who were then with me.

Vesalius' scientific career was virtually terminated, and he was henceforth "diverted to the mechanical practice of medicine, to numerous wars and to continuous travels," seeing in the advance of science "the accomplishment of those things whose blameless foundations I laid, in accordance with my ability and as my age and judgment then permitted." His old teacher, Sylvius, continued to assail him. In 1551, Sylvius denounced Vesalius to the Emperor Charles V as a monster of impiety, whom it was important to suppress completely "lest he poison the rest of Europe with his pestilential breath." [19]

The last days of Vesalius are beclouded with uncertainty. In the spring of 1564, he undertook a pilgrimage to Jerusalem. Why did Vesalius set forth on such a pilgrimage? The most widely told story had it that he had run afoul of the Inquisition. Vesalius's enemies, it was said, had accused him of having performed an autopsy on a body whose heart was still beating; they had denounced him to the Inquisition, which condemned him to death but commuted the sentence to a penitential pilgrimage to Jerusalem. "Another story is that he went abroad to escape the bad temper of his wife," and still another that he wanted to enrich himself. A fourth hypothesis is that Vesalius, under the pretext that he had to go to Jerusalem for his health, was actually making himself available for his old professorship at Padua, which had fallen vacant with the death of Falloppio.[20]

It seems most probable that Vesalius went on his pilgrimage to Jerusalem as a penance or by way of commuted sentence for dissections which had aroused the ire of the Inquisition. As George Sarton says, "the substitution of a pilgrimage instead of a judicial penalty was common practice." [21] Vesalius had been able to outwit the municipal authorities at Paris and Louvain when he climbed gibbets and dug in cemeteries, but the Spanish Inquisition, religious arm of a totalitarian state, was another matter. To say that he went to Jerusalem either to escape his wife or to enrich himself seems fanciful, for Vesalius could have sought out much more pleasant places in Europe if the first was his aim, and poverty-stricken Palestine was no place to make a fortune in the sixteenth century. Nor could Vesalius have pleaded that he had to go to Jerusalem for his health; the Holy Land was notoriously one of the unhealthiest spots of the Mediterranean world, and one that health-seeking Europeans avoided. The common version of Vesalius's pilgrimage seems, indeed, to have been the closest to the truth. The forces opposed to the scientific intellectuals, with their hedonist-libertarian ethic, were finally strong enough to exact penance from him. Vesaluis sailed to the Holy Land. On his return voyage, a violent storm evidently forced his ship to land off a desolate beach on the island of Zacynthos. There Vesalius died.

If we ponder the significance of the anatomical revolution, the work of Vesalius, and the story of human dissection, certain further considerations suggest themselves as to the character of the psychological revolution on which modern science was based. Freud, as we saw, described a case in which a physician's acute horror of dissection was founded on strong Oedipal feelings. We may venture, by analogy, the hypothesis that the psychological revolution of early modern times involved a decline in the intensity of Oedipal feelings, or at any rate the development of a social situation in which they could be resolved more satisfactorily. During the Middle Ages, mothers could secure their sons against the rivalry of other women by dedicating them to the celibate life of monk or priest. Ascetic religious devotion was the most effective way for making a permanent institution of unresolved Oedipal feelings. Ireland, in modern times, still remains an example of how celibate bachelorhood can be an institutionalized expression of undiminished Oedipal feelings. In the sixteenth century, however, contempt for priests and monks, which Vesalius shared, had become widespread. The eunuchoid monk became a figure of ridicule with a touch of the hypocrite. The Renaissance men experienced a sense of liberation from some emotional thralldom. We might say that the unresolved Oedipus complex ceased to dominate their feelings and perceptions. They could dissect bodies, picture nude women, without feeling that they were engaged in the violation of their mothers; they could depict and dissect men without thinking they were engaged in bodily vengeance against their fathers. The ordinary joys of life had become plentiful, there was a movement in the atmosphere, the climate of permanent anxiety that had been part of the Middle Ages ebbed. Instead there was opportunity and exploration. Vesalius' mother could raise her son to honor not priests and monks but the scientific heritage of his ancestors. No medieval mother would have done that. Women had come to find their own lives sufficiently pleasurable so that they had no need to enslave their sons. The scientific revolution, in this sense, may well have been founded on a conquest of the Oedipus complex. The man of the Renaissance, writes Castiglioni, wants first of all "to know how to see, and just in this is to be found the programme of the scientific Revival." [22] The emancipation of the eyes to see the things of the world, and the hands to feel them, may well have been the outcome of an emancipation of emotions from Oedipal imprisonment.

NOTES

1. Harvey Cushing, *A Bio-bibliography of Andreas Vesalius* (New York, 1943), p. 158. Charles Singer and C. Rabin, *A Prelude to Modern Science: Being a Discussion of the History, Sources and Circumstances of the "Tabulae Anatomical Sex" of Vesalius* (Cambridge, 1946), p. iii. Charles Singer, *The Evolution of Anatomy* (London, 1925), p. 64.

2. Charles and Dorothea Singer, "The Origin of the Medical School of Salerno, the First European University: An Attempted Reconstruction," in *Essays on the History of Medicine*, ed. Charles Singer and Henry E. Sigerist (London, 1924), p. 135. Arturo Castiglioni, *The Renaissance of Medicine in Italy* (Baltimore, 1934), pp. 14-15.

3. Charles Singer, *The Evolution of Anatomy*, pp. 90, 116.

4. Charles Singer and C. Rabin, *op. cit.*, p. xiii. Harvey Cushing, *op. cit.*, p. xxiv.

5. Benjamin Farrington, "The Preface of Andreas Vesalius to *De Fabrica Corporis Humani*, 1543," *Proceedings of the Royal Society of Medicine*, XXV (1932). Benjamin Farrington, "The Hand in Healing: A Study in Greek Medicine from Hippocrates to Ramazzini," in *Head and Hand in Ancient Greece* (London, 1947), pp. 30-4.

6. Sigmund Freud, "A Religious Experience," in *Collected Papers*, ed. James Strachey (London, 1950), Vol. V, pp. 242-6.

7. A. M. Lassek, *Human Dissection: Its Drama and Struggle* (Springfield, 1958), pp. 74-8. H. Hopstock, "Leonardo as Anatomist," trans. E. A. Fleming, in *Studies in the History and Method of Science*, ed. Charles Singer (Oxford, 1921), Vol. II, pp. 154-5, 188. Edward MacCurdy, *The Notebooks of Leonardo da Vinci* (New York, 1938), Vol. I, pp. 30, 37, 95. Rachel Armand Taylor, *Leonardo the Florentine* (New York, 1927), pp. 538-9.

8. Cf. Thomas D. Merrigan, "Anatomy," *Catholic Encyclopedia*

(New York, 1907), Vol. I, p. 459. Charles Singer, *Evolution of Anatomy*, pp. 85-6. Fielding H. Garrison, *The Principles of Anatomic Illustration Before Vesalius* (New York, 1926), pp. 40-1. James J. Walsh, *The Popes and Science* (New York, 1908), pp. 28 ff. Joseph Glanvill, *Plus Ultra: or, the Progress and Advancement of Knowledge since the Days of Aristotle* (London, 1668, reprinted, Gainesville, Florida, 1958), p. 13. A. M. Lassek, *Human Dissection*, pp. 63, 71.

9. M. F. Ashley Montagu, "Vesalius and the Galenists," *Scientific Monthly*, LXXX (1955), 237-9. James Moores Ball, *Andreas Vesalius: The Reformer of Anatomy* (St. Louis, 1910), p. 59. Harvey Cushing, *op. cit.*, p. xxxi. Charles Singer and C. Rabin, *op. cit.*, p. iv.

10. *The Embryological Treatises of Hieronymus Fabricus of Aquapendente*, ed. Howard B. Adelmann (Ithaca, 1942), p. 20.

11. Harvey Cushing, *op. cit.*, pp. xxvii, 160. Charles Singer and C. Rabin, *op. cit.*, p. xxiii.

12. Benjamin Farrington, "The Preface of Andreas Vesalius to *De Fabrica Corporis Humani*, 1543," p. 1337. M. F. Ashley Montagu, *op. cit.*, p. 233. Harvey Cushing, *op. cit.*, pp. 44-5. Charles Singer and C. Rabin, *op. cit.*, p. xxi. John Farquhar Fulton, *Vesalius Four Centuries Later* (Lawrence, 1950), p. 9.

13. Charles Singer and C. Rabin, *op. cit.*, p. xxii. Charles Singer, *Evolution of Anatomy*, p. 120. Andreas Vesalius, *De Humani Corporis Fabrica* (2nd ed., Basel, 1555), p. 658. Mr. Otto J. Sadovszky kindly translated these passages for me.

14. M. Roth, *Andreas Vesalius Bruxellensis* (Berlin, 1892), pp. 60-1.

15. Arturo Castiglioni, "Fallopius and Vesalius," in Harvey Cushing, *op. cit.*, pp. 184, 189-90.

16. *The Epitome of Andreas Vesalius*, trans. L. R. Lind (New York, 1949), p. 87.

17. Harvey Cushing, *op. cit.*, p. 193. Possibly the woman at Paris, though the "first" for Vesalius, was not dissected independently by himself. In that case, the woman at Louvain would have been the first he dissected altogether on his own. On the other hand, the Louvain girl is stated to have been the first female he had opened. That could not have been the case if he had already dissected the hanged woman in Paris.

18. M. Roth, *op. cit.*, pp. 74-5. Harvey Cushing, *op. cit.*, p. xxvii. L. Crummer and J. B. de C. M. Saunders, "The anatomical compendium of Loys Vasse (1540)," *Annals of Medical History*, Ser. 3, I (1939), 351, quoted in Harvey Cushing, *op. cit.*, p. xxv.

19. Harvey Cushing, *op. cit.*, pp. xxx, 156, 192.

20. *The Epitome of Andreas Vesalius*, p. xix. C. Donald O'Malley, "Andreas Vesalius' Pilgrimage," *Isis*, XLV (1954), 139-41.

21. George Sarton, "The Death and Burial of Vesalius, and incidentally, of Cicero," *Isis*, XLV (1954), 136.

22. Arturo Castiglioni, *The Renaissance of Medicine in Italy*, p. 17.

VII

The Comparative Sociology of Science

WE HAVE SEEN HOW THE SCIENTIFIC INTELLECTUALS OF the seventeenth century were men inspired by a "new philosophy" which had its psychological source in the hedonist-libertarian ethics. We have traced the roots of this ethic to the emotion underlying the emergence of nominalism in the Middle Ages, and have seen it grow among the international community of scientists who fashioned the Copernican Revolution. During successive centuries, scientific movements arose in far-flung places in Europe. But whether it was Calvinist Edinburgh, Lutheran Stockholm, Catholic Paris, Greek Orthodox Moscow, or Jewish Minsk, the common philosophy and underlying emotion of the scientific intellectuals was hedonist-libertarian.

Such a generalization of social science must withstand the test of the facts about countries in different times and places. Let us therefore examine the scientific movements of several European and non-European centers, and see how the hedonist-libertarian ethic brought scientific zest and fecundity, while the ascetic-authoritarian ethic brought the decline of science.

☙ Arabic Science

George Sarton spoke of "the miracle of Arabic science." [1] Yet no European has yet written an essay trying to prove that the Moslem ethic was especially congenial to the rise of science. It was only where the Arabic spirit, transformed in centers of industry and trade, took a liberal hedonistic form that it became a fruitful inspiration for a movement of scientific intellectuals.

Islamic civilization, through the agency of Arab conquerors, came to embrace many societies of non-Arabs. The Arabs, during their conquests in the century after Mohammed's death, became a military aristocracy. They administered the state and officered its army. The cultivation of the arts and sciences tended to become the province of non-Arabs and persons of mixed blood. "It is a remarkable fact," wrote Ibn Khaldun, the Tunisian who was the most powerful sociological intelligence in fifteen hundred years, "that, with few exceptions, most Muslim scholars both in the religious and in the intellectual sciences have been non-Arabs." The centers of scientific culture were found in the cities, in Baghdad, Basra, and Kufa, where Arabs, Persians, Moslems, Christians, and Jews commingled. The pattern which was later to establish Venice as the center of European science was already exemplified in the first half of the eighth century. Secular science began to thrive in the invigorating atmosphere of the free commercial city, where religious and ethnic differences were unimportant, and where rationalistic attitudes prevailed despite the nominal creed.[2]

The great movement of Arabic science, it is noteworthy, flourished not under the more orthodox Umayyad caliphate in Damascus but, rather, under its more liberal Abbasid rival in Baghdad. The Umayyads were still close to the nomadic Puritan mores; the cultural heritage of the desert Bedouins persisted in their rude orthodoxy. The Abbasid revolt in 747 opened the way for Islam's golden age. The orthodox follower of Sunna, the code of custom, was not only rigidly opposed to science but was also a firm believer in predestination. These offspring of desert Calvinists would brook no thought of man's individual free will. Arab ascetics, whether saints or wandering beggars, emphasized the transience of life; human existence was something shadowy to them. Under the Abbasids, however, Arabic culture was enriched with an admixture of Persian hedonism.[3] The four greatest scientists of the second half of the ninth century were Persians. The thinkers of Baghdad became skeptics, and ventured even to affirm man's free will.

The dominant Persian influence at the Abbasid court introduced, as Sarton tells us, "a greater love of beauty, intellectual curiosity, and much fondness for discussion." These conditions were favorable for the progress of science, but, Sarton adds, "unfortunately free thought was often followed by libertinage and immorality." Baghdad was indeed a center of urban hedonism. Built on the west bank of the Tigris River, it became the *entrepôt* for trade between Mesopotamia, Syria, Armenia, and China. Its court life became proverbial for its wealth, glamour, and romance. Its merchants were leaders in the city; on the wharves, their ships loaded cargo to and from the Far East and Africa. Their goods reached far north to Scandinavia. The Market of the Perfumers was an important place in Baghdad; forty-three shops of perfume distillers provided it with products. At a time when ascetic Christian Europe was hostile to bathing, Baghdad in the tenth century boasted of twenty-seven thousand public baths. The maidens in the *Thousand and One Nights* were not only dedicated to Eros; they prided themselves on their learning in the sciences, mathematics, music, and philosophy. The trader was high in the Arab scale of prestige, even as the farmer was low. From this merchants' civilization issued the endowments of colleges, such as that of the Nizamiyah, which paid its professors and gave scholarships to poor students. A new philosophic and scientific terminology was created in the Arabic language, which had never previously been used for scientific purposes. Baghdad under Abbasid rule was, in Sarton's words, "a period of exaltation and youthful optimism."[4] It became, moreover, the center of an international community of scientific intellectuals which reached from Asia across North Africa to Cordova in Spain.[5] The golden age of Arabic science came in the first half of the eleventh century. The poetry of Omar

Khayyam, algebraist and astronomer, has become for every schoolboy the epitome of the hedonistic way of life; he lived in the second half of the eleventh century.

When orthodox reaction ensued, the scientists invariably suffered persecution. The turning point in the intellectual history of Islam is said to have come around 1106 A.D., with the triumph of the orthodox faith; it put an end to the spirit of free scientific inquiry. A great Orientalist, according to Sarton, wrote, "But for al-Ash'ari and al-Ghazzali the Arabs might have been a nation of Galileos, Keplers, and Newtons." This may indeed overstate the significance of purely philosophic ideas in history. It does, however, serve to emphasize the common roots of science, in all civilizations, in a concern for the earthly happiness, welfare, and status of men.

Ibn Khaldun, writing at the end of the fourteenth century out of his own rich experience from Spain to Syria, thus said that where a civilization is "abundant," science flourishes. He could recall Christian Castile as he had seen it under Pedro the Cruel when he wrote that when "civilizational activity" stopped in Spain, the sciences declined, and that under the Christian Roman Emperor, "the intellectual sciences were shunned by them, as religious groups and their laws require." In the East and Iraq, where civilization continued "abundant," scientific activity still continued with vitality.[6]

Alexandrian Science

THE MOST CELEBRATED SCHOOL OF SCIENCE in antiquity, that of Alexandria, is still another instance of the fructifying influence of the hedonistic ethics. There are two Alexandrias in the history of thought. The first is associated with the early Ptolemies, in the third and second centuries B.C., and the efflorescence of a scientific movement. The second period begins approximately with the opening of the Christian era; it sees the triumph of Plato with the support of various Oriental mystical influences. The scientists of early Alexandria—Eratosthenes, Euclid, Aristarchus, Hipparchus—shunned mystical modes of thought. They constituted in the renowned Museum a scientific institute, embracing all fields of study. Their successors, too, remained aloof to all the varieties of Christian and Gnostic speculation. The philosophical school of Alexandrian Neo-Platonism was, on the other hand, hostile to the scientific venture, and the spread of its influence from Egypt throughout Europe, among tired peoples, helped to extinguish the scientific spirit.[7]

The urban civilization of Alexandria provided the basis for its liberal hedonism. Alexandria under Ptolemy Philadelphus became the largest city of the Greek world. It was the crossroads of trade between Arabia, Africa, India, and the countries along the Aegean and Euxine Seas. Its splendor was proverbial. The royal palace, which filled a third of the city, was a marvel of elegant furniture, colored walls, lovely rugs, floors adorned with fine mosaic. Then there were the buildings of the Library, the Museum, the Academy of Sciences and Letters, and the Zoo. Many languages and peoples mixed in Alexandria—Greek, Egyptian, Hebrew. The official and business classes—all the upper class, indeed—were Greek, but something of their prosperity had reached the lower class; the wages of workingmen were higher in Egypt during the reign of Ptolemy Philadelphus than they were in Greece. The economic spirit was dominant in this city of businessmen, bureaucrats, artisans, shopkeepers, longshoremen, peddlers, sailors, philosophers, scholars, and slaves. But although material interests were primary, the men of the well-to-do and middle classes were also fond of the theatre, music, sport, and their Greek classics.

The prevailing mood of the early Alexandrian Greeks, as Rostovtzeff describes it, was "not one of depression and pessimism. . . . On the contrary, a buoyant optimism prevailed. There was confidence, a faith, supported by the teachings of the leading philosophical schools, in the unlimited capabilities of man and his reason; there was an aggressiveness, a striving for life and happiness."[8] The Alexandrian, whether poet, civil servant, engineer, actor, or scientist, was "engaged not in routine, but in creative work. They were bringing new values into existence." The Alexandrian was something of a revolutionary, recasting the old life. This was a society that gave high official status to its Dionysiac *technitai*—its professional associations of artists, stage managers, actors, musicians, and dancers. And this society, too, gave a home to its distinguished scientists and scholars, in the Museum. There they lived in comfort, and were provided with their food. They were exempted from taxation, and devoted themselves to their work.

If the Royal Society, with its Baconian ethics and Charles II as its godfather, can be said to have had a predecessor in antiquity, it was indeed the Academy of Scientists at the Museum of Alexandria; Ptolemy Philadelphus, their founder, has been likened to "the American millionaires of to-day" with their foundations for the promotion of scientific research.[9] Among the Alexandrian scientists were Eratosthenes, the creator of scientific geography and discoverer of an accurate method for measuring the earth's circumference; Ctesibius, investigator into the mechanics of catapults and levers; Herophilus, founder of the medical school and creator of the science of human anatomy. Medicine made progress in Alexandria because dissections, which had been forbidden in Greece, were allowed in Egypt. The name of Euclid, in geometry, and of Apollonius, immortalized in *Conic Sections*, gave luster to Alexandrian mathematics. Both men taught at Alexandria; Eratosthenes was librarian. Archimedes of Syracuse, probably the greatest physicist of the ancient world, published his works in Alexandria, and dedicated them to several of its scientists, Eratosthenes among them. The decline of Alexandrian science was coeval with the decline of its optimist striving for human happiness, and the rise of an otherworldly standpoint.

◆§ Catholic Authoritarian Asceticism in Spain and Portugal

When catholic thinkers have, under favorable social circumstances, grown to maturity in relative freedom from an ascetic authoritarian ethic, they have been among the foremost names in science. As we have seen, Padua was for a century, thanks to Vesalius's influence, "the center of anatomical study" in Europe, with such distinguished names as Gabriele Falloppio, the anatomist of the sexual organs, and Fabricius ab Aquapendente, pioneer of modern comparative embryology and discoverer of the venous valves. Giovanni Borelli, the founder of experimental biology, although a political rebel, always remained within the Catholic fold.[10]

The language of the science of electricity was later an abundant tribute to the contribution of Roman Catholic scientific intellectuals—volts, amperes, coulombs, ohms, the galvanometer. Alessandro Volta at the University of Turin at the beginning of the nineteenth century, Luigi Galvani at the University of Bologna in 1780, Ampère at the Ecole Polytechnique, Coulomb working under the *ancien régime* as an engineering official, Ohm at Nuremberg were brilliant pathfinders in the new electrical science.[11] Scientific creativity at the end of the eighteenth century had not become the exclusive province of Protestant virtues.

In Spain, on the other hand, a blight was cast over any incipient scientific movement. "There have been good scientists in Spain from time to time," writes Américo Castro in his penetrating *The Structure of Spanish History*, but "there has never been in Spain any authentic scientific thought." A scientific movement never flourished in Christian Spain. The scientific roots that had been planted by Moslem and Jewish intellectuals in an earlier era did not survive the Christian hegemony. What ingredient was it in the Spanish species of Roman Catholic psychology which could extirpate science? For in the Italian towns, as we have seen, where the "life-structure," in Castro's words, "has been essentially this-worldly," Catholic society could produce a Campanella, a Bruno, a Galileo, a Borelli, and a Malpighi.

What destroyed the scientific spirit in Spain was the oppressive asceticism which engulfed its intellectual life. The sixteenth-century Spaniard, unlike his Moslem and Jewish forebears, "writhed desperately beneath a burdensome mass of ascetic treatises." The New Englanders were Puritans because they were utilitarian ascetics; asceticism was a rational response in a frontier where goods had to be accumulated from scarce means. But the Spanish Christians were masochist ascetics. They found sanctity in "abstinence in itself," and felt fortified by fasts in triumphant self-aggression.

> I am strong like Spain,
> For lack of sustenance.

sang Quevedo.

A mode of consciousness arose in which the emphasis was on

the agony and anguish of the individual; in this mode of masochist perception, there was a "sustained consciousness of existence as a non-existence." The Hispanic sense of reality, says Castro, became imbued with an insecurity and doubt concerning its own existence. "The ascetic negation of the value of all things human in sixteenth-century Spain was based on a tradition that put no faith in the substantial reality of things. Everything seemed; nothing was." If masochist asceticism had been confined to a handful of mystics, it would not have warped the sense of reality of a whole intellectual class. But, as was noted in 1646, the religious orders were enrolling "the bravest men, the healthiest, the most upstanding, those with the best faces, the most talented and skillful. There is not among them . . . one that is ugly, or dull, or ignorant. . . . In the world [remain] only the dregs and dross of men." [12] Masochist asceticism, with its ideology enforced by an Inquisition, stifled any tendency to a hedonist-libertarian ethic, and prevented the growth of a scientific movement.

It was not until the end of the nineteenth century that a genuine scientific movement arose again in Spain. This Spanish scientific renaissance, linked especially with the name of Santiago Ramón y Cajal, was founded on a revival of the hedonist-libertarian ethic against Catholic authoritarian asceticism. His life story deserves our consideration as a case study in the psychological liberation of scientific curiosity. Ramón, the first Spaniard to become a Nobel Laureate in the sciences, pondered this problem of the emotional reawakening of science in Spain. "It is entirely a matter of awakening the scientific curiosity, which has slept through four centuries of mental slavery, and of inoculating by example the sacred fire of personal inquiry," he wrote. Founder of the Spanish school of histology and pioneer investigator of the neuron, Ramón in his life experienced the full measure of a revolt against that asceticism which commanded the self-destruction of the intellect and perception.

The son of a poor village doctor, he was animated by a "madness over art." He filled the wide margins of the catechism with drawings; he painted laborers, trees, and taverns, and when he drew saints, it was the active ones, the fighters, not the contemplative ones. The father hated the boy's artistic interests, and called upon his teachers, friars and monks, to exorcise this madness from him. "The persecution of my poor pencils, charcoals, and papers was consequently redoubled, and I had to employ all the arts of dissimulation to hide them and to conceal myself when, swept away by my favorite passion, I amused myself with sketching bulls, horses, soldiers, and landscapes." Between father and son there then ensued, says Ramón, "a silent war of duty against desire."

Ramón's teachers did all they could to drive desire from him. At the age of eleven, he was imprisoned for a bold experiment with homemade artillery. "At the bottom of my interest in firearms," he writes, "there existed besides the desire for excitement, a sincere and lively admiration for science and an insatiable curiosity regarding the forces of nature." The friars tried in vain to condition in him a devotion to Latin grammar instead, but in "that silent and persistent physical and moral struggle between brain and book," the latter always came out worst. Ramón's teacher in logic and ethics was a zealous master who prostrated himself for hours in the cathedral, "with his arms spread out in a cross and his soul in ecstasy. . . . A fervent admirer of scholasticism, for him there had lived only two great philosophic geniuses, Aristotle and Saint Thomas Aquinas." The young Ramón wondered why the ascetic master hated Locke and Voltaire so much. He did his best to work out a defensive concatenation of words like "essence and existence" whose meaning always eluded him, but once again ran afoul of clerical discipline. Unable to resist the white surface of the town wall, he drew his master's portrait upon it. The examining tribunal submitted him to a special session of "deep waters and metaphysical quibbles." For a few days, Ramón and his companions ran away from school to recover their healthy sense of reality.

An incident in 1860 especially impressed the child Ramón. One afternoon, as the schoolchildren were saying the Paternoster, the sky grew dark, and there were violent peals of thunder. As the children uttered "Lord deliver us from all evil," there was a terrific crash, and the building collapsed. The priest was found mortally wounded beside the bell he had tried to toll to ward off the danger; the lightning had killed him. "It is unnecessary to emphasize how stupefied I was by this tragic event," writes Ramón. "For the first time there crossed my mind, already deeply moved, the idea of disorder and lack of harmony. . . . The scientific conception of law penetrates the brain very slowly with the revolutionary doctrines of physics and astronomy." The world of the ascetic priest was then a fantasy world, and the austerities and ecstasies were not the path to knowledge.

As Ramón in later years looked back upon his childhood, he saw its significance in his resistance to the ascetic's mode of life and thought. "I reacted obstinately against so gloomy an ideal of life, which killed in flower all my boyish illusions and cut off sharply the impulses of my budding fantasy." "The mysterious attractiveness of forbidden fruit," he writes, helped to give his imagination a "hypertrophic development." The ascetic way of life, he said, "banishes from the hearth the happiness which ordinarily springs from the satisfaction of a thousand innocent caprices . . . it prevents the desirable relaxations of the novel, the theater, painting, and music, which are not vices but instinctive necessities for young people," and it makes children regard "their parents as the perpetual preventers of present happiness." Compelled to stand as a child alone against the social forces of family and church, Ramón found encouragement, appropriately, in the figure of Robinson Crusoe, who symbolized for him the power of man who, with his unaided efforts, achieved sovereignty over nature.

Ramón's own philosophy in maturity was that which reigned in the anticlerical cafés of Madrid. The "gang" of the Royal Society in the seventeenth century had their coffeehouses; Ramón and his co-workers of the Spanish Renaissance had their cafés. The café in the nineties was the symbol of intellectual liberty in Spain. "It was out of the theories of men like Ramón y Cajal over the café tables," writes Harley Williams, "that our modern scientific and materialistic world has been created." [13] Here were hatched new movements in art, politics, and science. Ramón was one of the so-called "men of '98," the scientific and political intellectuals who sought to lift Spain, after its humiliating defeat by the United States, from the decadence into which it had been cast by clerical asceticism and mysticism. He had no use for what he regarded as the "charlatanism" of idealist metaphysicians. He was an empiricist who had realized his childhood hope to become a painter by painting the microscopic world of the body's tissues in their amazing variety. The renaissance of *Hispanidad*, Ramón saw, must come through a psychological revolution against masochist asceticism and its thought-ways.

The Roman Catholic religion became predominantly a retarding factor in Western Europe when, rendered anxious and insecure by the Protestant revolt against its hierarchy, it turned for aid to single-minded clerical managerialists. The Jesuits, for instance, simply saw the scientific intellectuals as rivals for the hegemony over the European mind. They were ready to extirpate heresy by every means. In Portugal they virtually eradicated all scientific inquiry. Established in Portugal by a papal bull in 1540, the Society of Jesus by the eighteenth century had thousands of Jesuits distributed in a network throughout the Portuguese dominions. At the University of Coimbra, which they soon brought under their intellectual management, the curriculum declined into a recital of the miracles wrought by Jesuits, the sufferings of their martyrs, the punishments that awaited heretics, and the powers of wonder-working relics. The managerial inclinations of the Jesuits reached their fullest development in distant Paraguay, where, in the middle of the eighteenth century, they ruled as bureaucratic theocrats over a domain of a hundred thousand Indians, organized in a totalitarian society.

When the able statesman the Marquess of Pombal undertook during the twenty-seven years from 1749 to 1777 to restore the arts and sciences to Portugal, he recognized that he had first to come to grips with the Inquisition and the Jesuits. Therefore, in 1751, he terminated the institution of the auto-da-fé, and gave the government the power to review any clerical judgment. Finally, in 1759, he secured a decree which directed the immediate and complete expulsion of all Jesuits from Portugal. The way was then clear for a revival of the sciences. Faculties in natural history and mathematics were established at the University of Coimbra which "excited the enmity of the clergy, who exclaimed it was heretical." Pombal founded an astronomical observatory, a botanical garden, and museums of chemistry and natural science. He imported Italian professors. The objective was to promote "all sciences that either sweeten life or improve the condition of man." The Bishop of Coimbra retaliated by forbidding the reading of Voltaire's works, Ecclesiastes, the Song of Songs, Rousseau, and the Encyclopédie. In short, the Bishop tried to ban any book of hedonistic-libertarian ethics, whether it was the Encyclopédie or part of the Bible itself. For such authors, he said, were with "the deadly poison of their knowledge" subverting the unity between the priesthood and the temporal power. Pombal replied by having Molière's *Tartuffe* translated and performed many times to large, applauding audiences; the ascetic-authoritarian ethic was being linked to an underlying hypocrisy. The hedonistic-libertarian spirit which sought the revival of the sciences was part of a contagion for freedom. It was Pombal who decreed in 1761 that any slave arriving on Portuguese soil became automatically a free man.[14]

☙ The Philosophers of the Scientific Revolution as Spokesmen for the Psychological Revolution

THE LEADING PHILOSOPHERS of the seventeenth century were not aloof from the scientific and social movements of their time. Without exception, they were men of the world, concerned with statecraft or with active research in science. Their thought, therefore, can be taken as indicative of an underlying cultural trend.

Great aspirations are born in utopian swaddling clothes. In the sixteenth century, Thomas More, later the martyred Chancellor of England, made his Utopia the projective home of the hedonist ethics:

> They [the inhabitants of Utopia] seem, indeed, more inclinable to that opinion which places, if not the whole, yet the chief part of a man's happiness in pleasure; and, what may seem yet more strange, they make use of arguments even from religion, notwithstanding its severity and roughness, for the support of that opinion so indulgent to pleasure; . . . they reckon that all our actions, and even all our virtues, terminate in pleasure, as in our chief and greatest happiness; and they call every notion or state, either of body or mind, in which Nature teaches us to delight, a pleasure.[15]

Thus Thomas More in 1516, young Under-Sheriff of the City of London, friend of Erasmus, enunciated hedonism as the ethics of

Utopia. This fantasy expressed the growing self-conscious concern with happiness as the standard for the judgment of a social order.

A century later another Lord Chancellor, Francis Bacon, affirmed forthrightly in his *Novum Organum* the utilitarian aim of science. "Now the true and lawful goal of the sciences is none other than this: that human life be endowed with new discoveries and powers." The Baconian ethic became the moral philosophy of the Royal Society, and had an immense influence on scientific Englishmen in the seventeenth century. What was the Baconian ethic? It was first and foremost the assertion that the increase of pleasure, even if it meant an increase of men's desires, was a higher good. The philosophers of feudalism and antiquity had generally prized tranquility and equanimity; they proposed to secure their goal by renouncing desires. But Bacon would not renounce the pleasures of human existence. He wrote that the " 'good of advancement is greater than good of simple preservation,' because every obtaining a desire has a show of advancing nature towards perfection. . . ." A mind, said Bacon, can enjoy both tranquility and vigor of fruition.

> For do we not often see some minds so constituted, as to take the greatest delight in enjoying pleasures when present, and yet nevertheless little annoyed at the loss and leaving of them? so that the philosophical progression, "Enjoy not, that you may not desire; desire not, that you may not fear," is the precaution of cowardice and pusillanimity.

The Baconian ethic proposed that men seek their good in this life, not in a preoccupation with the hereafter.

> Most of the doctrines of the philosophers seem to me to be more fearful and cautionary than the nature of things requires: thus they increase the fear of death in offering to cure it; for when they would have a man's whole life to be but a discipline or preparation to die, they must needs make men think that it is a terrible enemy against whom there is no end of preparing. Better says the poet (for a heathen):—
>
> Give me a soul which can grim death defy,
> And count it Nature's privilege to die.

Bacon recognized the evil in men, but he did not wish to make meditations on guilt the aim of life. Rather, he proposed that human behavior be studied in a scientific spirit, so that wise men would be able to cope with it, "so that we are much beholden to Machiavelli and other writers of that class, who openly and unfeignedly declare or describe what men do, and not what they ought to do." [16]

Thomas Hobbes, in his early manhood Bacon's amanuensis, affirmed the hedonistic ethics with all that bluntness which led Charles II to call him "the Bear." Hobbes said, "Whatsoever is the object of any mans Appetite or Desire; that is it, which he for his part calleth Good"; and "Pleasure therefore, (or Delight), is the appearance, or sense of Good." Mankind's Benefit was for Hobbes the aim of science. Hobbes like his fellow scientific philosophers went through the experience in his youth of a self-liberation from the received cultural norms. He went as a boy of fourteen to Oxford, and listened to the "Praelector, though still beardless," lecturing "with authority" on the Aristotelian moods of the syllogism. "These," wrote Hobbes in the Latin verse of his autobiography, "I was slow to learn, but I did learn them, and reject them and get leave to prove everything in my own way." This experience of rejecting the cultural superego and setting out for one's own intellectual journey with one's own independent strength was of the essence of the hedonist-libertarian recovery. Hobbes went on to listen to the Master of Physics, engaged in explaining phenomena by the effects of "Sympathy and Antipathy, with much more of the same sort," said Hobbes, "too high for me to grasp." His sense of reality rebelled, and he "turned to more inviting themes," studied astronomy, geography, and "picked out the tiny settlements of mankind." On his youthful travels, he pondered, as did Descartes in his wanderings, "the nature of things; and it seemed to me," said Hobbes, "that in the whole world only one thing is real, falsified though it be in many ways." Matter and the varieties of motion were alone real, and he must master, he felt, natural philosophy, the laws of motion. When the sense of reality was regained, reality was perceived through the senses, while that which was not given through the senses was literally non-sense. "And words whereby we conceive nothing but the sound, are those we call Absurd, Insignificant, and Non-sense." [17] The common men, Hobbes noted, rarely indulged in such speech, but the clerical intellectuals, or, as he called them, the "Schoolmen," were filled with this sort of "madness."

An absolutist government, in Hobbes's view, would alone guarantee that peace which would preserve men from fear, and allow the values of the hedonist-libertarian ethic to flourish. Hobbes was literally born into anxiety, he tells us. His mother was pregnant with him in the spring of 1588 as the rumor spread that the Spanish "Armada was bringing the day of doom to our race. Thus," Hobbes continues, "my mother was big with such fear that she brought twins to birth, myself and fear at the same time." But Hobbes did not let anxiety turn his ethic in a masochist-ascetic direction; he proposed to use political means to reduce its social sources. His conception of human nature, and of the political capacities of the ordinary man, was not flattering, but he did not aim to revenge himself upon this human nature. Rather, he wished as far as was practicable to fulfill it.

John Locke, the next in the great line of English empiricists, has been called the philosopher of the Glorious Revolution; he was also the philosopher of the Royal Society. This celebrated advocate of tolerance might be characterized as a "theological hedonist." It is "happiness and that alone," said Locke, which "moves desire," and to those who caviled at the pursuit of happiness, "the utmost pleasure," he replied, "God himself is under the necessity of being happy." Asceticism, from Locke's standpoint, is contrary to God's precept. "God has by an inseparable connexion joined Virtue and Public Happiness together." Technological advance was the handmaiden of public happiness. The American Indians, for instance, were so backward in the conveniences of life, Locke wrote, because they did not know how to use iron, "that one contemptible mineral," which, he said, "may be truly styled 'the father of arts and the author of plenty.' "

The liberal Christianity of John Locke was far removed from ascetic Protestantism. Locke's Christianity, as Thomas Fowler said, must have seemed "very attenuated" to the contending religious parties of his time. For his was "a Christianity which did not recognize the hereditary taint of original sin, and which passed over the mystery of the Atonement in silence." "Much less can the righteous God," said Locke, "be supposed, as a punishment of our sin, wherewith He is displeased, to put man under the necessity of sinning continually, so multiplying the provocation." In liberal fashion, Locke proposed to reform education by reducing traditional discipline and providing the child with studies it would truly enjoy. He ridiculed the tormenting of the boy's time with the making of Latin themes:

"the poor lad, who wants knowledge of those things he is to speak of . . . must set his invention on the rack to say something where he knows nothing; which is a sort of Egyptian tyranny. . . ." As a seventeenth-century progressive educator, Locke staunchly believed that education could be made enjoyable by appealing to the child's own interests. He condemned the massive memorization of "scraps of authors," and felt that the young gentleman, in addition to learning the languages and sciences, should graduate in dancing, fencing, wrestling, and riding, and, above all, learn "a trade, a manual trade, nay two or three, but one more particularly."

As a philosopher of the scientific community, Locke urged a toleration of all religious standpoints with one principal exception—he would not grant toleration to those who themselves refuse to tolerate others "in matters of mere religion," or who teach that "faith is not to be kept with heretics." The liberalism of the scientific community asked people to banish fanaticism from their hearts. Locke had himself experienced the vindictive powers of repression. At his college in Oxford, a self-appointed academic spy reported on Locke's activities: "March 14, 1681—John Locke lives a very cunning and unintelligible life here, being two days in town and three out; and no one knows where he goes, or when he goes, or when he returns. Certainly there is some Whig intrigue a managing. . . ." The latitudinarian Locke two years later fled to Holland, and was expelled from Oxford. Author of the classical statement of English empiricism and philosopher of the Revolution of 1688, Locke said, "Man's happiness, or misery, is most part of their own making." [18]

Montaigne, during the sixteenth century, had already expressed the weariness of French liberal intellectuals with the religious fanaticism which led to massacres and wars. The skepticism of Montaigne, his famous "*Que sais-je?*" was absorbed into the scientific context of Descartes's so-called method of doubt, the refusal to accept any statement on received authority. Montaigne, however, also had the hedonist's admiration for nature. Calvinists saw in primitive people the confirmation of the sinfulness of man. Montaigne, on the other hand, wrote in praise of the charms of savages, even of cannibals.[19] He adored the spontaneous products of "*notre grande et puissante mère nature*" ("our great and powerful mother nature"). This emotional change among French intellectuals which Montaigne exemplified underlay the revolutionary statements of Descartes's philosophy of the scientific intellectual.

What the Baconian ethic was to the English scientists, the Cartesian philosophy was to their French co-workers. French scientific groups held to a standpoint akin to their English associates. The constitution of the Montmor Academy, founded in 1657, declared, for instance: "The purpose of the conferences shall not be the vain exercise of the mind on useless subtleties, but the company shall set before itself the clearer knowledge of the works of God, and the improvement of the conveniences of life, in the Arts and Sciences which seek to establish them." It joined in Descartes's faith that "in Mathematics there are the subtlest discoveries and inventions which may accomplish much, both in satisfying the curious, and in furthering all the arts, and in diminishing man's labor."

Descartes was a scientific hedonist. "The enjoyment of the good consists," he wrote, in the emotion of "joy"; "for as a matter of fact the soul receives no other fruits from all the good things that it possesses. . . ." The passions, he affirmed, are the source of "all the good and evil of this life"; it is the function of prudence to direct the passions so as to produce the maximum of joy. Virtue, for Descartes, consists of those modes of behavior which increase joy. Descartes's approach to the problems of ethics was essentially medical: "For the mind is so dependent on the temper and disposition of the bodily organs, that if any means can ever be discovered to render men wiser and more capable than they have been, I believe that it is in the science of medicine that the means must be sought." [20] "The conservation of health," wrote Descartes in 1645 to the Marquis of Newcastle, "has always been the principal object of my studies, and I do not doubt that it will be possible to acquire vast medical knowledge that has remained unknown until the present."

The seventeenth century was one in which philosophers wrote intellectual autobiographies. Descartes, Spinoza, Hobbes, Leibniz wrote their personal intellectual histories because this was a time in which men experienced personal crises as they emancipated themselves from the dominant intellectual environment. Leibniz traced his liberation from the traditional philosophy to the fact that, his parents having died young, he pursued science and learning for the sheer pleasure they gave him. He grew spontaneously into a hedonist-libertarian, not constrained by a cultural superego. He wrote in 1672:

> Mainly because my parents died so early and I was thus left, almost without any direction, to my studies, I have had the good fortune to come upon books of many languages, religions and sciences yet in no proper order; and these I read, being at first impelled by the instinct of *delectatio*. Yet thereby I imperceptibly drew this profit: that I was freed from vulgar prejudices; that I happened upon many things I would otherwise never have considered. . . .

He was "almost an autodidact," Leibniz wrote eight years later, and he "sought out what was new in every science" as soon as he entered it, often even before he "had attained to a knowledge of its very elements." Therefore, he said,

> I did not fill my mind with empty things . . . the knowledge of which is generally accepted not on its own grounds, but on the authority of a teacher; and further, I was not contented until I had discovered the fibres and roots of every science and until I had reached its very principles. . . .

In his maturity, Leibniz became above all the would-be conciliator of warring schools of philosophy and religion. He dreamed of being the architect of the rapprochement between Calvinsim and Catholicism. It is remarkable therefore that the hedonistic standpoint continued to guide his ethical definitions; it remained the common ground of philosophers in the seventeenth century. "For whatever produces pleasure immediately through itself," wrote Leibniz, "is also desired for itself, as constituting (at least in part) the end of our wishes. . . ." Wisdom, he declared "is nothing but the science of happiness," and happiness, in turn, "is the basis of justice." Like a good utilitarian, Leibniz held that jurisprudence "ought to begin by establishing the science of happiness. . . ." And happiness itself he defined straightforwardly in terms of pleasure—"happiness . . . consists in a lasting condition of what is necessary in order to taste pleasure"; "happiness is durable joy." [21] Such was the ethics which motivated Leibniz as he pursued his multifarious projects—new machines, new technologies, a universal language, and a scheme to insure the peace of Europe.

Every age, no matter how bold and revolutionary its philosophy, seeks to justify itself by the approving image of an ancestor.

The Middle Ages looked to Aristotle, the Renaissance sat at Plato's feet, but the seventeenth century turned its back on both, and revered the ancient hedonist Epicurus. Spinoza was typical of philosophers in the seventeenth century when he wrote, "The authority of Plato, Aristotle, and Socrates has not much weight with me." His respect was reserved for "Epicurus, Democritus, Lucretius," the hedonistic atomists. When Sir Thomas Stanley published a *History of Philosophy* in 1656, he allotted a hundred and twelve pages to Epicurus, more than any other thinker received. That same year, John Evelyn published his *Essay on Lucretius*, which sang Epicurus's praise, while Gassendi at Paris had avowed himself a disciple of Epicurus, and defended his master's personality as well as his philosophy. Charleton in 1656 published an *Apologie for Epicurus*, which described the ancient sage as "a great Master of Temperance, Sobriety, Continence, Fortitude, and all other Vertues," but as he explained in another work, *Epicurus' Morals*, the ground of virtue is pleasure: "Forasmuch as it's sweet, or pleasant, for a man to live without pain; and sweet, or pleasant likewise, to enjoy good things and be recreated by them: it is an evident truth that without both these sweetnesses or Pleasures, or one of them at least, Felicity cannot be understood." Sir William Temple, in political retirement, wrote essays on gardening and the cure of the gout, and paid a disciple's homage to Epicurus. The vogue of Epicurus was widespread and influential. In France, notes Leonora Cohen Rosenfield, the empiricists in the first half of the seventeenth century were Epicureans, and in the second half freethinkers. The new Epicureans, however, differed from those of antiquity in one basic respect; together with the Cartesians, they shared a faith in human progress.[22] Their proposed revolt against the received intellectual authority was not conceived as part of a historical cycle but as the means for ever-continuing human betterment.

Dutch Scientists and the Hedonist-Libertarian Ethic in the Seventeenth Century

ALTHOUGH THE NETHERLANDS ACHIEVED their independence from Spain under the Calvinist aegis, and although the Calvinist clerics exercised a considerable influence on Dutch life, Dutch science, on the contrary, was the product of its hedonist-libertarian-minded intellectuals.

Until the United Provinces of the Northern Netherlands achieved their independence, the scientific leadership was held by the southern, Catholic provinces, later the country of Belgium. Antwerp, the most important commercial town, was the center, for instance, of such mathematical education and work as existed in the first half of the sixteenth century. Teachers in reckoning, "*rekenmeesters*," required to satisfy the need for training in accountancy, bookkeeping, computation, and navigation, were the principal mathematical scholars; they pursued their work privately, outside the halls of the universities. The most distinguished worker of this scientific movement was Simon Stevin, whom George Sarton has characterized as "perhaps the most original man of science of the second half of the sixteenth century." He was a practical man of affairs who had no taste for either religious disputation or dogma.

Born in Bruges in 1548, Simon Stevin worked as a bookkeeper and cashier in Antwerp. Some persons have speculated that the model for the commercial equilibrium of a business enterprise may have guided his reflections on the conditions for hydrostatic equilibrium. In 1571, however, Stevin, discomfited by the authorities' refusal to exempt him from the tax on beer, left Antwerp, and settled in the Northern Netherlands, which were now liberated from Spain. In 1583 he became a student and later a professor of mathematics at the University of Leyden. The Calvinist Prince Maurice of Nassau, who said later that he "knew nothing of predestination, whether it is green or whether it is blue," was his pupil, befriended him, and drew him into the civil service; Stevin served as director for roads and waterways at Delft, and as Quartermaster General of the Dutch armies. He was in many ways the scientific intellectual turned scientific administrator. He was, says Sarton, "the first man to perform duties comparable to those of a public accountant and to rationalize those duties." [23] In 1600, Stevin organized the mathematical teaching at the school of engineering in Leyden, which he made notable for his enthusiasm and his insistence on teaching in Dutch, the people's language, rather than the academic Latin of the universities.

For the linguistic revolution was part of the psychological revolution. The Dutch language was not only simpler and technically superior to Latin, said Stevin, but it had a greater emotional power. Scientists, too, wished to speak in the homely, everyday idiom, which was close to their spontaneous emotions and in which they felt naturally expressive. Latin enclosed them with a repressive schol arly tradition, its accumulation of medieval verbiage, as Hobbes said, with its expressions for "Entity, Intentionality, Quiddity, and other insignificant words of the school." "If any man require," challenged Hobbes, "let him take a Schoole-man into his hands, and see if he can translate any one chapter . . . into any of the moderne tongues, so as to make the same intelligible. . . ." [24] The "vulgar" idiom would sift sense from nonsense. The liberation of "vulgar" emotion, taking one from the mode of masochist to realistic perception, expressed itself in recourse to the hitherto despised "vulgar" speech.

Stevin, as a typical scientific intellectual, had, as Sarton judges, "little interest in theological differences." Although born a Catholic, his advice to all religionists in his *Vita Politica* (1590) was that they should not disturb the public order; if a person's religion differed from that of his Prince, said Stevin, he should practice it privately, and not create public issues; if he found himself unable to do so, he should leave the country. Stevin was proud that he was always in accord with the executive power; very much like Hobbes, he wanted the arts of peace and no part of religious fanaticism.

The Netherlands were the most Calvinist of the European countries, but its scientists, like their English contemporaries, were remarkable for their hedonist ethics and anti-Calvinist outlook. Christian Huygens, the greatest of the Dutch scientists, was typical in this respect. Brought up on Erasmus, from his youth Huygens found questions of religious dogma distasteful. He gave vent to his skepticism in his writings. He mocked at the system-makers in 1686: ". . . *les philosophes . . . que pouvaient-ils faire? . . . Avouer qu'il surpasse de bien loin l'homme d'avoir une idée de Dieu*" ("As for the philosophers . . . what could they do? . . . Admit that it is far beyond man to have an idea of God"). Huygens realized how great was the need many people had for certitude, but he avowed his own freethinking in a fragment entitled *Que Penser de Dieu?*: "*Il ne faut pas croire sans qu'on ait raison de croire; autrement que ne croit on les fables et les comptes de vieilles, et pour-*

quoy les Turcs n'ont ils point raison de croire à l'Alcoran?" ("One must not believe without reason for believing; otherwise why doesn't one believe the fables and tales of old women, and why aren't the Turks right in believing the Koran?") Although he admired Descartes greatly, he found no cogency in the Cartesian proofs of God's existence. Religious doubt did not desert him even as he lay dying. He made no avowals of belief in God, and when a relative suggested calling a minister, "*Il commenca à jurer et à tempêter*" ("He began to swear and storm").

The seventeenth century saw the rise of science fiction as a definite literary genre. Huygens' hedonistic creed was most explicitly expressed in a curious work, a mixture of science and science fiction, entitled (as translated) *The Celestial Worlds Discover'd: or, Conjectures Concerning the Inhabitants, Plants and Productions of the Worlds in the Planets.* He envisaged the inhabitants of other planets; they probably "enjoy," he wrote, "not only the Profit, but the Pleasures arising from Society; such as Conversation, Amours, Jesting, and Shews. Otherwise we should make them live without Diversion or Merriment; we should deprive them of the great Sweetness of Life, which it can't well be without. . . ." Huygens granted his alien planetarians "these Blessings": "the Pleasures of Eating and Copulation," the "Smell in Flowers and Perfumes," "the Sight in the Contemplation of beauteous Shapes and Colours," "the Hearing in the Sweetness and Harmony of Sounds." He gave a hedonist's thanksgiving: "what an admirable Providence it is that there's such a Thing as Pleasure in the World." Huygens acknowledged that the fear of poverty and misery had been the schoolmistress of the arts; necessity, he said, had been the greatest cause of human inventions and discoveries. Men of science themselves, however, were moved by "that Happiness and Contentment which they have pretended to above all others." For "the Profit and Advantage of their Inventions" has spread all over the world.

Huygens scorned the Calvinist political fanaticism of the Dutch lower classes. When the mob at the Hague lynched the statesman-scientist John de Witt, Huygens took consolation in the wisdom of Epicurus: "*Quand on voit des choses comme celle-ci, l'on diroit que Messieurs les Epicuriens n'avoyent pas tort de dire, 'versari in Republica non est sapientia'* " ("When one sees such things as this, one would say that the Epicurean gentlemen weren't wrong in saying, *it is not wisdom to be mixed up in politics*" [26]

John de Witt, the remarkable Grand Pensionary of Holland, symbolized above all the union of the hedonistic ethics with the scientific spirit. His mathematical work was admired by Descartes, and the *Elementa Linearum Curvarum,* which he published at Leyden in 1650, was recommended by Isaac Newton as a sound preparation for reading the *Principia.* De Witt rose to become the leader of the liberal Republicans in Holland. He worked to promote the freedom of thought and religion. He was bitterly hated by the Calvinists, who remembered that de Witt and his friends were once united in a kind of underground hedonistic society called "L'Ordre de l'Union et de la Joye." Its ruling proverb was that of Rabelais's Abbey of Thélème—"*Fais ce que vouldras*" ("Do what thou wouldst")—and it aimed to promote dancing, music, and versifying, and to chase away, in the words of a correspondent of de Witt,

> Dame Mélancolie
> Qui ne fit jamais en sa vie,
> Que nes maux de coeur et de teste,
> Et troubla mainte belle feste;
>
> (Lady Melancholy
> Who never in her life made
> Anything but trouble for the heart and head
> And was a killjoy at many a fine party;)

To join this circle, one was required to have "*envie de rire, danser, gambader, et se réjouir*" ("the intention to laugh, dance, frolic, and have fun"). De Witt himself had translated Corneille's *Horace* into Dutch, was a talented violinist, a skilled tennis player, and even indulged in backgammon and card magic. His brother Cornelius, during the hours before his death, was reading Molière's plays *L'Avare* and *Tartuffe.* The liberal republicans had a philosophy akin to Spinoza's idea of the free man, the antithesis of the whole Calvinist doctrine. They regarded themselves as in the lineage of the gay, kindly, tolerant Erasmus.[27]

Predestination, damnation, election, and asceticism receded as Dutch liberalism and science came to flourish in the latter half of the seventeenth century.[28] During the middle of the century, the

University of Leyden was the leading center for education in science. It admitted to matriculation men of all religions—Catholic, Jewish, Protestant. Large numbers of students flocked to Leyden from all parts of the world. Englishmen, during the time of their civil war, found it a special haven. Leyden's medical school was especially famous, but its work in other branches of science, notably astronomy, was also pre-eminent. In 1632, the first observatory ever officially associated with a university was authorized at Leyden, and Jacobus Golius, who had studied Arabic science in the Middle East for several years, became its first director.[29]

Switzerland: Municipal Experiments in Calvinism and Liberalism

THE SCIENTIFIC INTELLECTUAL came into his own in Switzerland only after the constraining weight of the Calvinist ethic was attenuated. This land of free towns and cantons, of Catholics and Protestants, affords a testing ground for measuring the relative power of the hedonist-libertarian and Calvinist ethics in stimulating the growth of a scientific movement. Geneva was the "Protestant Rome" where Calvin himself ruled theocratically. And Geneva itself was a vivid experimental demonstration of the repressive effect of the Calvinist ethic on scientific work.

For two centuries, from 1535 to 1725, Geneva was under clerical domination. The curricula and lectures at its college and academy were held to Calvinist principles. During that entire period, as de Candolle tells us, not a single Genevese distinguished himself in science. The awakening of science in Geneva began with the enfeeblement of Calvinist authority. It was during the decade from 1720 to 1730 that education and morals changed in a liberal direction. In 1739, finally, a Genevese was elected for the first time to one of the three great scientific societies of Europe. Thenceforth, the city produced scientists of all branches in numbers far greater than its small population would have led one to expect. Calvin's Geneva, as a crucial sociological experiment, confirms the theory of the scientific fertility of the hedonist-libertarian ethics.

Geneva, as the Protestant Rome, with its attraction for visitors from all parts of Protestant Europe, always had about it something of the cosmopolitan. But only slowly did its atmosphere become one favorable to science. As in Sweden, the liberal philosophy made its first intrusion into Geneva in the guise of the Cartesian philosophy. Jean Robert Chouet, appointed professor of philosophy at the Academy of Geneva in 1669, was notable for his solitary achievement of a self-liberation from theology. He expounded the Cartesian and experimental methods to his classes, and contested the Calvinist scholasticism. Then, toward the end of the seventeenth century, theologians themselves began to lay hands on Calvinist dogma. The spirit of tolerance grew sufficiently strong so that in 1735 ministers were excused from making an official declaration of faith. "The liberty accorded on so essential a point," says de Candolle, "marked a new era for Geneva. Theology ceased to be an exclusive and dominant science. The intellectual forces . . . began to direct themselves into the sciences, letters, politics, with a growing intensity." [30]

Basel, a smaller town than Geneva, was nevertheless, in the late seventeeth and early eighteenth centuries, already a scientific center. At Basel, there were the eight members of the illustrious Bernoulli family, the mathematician Euler, and the astronomer Huber. Basel, situated nearer to the German free cities, was less weighted with Calvinist dogma. Although little more than a small village (as late as 1779, it had only fifteen thousand inhabitants), it preserved a free spirit, and attracted to its domain those who had seen the horrors of religious fanaticism. The family of Jacob Bernoulli, for instance, resident in the Low Countries, had seen the armies of the Duke of Alva massacre twenty thousand persons to further the cause of Catholic unity.[31] Nonetheless, the Bernoullis recognized the high achievement of Catholic scientific intellectuals. At the age of eleven, the gifted Daniel Bernoulli (1700-1782) was sent for his education to Italy. His uncle, Jacques Bernoulli (1654-1705), the first outstanding scientist of the family, had characteristically refused to become a clergyman, and insisted on a mathematician's career.

As late as 1869, true enough, the Catholic cantons of Switzerland, although numbering one-fourth of the population, had only one-seventh of the members of the Société Helvétique des Sciences Naturelles. Members with Protestant backgrounds likewise predominated in the mixed cantons. Can we, however, at once draw the inference, as some scholars have, that Protestant asceticism is more conducive to the cultivation of science than Catholic indulgence? [32]

That a higher percentage of persons born Protestant than of persons born Catholic is drawn to science is unquestionable. A similar situation obtains in the United States, and has lately been a matter of serious concern for the leaders of the Roman Catholic Church in America. Monsignor John Tracy Ellis, a professor of church history at the Catholic University of America, and John J. Cavanaugh, the former president of the University of Notre Dame, have expressed themselves vigorously on this question. Why, they ask, were there no Catholic institutions among the fifty which were producing the most scientists in 1952? "Even casual observation of the daily newspapers and the weekly news magazines," said Father Cavanaugh, "leads a Catholic to ask, where are the Catholic Salks, Oppenheimers, Einsteins?" [33] But could one infer from the statistical facts concerning American scientists that Protestant asceticism has been the mainspring of the scientific movement?

The word "Protestant," as we have had cause to see, covers a multitude of persons. It extends in America from the fundamentalist ascetics of the Bible Belt, inveighing in Alabama, Mississippi, and Tennessee against the teaching of the theory of natural selection, to the Christian Scientists in New York, who have succeeded in barring questions on the germ theory of disease from the state's examinations in the high schools, to the Unitarians, atheists, and agnostics who have abounded in America's leading universities. The American case might well guide us in our analysis of the Swiss data. For in the United States, to the extent that "Protestant" has denoted an adherence to asecticism, or the distinctive tenets of Calvinist theology—to that extent the impact of the "Protestant ethic" on science has been an overwhelmingly negative one. In the measure, however, that "Protestant" has been loosely used to denote deists, liberals, and agnostics—to that extent, metamorphosed except in name into the liberal ethic, it has encouraged the rise of the scientific spirit. In other words, a crude statistical analysis has attributed to the Protestant ethic what was, rather, the contribution of liberals, who were only in the most formal sense Protestants. The liberal ethic is hedonist-libertarian; the Protestant ethic, especially in its Calvinist form, is ascetic-authoritarian. And the general theorem that applies to the Swiss instance as to others is: an ethic, insofar as it is ascetic-authoritarian, will discourage the rise of the scientific spirit, whereas an ethic, insofar as it is hedonist-libertarian, will promote the growth of scientific inquiry. The liberals during the revolutionary ferment in the mid-nineteenth century won their first victories in the "Protestant" cantons, but their ethic was not that of Calvin's Geneva. Their liberalism was philosophical as well as political.[34]

The Scottish Renaissance

THE RISE OF SCIENCE IN SCOTLAND has been explained as a clear instance of the provocation to intellectual fertility of Protestant asceticism; "the efflorescence of science in the late eighteenth century depended heavily on Scotland, where ascetic Protestantism had thoroughly penetrated."[35] The truth of the matter is, however, quite the opposite. What has been called the "Scottish Renaissance," which brought the Scottish universities to the forefront of European intellectual life and made of Edinburgh a scientific and philosophical center of the very highest order, was precisely the efflorescence in Scotland of the hedonist-libertarian ethic and a revolt against Calvinist asceticism.[36]

An era of industrial expansion commenced in Scotland after the suppression of the Jacobite rising of 1745. In the words of the historian P. Hume Brown, it diverted "the minds of the most energetic section of the community from the theological interests of their fathers," and disposed them to plant their feet more firmly in this world and to think less of the next. Among the educated classes, a spirit of skepticism became fashionable. "In my younger days," recalled Professor John Gregory in 1766, "many of my friends were no Christians." "At that time," according to Ramsay, "Deism . . . was making rapid progress in Scotland."[37] A religious party, known as the Moderates, which was strong among the upper class, came to dominate the Scottish church. A "Moderate man" was defined as one who "expelled mortification, self-denial, humility and silence from among the number of virtues." Its creed was a liberal ethic rather than Calvinist theology, so that when David Hume, greatest of skeptics, listened to a sermon by the Moderate Reverend

Dr. Alexander Carlyle, he remarked that it was nothing but "heathen morality." [38] The Moderates had departed far from the Covenanters' harsh standpoint; they were agreeable toward the pleasures of life. They modeled themselves on the easy ways of the clergy of the Church of England. "Instead of the Sectarian sourness of the covenanting period," said a historian of their controversies, "they verged to an opposite extreme of softness and complacency, chiming in with the literature and amusements of the age. The strong points of Calvinistic theology were thrown into the shade. . . . The Cross of Christ was merely referred to in the way of distant allusion." [39] They reconstructed God in the image of a Benign Moderate, genially disposed toward the theater, the arts, and social pleasures, a God liberated from the accusative thunder of Calvin and Knox. The Popular Party, which held the allegiance of the poor especially in the rural areas, held steadfastly to the ancient teachings. They dealt harshly, when they could, with the liberals. In 1729, after four years in which the country was kept in the ferment of a trial for heresy, they drove from his office John Simson, professor of divinity at the University of Glasgow. When Thomas Reid, later the philosopher of common sense, came to preach at his first church, "he was reviled by the populace, some of whom pulled off his hat and wig in the fray." [40] In 1756, they stormed against the performance in the Edinburgh playhouse of the tragedy *Douglas*, written by John Hume, minister of Athelstaneford. Adam Ferguson took time from his lectures on moral philosophy at the University of Edinburgh to write a pamphlet in defense of theater-going, *The Morality of Stage Plays Seriously Considered.*

The philosophers of the Scottish Renaissance made one great innovation in their conception of human nature. They regarded man as essentially benevolent toward his fellow human beings. Whereas Hobbes had seen malevolence as original in human nature, and had given to Calvinist original sin a secular equivalent, the Scottish philosophers found that sympathy and "fellow-feeling" were instinctive to man. Their optimistic conception of human nature, with its vitality and confidence in man's powers, was part of the hedonist-libertarian ethic which assisted the growth of science. So Adam Smith began his *The Theory of Moral Sentiments* by describing those principles in man's nature "which interest him in the fortune of others, and render their happiness necessary to him, though he derives nothing from it, except the pleasure of seeing it." Actions were evaluated by their tendency "to promote the happiness either of the individual or society," and "fellow-feeling" linked society's happiness to the individual's. David Hume wrote that the sight of the happiness of others "like sunshine . . . communicates a secret joy and satisfaction," while the view of misery "throws a melancholy damp over the imagination."[41] The scientist's life seemed to Adam Smith the freest and the happiest existence, for in the scientist's life the hedonist-libertarian outlook was most fulfilled:

> Mathematicians and natural philosophers, from their independency upon the public opinion, have little temptation to form themselves into factions and cabals, either for the support of their own reputation, or for the depression of that of their rivals. They are almost always men of the most amiable simplicity of manners, who live in good harmony with one another, are the friends of one another's reputation, enter into no intrigue in order to secure the public applause, but are pleased when their works are approved of, without being either much vexed or very angry when they are neglected.[42]

Perhaps Adam Smith's picture of the scientist was overdrawn, but he said he had taken his picture from life, that the two greatest mathematicians he had known, Robert Simpson of Glasgow and Matthew Stewart of Edinburgh, had been men of the greatest tranquility of spirit.

David Hume was not an isolated analyst of ideas; he was a philosopher who was thoroughly representative of the temper of intellect and feeling of the Scottish Renaissance. As Hume Brown states: "There is concurrent testimony that Hume only systematized and gave precision to modes of thinking which widely prevailed in Scotland during the greater part of the eighteenth century."[43] Even among the clergy, the young were drawn to Hume with an intimacy which "enraged the zealots on the opposite side."[44] Hume was indeed a warm friend of leading Scottish moderates. A "pagan naturalism" prevailed at Edinburgh which regarded Christianity as a "temporary aberration" of the human mind. So widespread was this attitude that Edinburgh publishers refused to print Beattie's *Essay on Truth*, written as a reply to Hume's skepticism. "Absolute dogmatic atheism is the present tone," wrote Dr. John Gregory, Professor of the Practice of Physic at Edinburgh, to Beattie in 1766. In the House of Commons, Thomas Townshend took the opportunity to affirm that "the Scots were not all freethinkers."

The years between 1720 and 1740 had prepared the way for the outburst of amazing originality in Scottish thought. At Glasgow, Professor Francis Hutcheson, "the father of Scottish philosophy," had dared to be the first in 1729 to address his classes not in Latin but in English. He spoke moreover on the dignity of human nature and the "harmony of the passions," and as he spoke, "Calvinistic dogmas seemed to lose all their meaning; the orthodox doctrines of the Kirk of the total corruption of human nature, of reprobation, of salvation by faith alone, became to his audience strangely unreal." [45] Hutcheson imparted to his students "a turn for free inquiry." [46] By 1740, the conception of a civilized hedonistic life was dominant in the intellectual centers. During the following years, the Universities of Edinburgh, Glasgow, and Aberdeen led the world in philosophy and the social and physical sciences. The leader of the Moderate Party, William Robertson, became principal of the University of Edinburgh in 1762; his varied historical investigations called forth the enthusiasm both of Hume and Gibbon.[47]

Scientific and literary societies proliferated in Edinburgh. The Select Society, founded in 1754, joined together philosophers, painters, writers, and clergymen under a common banner for "the liberal and ennobling discussions of literature and philosophy." [48] Among its founders were David Hume, Adam Smith, and William Robertson. The Society for the Publication of Medical Essays, which came into being in 1731, was transformed into the Philosophical Society of Edinburgh in 1739—with such distinguished non-medical members as Colin Maclaurin, the Professor of Mathematics—and finally reconstituted in 1783 as the Royal Society of Edinburgh.[49]

Scotland, whose population in 1755 was estimated as only slightly more than a million and a quarter, was the motherland of David Hume in philosophy, Adam Smith in economics, Hutton in geology, Black in chemistry, and Watt in technology.[50] They were the offspring, however, not of Protestant asceticism but of the hedonist-libertarian revival. Robertson used to say "that in Mr. Hume's gaiety there was something which approached to *infantine;* and that he found the same thing so often exemplified in the circle of his other friends, that he was almost disposed to consider it as characteristical of genius." [51] The underlying emotion of the Scottish Renaissance perhaps was best expressed in the poems of Robert Burns, who sang of the joy in life's natural expression, and put to flight the Calvinist gloom.

The relations between the scientists and the hedonist philosophers were close, cordial, and collaborative. Joseph Black, professor of chemistry and medicine at Edinburgh in 1766, discoverer of "fixed air" (carbon dioxide), and propounder of the theory of latent heat, used to forgather often with his friends David Hume, Adam Smith, John Home, Adam Ferguson, and Alexander Carlyle, men with whom he was united not by technical interests but by a common "experience of ingenuity and candor." [52] Adam Smith said of Black that he "had less nonsense in his head than any man living." [53] A society known as the Oyster Club, whose original members were Adam Smith, Black, and James Hutton, used to meet weekly. Its atmosphere was very much like the early meetings of the Invisible College in London.

> They were all three equally amused; were equally prepared to speak and to listen . . . it would be hard to find an example, where every thing favorable to good society was more perfectly united, and every thing adverse more entirely excluded. The conversation was always free, often scientific, but never didactic or disputatious; and as this club was much the resort of the strangers who visited Edinburgh, from any object connected with art or with science, derived from thence an extraordinary degree of variety and interest.[54]

The most intimate friend of Joseph Black was James Hutton, later the famous author of *Theory of the Earth*, who took a similar delight in the Edinburgh circle. As John Playfair wrote, Hutton "was, perhaps, in the most enviable situation in which a man of science can be placed. He was in the midst of a literary society of men of the first abilities, to all of whom he was peculiarly acceptable, as bringing along with him a vast fund of information and originality, combined with that gayety and animation which so rarely accompany the profounder attainments of science." It is striking that the biographical memoirs of Black and Hutton have not a single reference to or indication of theological belief or religious observance. Hutton was filled, in Playfair's words, with a "sensibility to intellectual pleasure." "The fire of his expression, on such occasions, and the animation of his countenance and manner, are not to be described. . . ." "With this exquisite relish for whatever is beautiful and sublime in science, we may easily conceive what pleasure he derived from his own geological speculations." To his ever-present "gaiety and humor," there was superadded in Hutton the trait of never conceding "anything to authority"; he was indifferent to "opinions of former theorists" and "books of opinion" generally. Death for the Scottish scientists did not come with a menace of perdition and predestination. They looked at its advent with that same terrorless equanimity with which David Hume had faced his last days; Adam Ferguson's description of Black's closing days recalls the last sentence of Hume's famous autobiography: "A life so prolonged had the advantage of present ease, and the prospect, when the just period should arrive, of a calm dissolution." They told warmly of Hutton that "a brighter tint of gaiety and cheerfulness spread itself over every countenance when the Doctor entered the room. . . ." This is a portrait of the scientific hedonist-libertarian in the Scottish Renaissance.[55]

The hedonist-libertarian ethic of science, in the form it took in the Scottish Renaissance, was expounded by Adam Smith in his lesser-known work, *The History of Astronomy*. "Wonder," said Adam Smith, "and not any expectation of advantage from its discoveries, is the first principle which prompts mankind to the study of Philosophy . . . and they pursue this study for its own sake, as an original pleasure or good in itself. . . ." Joy in science, according to Smith, was part of the psychological nature of man: "It is evident that the mind takes pleasure in observing the resemblances that are discoverable betwixt different objects."[56]

Virtually alone among the Scottish scientists, Colin Maclaurin, professor of mathematics at Edinburgh University and "the most distinguished disciple of Isaac Newton," was clearly a person of devout religious convictions. However, Maclaurin, a pastor's son, fashioned a God who was scarcely Calvin's but, rather, a Benevolent Guide to Mathematical Truth. If man were to perish "without ever arriving at a more complete knowledge of nature," something would be unfulfilled in "the beautiful scheme of nature." Therefore, reasoned Maclaurin, God must have designed us for admission, "after due preparation," to higher mathematical powers. The reasoning was scarcely cogent, but the prospect of a Higher Mathematics was such a joyful one for Maclaurin that he abandoned original sin for the optimist vision of a Fellow Mathematician. He had occasion, however, to bewail the havoc that Eros could play, in exotic places, with the pursuit of science. To his friend Stirling, Maclaurin wrote sadly in 1740, ". . . an unlucky accident has happened to the french mathematicians at Peru. It seems they were shewing some french gallantry to the natives wives, who have murdered their servants destroyed their Instruments and burn't their papers, the Gentlemen escaping narrowly themselves. What an ugly Article this will make in a journal." [57]

Mathematical education in Scotland, however, had a long, honorable tradition founded on more practical needs. In Edinburgh and Glasgow, commercial schools taught the arithmetic required for bookkeeping and accountancy, while in the coastal towns the emphasis was on geometry and trigonometry as aids to navigation. Colin Maclaurin in the eighteenth century and David Gregory at the end of the seventeenth taught whole generations of the teachers of these schools.[58]

The orthodox Calvinist party fulminated against Smith and Hume, and disliked the scientists' alliance with them. The influence of Scottish orthodoxy prevented Hume from ever becoming a professor in his native land. The accusations of "heresy, Deism, scepticism, Atheism, etc., etc., etc.," kept him from the Chair of Ethics at Edinburgh in 1744, while the Glasgow clergy barred his way to becoming Adam Smith's successor to the Chair of Logic at Glasgow in 1752. A half century later, John Leslie, professor of mathematics at Edinburgh in 1805, had a sentence which praised Hume in his treatise, *An Experimental Inquiry into the Nature and Propation of Heat* (1804). Hume, he said, was the "first who treated of causation in a truly philosophic manner." As a consequence, Leslie was accused of being an atheist, and his appointment was vigorously contested.[59]

In its philosophy, the aim of the Scottish Renaissance was simply, in Dugald Stewart's words, "the advancement of useful knowledge and of human happiness." It prized its continuous intellectual relations with France, Italy, and Holland; it maintained no aloofness of a Calvinist elect. "The constant influx of information and of liberality from abroad," wrote Stewart, "may help to account for the sudden burst of genius, which to a foreigner must seem to have sprung up in this country by a sort of enchantment, soon after the Rebellion of 1745." [60] Black prided himself that his father, who had settled as a merchant in Bordeaux, was "honored with President Montesquieu's friendship." The Scottish historians were regarded as social scientists who had best followed the road which Montesquieu had opened for the understanding of society. "On this interesting subject," said Edward Gibbon, "a strong ray of philosophic light has broke from Scotland in our own times; and it is with private as well as public regard that, I repeat the names of Hume, Robertson, and Adam Smith." [61] James Gregory (contributor to the theory of convergent series) was a student for several years at Padua; his two nephews, David and James Gregory, who followed him as professors of mathematics at Edinburgh, introduced Newton's physics at their university while Cartesian vortices still occupied the curriculum at Cambridge. Then, too, there was James Stirling, member in 1738 of the Edinburgh Philosophical Society, who had spent formative years at Padua and Venice, a "favorite haunt" of the Bernoulli family. Stirling was a good friend of Nicholas Bernoulli, then a professor at Padua. When Stirling moved to London, he saw Newton often and frequented "french Coffeehouses." [62] "Stirlings Series" perpetuated his name in mathematics.

Above all, the Scottish Renaissance issued from a new sense of the pleasures and possibilities in human existence which was stirring among the people as a whole. The young Scotsman with talent found his way encouraged. "In the eighteenth century there was a greater proportion of the population possessed of a university education in Scotland than in any other country in Europe." The students came from every class—farmers, lairds, mechanics, and schoolmasters. The great majority of them were extremely poor, lived in garrets, and brought with them for their semesters in October supplies of oat and barley meal. Meal sold to students was, in view of their poverty, exempt from the local imposts; when the exemption was violated, the University of Glasgow delegated Professor Adam Smith to demand continuance of the ancient privilege from the Town Council. Among the classes themselves, the differences in mode of life were not considerable; laird, farmer, and tenant all worked on the land, and in the bleak Scottish soil had perforce to practice the same frugality. David Hume said there was no middle class in Scotland, only "gentlemen who have some rank and education and the meanest starving poor." [63] There were students who came from lonely areas in which English itself was a foreign language. Well into the nineteenth century, Sir William Ramsay recalled a fellow-student at Glasgow to whom explanations of Horace had to be given in Gaelic. But there was an animation among the students, a sense of confidence in their abilities and the alterability of their stations.[64] Dugald Stewart, speaking for the Scottish philosophers, stated as a general principle of history: ". . . it was the general diffusion of wealth among the lower orders of men, which first gave birth to the spirit of independence in modern Europe, and which has produced under some of its governments, and especially under our own, a more equal diffusion of freedom and of happiness than took place under the most celebrated constitutions of antiquity." This was the philosophy of history of the Scottish Renaissance.

☙ Swedish Science

A RENAISSANCE OF THE SCIENTIFIC SPIRIT took place in Scandinavia during the eighteenth century. Stockholm, by the beginning of the nineteenth century, was one of the principal scientific centers of Europe. Young Germans who wished to become master chemists journeyed to Stockholm to study in the laboratory of Jöns Jacob Berzelius; Metscherlich, the discoverer of isomorphism, and Wöhler, later famous for his synthesis of urea, were pupils of the famed Swedish chemist.[65] What psychological conditions produced the scientific movement in Scandinavia in the eighteenth century? "The real driving force in scientific studies" in Sweden, says Sten Lindroth, "has been a primary, emotionally colored interest in nature, understandable enough in a melancholy people and in a country where it was always a long way between homesteads." [66] This "emotionally colored interest in nature" was expressed by the botanist Elias Fries in his admonition to the aspiring scientist to give himself to nature while his senses "are still open" to its impressions, with "the pure affection which loves without asking why." But the Swedish interest in science has fluctuated; it has not been a constant. The Swedes of the mid-nineteenth century were to turn to theology and metaphysics rather than science. What, then, gave rise to the scientific movement of the eighteenth century?

At first sight, one is tempted to say that the Scandinavian scientific development was the by-product of the Protestant ethic. The rise of capitalism in Norway has been ascribed to this influence, and it might seem reasonable similarly to explain the origins of science.[67] Indeed, a disproportionately large number of the Swedish scientists of the seventeenth and eighteenth centuries were the sons of Lutheran pastors and had had a distinctly clerical upbringing. Olaus Rudbeck, the outstanding anatomist in the seventeenth century, was born to a churchman who became a bishop. The father of the noted chemist Urban Hiärne, was an impoverished pastor; Nils Rosen von Rosenstein, the founder of pediatrics, was the son of a vicar to several congregations; the father of Carl Linnaeus, greatest of botanists, was a curate and his mother a pastor's daughter; both grandfathers of the physicist Klingenstierna were bishops; Swedenborg, more renowned as a mystic than for his geological researches, founded in 1716 the first scientific journal in Sweden—his father was court chaplain and later professor of theology at the University of Uppsala; the mineralogist Johan Gottschalk Wallerius also came from a family of clergymen; Pehr Wilhelm Wargentin, Sweden's leading astronomer in the eighteenth century, and a pioneer in statistical science, as well, was a pastor's son; Berzelius, orphaned at the age of eight, was brought up by a foster father who was a pastor; the botanist Elias Fries, born in the eighteenth century and later the Grand Old Man of Swedish natural science, was also a vicar's son; and the father of the distinguished physicist Anders Jonas Angström, famous for his basic researches on spectra, was preacher to a mill town, and later a curate.[68] Of the twenty scientists in *Swedish Men of Science* who were born before 1815, twelve came from clerical backgrounds.

And yet it would be a profound mistake to conclude that Scandinavian science received its impetus from Protestant asceticism. For a closer scrutiny of the facts shows that the Swedish Renaissance, too, was an outgrowth of a revival of the hedonist-libertarian ethic. Science flourished in Sweden especially during the years known in its history as the Era of Freedom (1718-1772). The death of the ill-fated military genius Charles XII, in 1718, brought the end of absolute monarchy; a constitution gave all political power to the Riksdag (the Swedish Parliament), representing all classes of the people. A vigorous economic growth began in 1739 under the leadership of the party known as the "Hats," composed of young officials and burghers, who were economic rationalists dedicated to goals of material development. Their regime of about twenty-five years was the zenith of the Era of Freedom. They sponsored manufactures and the sciences. In Sweden, "scientific progress did not come until the end of the heroic age," and by "heroic age" is meant an age whose action was dominated by military leaders and whose thought was formed by Protestant religious leaders. Now, "the middle class pushed forward," "an energetic and worldly-wise class of burghers," tired of war and theological disputation, and finding in science both a world view they liked and the basis for future material advance. The culture of this class was that of the Newtonian enlightenment, and it "regarded propagandizing for experimental science as one of its most holy missions." In proportion as religious ideas became recessive in the outlook of the new Scandinavian middle class, "science alone appeared capable of rendering definite decisions about man and universe." Thus, the eighteenth century became for Swedish science "an enchanting period," and "there was something of spring-like freshness about it, perhaps more than any other an epoch of awakening minds and of germination of a true scientific life. . . ." [69]

The new scientists came into conflict with the old theological mode of thought. The decisive encounter in the latter part of the seventeenth century was at the University of Uppsala, which subsequently emerged as a scientific center. Cartesian philosophy was the ideology of the new scientific movement; its ideas began to spread in the early 1660's. Olaus Rudbeck, though a bishop's son, was, as professor of medicine and Rector, the principal force on the Uppsala faculty in securing the introduction of the new ideas. He "vehemently opposed the attempts of the theologians to suppress the dangerous new philosophy"; it was the cause of free research against a closed scholasticism. By his side in the battle of ideas was the then medical student Urban Hiärne, who, though also a pastor's son, fought with his Cartesian professors against the conservative majority. The pastor's son was finding a new philosophy of life; he was the leading spirit of "a circle of gifted and spirited students, a merry communion, which enjoyed seeing its existence in the light of the *littérature galante* of the period." As a young man, Hiärne wrote a pastoral novel and lyric love poems. In this wise, the soil was prepared for that "optimistic ferment," in Lindroth's words, out of which "Swedish natural science was gradually to grow strong and purposeful." [70]

The formation of the Swedish Academy of Science in 1739 was an intellectual consequence of the victory that year of the liberal party, the Hats. Soon the new society had all the country's experimental scientists among its members, together with a large representation of "science lovers," and it commenced publication of its annual *Handlingar* (*Transactions*). The development of science in Sweden was, however, not a continuous one. Despite the growth of commerce and industry, there was a decline of science-mindedness between 1810 and 1880. Swedish culture during that time became permeated with metaphysical idealism. "It was, in its most characteristic expressions, nurtured by Platonism, which saw nothing in the material world, but personified metaphysical concepts." The German *Naturphilosophie*, which looked at nature in theological terms, became influential in Sweden; the categories of the Protestant ethic were projected in cosmological terms, to the ruination of Swedish science. Schelling's philosophy especially was promulgated with enthusiasm by the so-called Phosphorist groups. A controversy ensued in 1829, ostensibly over the organization of medical education but actually between the experimental and metaphysico-religious modes of thought. The chemist Berzelius was attacked as a "leader of one of the types of materialistic research carried out most boldly and actively," and as a promoter of irreligion. Berzelius, who did indeed represent the empiricism of the eighteenth-century scientists, became a voice of the past in nineteenth-century Sweden. "In the middle of the nineteenth century, Sweden was a little country of civil servants . . . atrophied in old forms, an out-of-the-way corner of the world well protected from life-giving impulses from the outside." [71] An idealistic orthodoxy prevailed in the universities; creative intellectual life was in stagnation. One is reminded of the intellectual evolution of the United States in the nineteenth century, when the revival of the Protestant ethic was coeval with the decline of the scientific spirit.

Berzelius, who gave to chemistry the principles of its symbolic notation, went through an intellectual transition which was typical of the scientists nurtured in the liberation of the eighteenth century. He experienced an adolescent's passage from the theological to the scientific stage. At the age of fifteen, he wrote, as he went about collecting flowers and insects, a new intention in life welled up in him: "Up to this time it had been my firm purpose to become a clergyman like my father, my grandfather, and great-grandfather, which my mother also had said many times was her wish. But now I pursued with zeal botany and entomology, sciences which according to my understanding at that time were unnecessary for a clergyman. After some consideration, I therefore came to the conclusion to study medicine, in which I believed I would have some need of this knowledge." The authorities of the gymnasium, at which the young Berzelius was a student, did their best to break him of his scientific interests. The rector, as Berzelius later related, "censored me for occupying myself in the study of natural history with so much zeal. He gave himself much trouble to demonstrate the uselessness of this subject and finally advised me to cease wasting my time in such a purposeless manner." When young Berzelius persisted in his scientific activities, the rector tried to avail himself of a technical infraction of rules to have Berzelius whipped. Several years later, when Berzelius was well established in his career, with a royal appointment, his old rector wrote asking him "to forgive the castigation which was aimed at me during my gymnasium days, with the plea that the incident had occurred with the good intention of winning me back for the priesthood." Berzelius's certificate of graduation stated that he "was a youth of good natural gifts but with bad manners and of doubtful expectations."

A few years later, Berzelius made the next transition, from the collector's taxonomic activity to actual experimental work in chemistry. Again there was the sense of emotional awakening: "Immediately with the first participation in them I was seized with a feeling never previously experienced; I was irrevocably gripped by this method of pursuing knowledge. I must needs repeat for myself the experiments I had seen him [Ekmarck] perform, and although I was unable to buy any instruments, I improvised apparatus, with his help, which I myself could make." He pursued his chemical studies "with the most joyous hopes that my lively curiosity would be satisfied. . . ." When he first collected oxygen in a laboratory exercise, he wrote, "I . . . have seldom experienced a moment of such pure and deep happiness as when the glowing stick which was thrust into it lighted up and illuminated with unaccustomed brilliancy my windowless laboratory." [72] Berzelius, the descendant of Lutheran clergymen, would probably be classified in a statistical analysis as a person predisposed to science by an ascetic Protestant upbringing. In his own experience, however, he had moved at great emotional cost from the theological to the scientific mode of thought and feeling. What must control our sociological understanding of the rise of science is the actual "phenomenological experience" of scientists; whatever their social circumstances and backgrounds, what is finally most important is how they viewed their existence and their scientific work.

It is a risky matter to trace the content of specific scientific discoveries to underlying emotional changes among scientific intellectuals. Nevertheless, the epoch-making sexual classification of plants which Linnaeus introduced seems to have been especially related to the psychological revolution on which modern science was founded. The first demonstration of the sexuality of plants was made by a professor of medicine at Tübingen, Rudolph Jacob Camerarius, who in his *De Sexu Plantarum*, in 1694, reported his numerous experiments which determined the functions of pistil and stamen. When Linnaeus read about these experiments, which most botanists had ignored, his enthusiasm was aroused. He was in 1730 a young man of twenty-three, filled with ardor and the conviction that God was opening for him the secrets of nature, when he began to arrange plants according to a sexual system.

Were the discovery of sexuality in plants and the origin of the sexual classification at this time in the history of science purely fortuitous? Or were observers prepared to recognize the sexuality of plants because a psychological revolution in their era was enabling them to overcome resistances which had previously distorted their observation and repressed their inquiry? According to George Sarton,

> The discovery of the sexuality of higher plants by Camerarius in 1694 could have been made two thousand years earlier, if the experimental method had been applied to it. It was retarded by non-experimental thinking and by prejudices. . . . Similar remarks would be offered with regard to almost every fundamental discovery of modern science down to the theory of evolution. Each discovery was delayed by a kind of intellectual inertia. . . .

With respect to the sexuality of plants, however, the resistance to recognition and discovery seems to have been more than ordinary inertia; there was a definite resistance to finding sexuality so pervasive in nature, or to making it a theme for experimental study. For thousands of years, the cultivators of the date-palm in the Near East had known of the phenomenon of fertilization of female by male. But the idea that plants had organs which functioned sexually was abhorrent to many scholars, and well into the nineteenth century adherents of *Naturphilosophie* were proving the impossibility of sexuality in plants on "philosophical" grounds.[73] But Camerarius, a meticulous experimenter, had dared to write to the contrary.

Now, Linnaeus was a person of strong emotions with a passion for classifying things. He once classified all living botanists according to military rank, with himself as general. He disliked the ascetic, cold-blooded animals, and his commentary on the amphibians was, "Terrible are Thy works, O Lord!" Camerarius's discovery of sexuality in plants moved him immensely, because in his youth and manhood Linnaeus was an enthusiastic pantheist who identified Nature's vitality with God's life: "Should we call Him Nature," he said, "we should not be wrong. . . ."[74] In Holland, where he had spent three productive years, he felt his closest kinship with the Spinozist scientist Boerhaave. His childhood had been hard, and he grew bitter and pessimistic in his later years. The insight of the sexual classification, however, came to him in his animated youth, when he was most conspicuous for "his naïvete, his ability to regard nature with wide-eyed wonder, as though everything were new and miraculous as on the first day of creation"; he made a hedonistic principle the pervasive category in classifying the plant kingdom and reveled in Nature's anti-asceticism. To this extent, we might say that the emergence and use of the doctrine of sexuality in plants bore an intimate relationship to the hedonistic-libertarian ethic of the scientific revolution.

The life of Linnaeus was indeed a dramatic contest between the hedonist-libertarian zest and the Protestant heritage of gloom; the former inspired his scientific work, the latter shaped him into a metaphysician of Nemesis. The first draft of Linnaeus's natural system, written when he was barely twenty years old, was a biological prose poem, an ode to the joy of nature:

> This sun affords such joy to all living things that words cannot express it; the black cock and the woodgrouse can be seen to mate, the fish to play, why, all animals feel the sexual urge. Love even seizes the very plants. . . .

Then Linnaeus described the florial nuptials in a botanical Song of Songs:

> The actual petals of the flower contribute nothing to generation, serving only as Bridal Beds, which the great Creator has so gloriously arranged, adorned with such noble Bed Curtains and perfumed with so many sweet scents, that the Bridegroom may there celebrate his Nuptials with his bride. . . . When the bed is thus prepared, it is time for the Bridegroom to embrace his beloved Bride and surrender his gifts to her: I mean, one can see how *testiculi* open and emit *pulverem genitalem*, which fall upon *tubam* and fertilize *ovarium*.

The diary of his scientific expedition into Lappland at the age of twenty-five was a Lucretian record of observations; *Andromeda polifolia* became for him "a virgin of most exquisite and unrivalled charms," surrounded by "dragons and venomous serpents" so that the "distressed virgin cast down her blushing face through excessive affliction." The clergymen he met scandalized him with their ignorance, and he felt they should be "placed as far as possible from civilized society." On the other hand, as his journey progressed, he reported that "the wenches in Finland have bigger breasts than the girls in Lappland." *A Tour in Lappland*, says Linnaeus's biographer, was "a document of his happiness." In *Flora Lapponica*, Linnaeus paid tribute to the Lappland youth who hung a mushroom in a little pocket hanging at his waist so "that its grateful perfume may render him more acceptable to his favorite fair one." Distinguished botanists of Europe were sorely troubled by the language of their young Swedish colleague. Was he sound? "Was not this tone in itself testimony that the lewd sexual system involved the most dangerous consequences?" [75]

At Uppsala, Linnaeus's lectures on dietetics were lectures on ethics and man's condition. The primary condition for happiness, said Linnaeus, was "to be born of healthy parents in the most ardent sexual excitement." He thought his own genius came from having been his parents' first-born. With his medical standpoint, he affirmed that the "*mores* should never be against nature." The title of his book *Curiositas Naturalis* (*Curiosity of Nature*), 1748, was the statement of his philosophy as a scientist; the study of nature was "a constant joy to the soul" and the "highest point of human happiness." The book provoked criticism from the theologians, who noted that Linnaeus did not speak of an afterlife and that the Saviour was almost never mentioned. The religion into which Linnaeus had been raised, as a matter of fact, "hardly influenced his way of thinking." He continued to accept God's reality but transformed Him, as other scientists had, from a Protestant Deity into God, Honorary Member of the Royal Academy of Sciences. He wrote in his *Memoranda:* "God has inspired him with such a burning desire for science that this has become the most pleasant of all. . . . God has suffered him to peep into his secret cabinet." The peeping Linnaeus gloried that "None before him has made more observations in nature-study." The young boy who pleaded with his father, the curate, never to ask him again to be a priest, "because for that I have no inclination at all," perhaps had imbibed something of the primitive nature cult to which the peasants of the countryside still adhered. There was in him an upsurge of feeling wholly alien to the theological way of life.

But Linnaeus's self-giving to Nature's delights and its sexual beauties exacted a terrific price of guilt. The Protestant ethic took its vengeance. It was evidently in 1741, the year of his son's birth, that he began to keep notes on *Nemesis Divinia*, which grew into a vast collection in which he documented the law of retribution of the universe, "always punitive, avenging, hardly ever rewarding or reparative." The master who exploited his peasants awaited Nemesis: "God exterminates the master's seed and finally makes them poor." Above all, however, Linnaeus accumulated case histories on the sexualia of unfaithful wives, and wrote a meticulous sketch of the "Character of a wife who is a whore." Nemesis awaited the transgressor of the moral code, and restored the balance of existence. A Strindbergian torment awaited husbands concerning the paternity of children: "When she evades her husband . . . in order to please the adulterer, she loses the tender love of her husband. . . . Strange children become involved.—Must share with them that due to the rightful heirs. . . ." The notes were addressed to his son, who never married. Was Linnaeus speaking from some stark personal experience, or was his Lutheran upbringing rebuking him for a moral laxity which was common in Sweden at that time, and to which his own scientific labors may very well have contributed? His wife hated their son so much that it was said "in the whole wide world he had no more bitter enemy than his mother." And Linnaeus, in his will, left last words of animosity toward her: "if she contracts another marriage to her misfortune, as I do anticipate," she was to have no part of what he had secured through his labors. In his *Philosophia Humana*, he tried to explain why some women are more unchaste than others; he argued that some families transmit a hereditary wantonness, whose physiological mechanism he describes in detail; blood flows to genitalia in unusual quantities, "the girl acquires lustrous and moist eyes." [76] A physiological determinism was the counterpart of the law of Nemesis. His view of nature itself grew more somber.

No man ever felt a greater identification with nature than Linnaeus. It extended even to his theory of names for plants. For the names were not merely conventions, but expressed a linkage between the characters of the plant family thus named and of the discoverer—Pisonia, a somber tree, named after Piso, a somber man; Dorstenia, with withered flowers, like her namer, Dorsten. Each named in nature what corresponded to his own temperament. And Linnaeus, oscillating between his naturalistic, hedonistic ethic and the guilt of Nemesis, saw nature alternately in bridal splendors and sordid whoredom.

Conclusion: Protestant Politics, Protestant Family, and the Hedonistic-Libertarian Ethic

WHAT THEN WAS THE RELATIONSHIP of the Protestant ethic to the rise of modern science? It ought to be clear by now that the so-called virtues of the Protestant ethic—asceticism, frugality, self-denial—did not nurture the growth of science. But a historical movement, however, always achieves more than its conscious aims. Protestantism, as a doctrine of protest, called upon men to liberate themselves from the immediate past and its traditions. Luther and Calvin themselves intended systems as rigorous, in some respects, as the Roman Catholic. Like Asian magicians, they summoned up, however, forces of the deep beyond their mastery.

To succeed, a revolution against the past must enlist in its services the repressed energies of the unconscious. The liberated forces cannot, however, always be restrained within an arbitrary goal's domain; they overflow, upset old landmarks, and give to the individual a self-confidence and respect for his powers which he had never enjoyed. This total experience of liberation from the cultural tradition, this weakening of the burden of historical submissiveness, this sense of the individual's own importance—this constituted the common ground which the Protestant Reformation shared with the hedonistic revival of the seventeenth century.

On the conscious level, the Calvinist ethic was, of course, thoroughly anti-hedonist, and its revolutionary partisans regarded themselves as warriors against pleasure. David Hume has left us a sardonic portrait of the Puritan spirit under the Commonwealth. The republicans, the Lord's chosen, were "intoxicated with their saintly character," enflamed with "speculative principles" and political theology, "consecrated by their own fond imaginations" against the established churchmen. The saints were predominantly men of the lower classes. As for their representatives in Parliament, "the far greater part were mechanics . . . the very dregs of the fanatics." To them, pleasure signified not only the Devil's experience but political reaction; delight in pleasure, in their eyes, was "a sure pledge of attachment to the church and monarchy." [77] They frowned on both science and the playhouse, on whatever seemed to liberate people from the anxiety over their human status.

And, indeed, in times of social revolution, the men of the lower classes are invariably advocates of asceticism. For the revolutionist must construct for himself a new conscience which can dethrone the old, and this new conscience must have strength even to sanction parricide (for such to him is the latent significance of regicide). Only the ascetic who punishes himself with deprivation can claim that he has killed not for private gain but for the public good or God's will. Only the ascetic, by partially destroying himself, proves both to himself and the world at large that he is selfless.

But asceticism remains, however, only half the Puritan's story, and the other half was his individualistic revolt against institutions and personages which were deeply embedded in his traditional conscience. The ancient institutions instilled in man a sense of his own insignificance; the individual questioner then sensed himself presumptuous against historical wisdom. The experience of individual judgment, however, brought with it a new feeling of what it was to be one's self, and in this sense the revolutionary experience has itself always been a hedonistic one.[78]

The Protestant Reformation liberated the individual by the revolutionary means it was compelled to employ; a stable Puritan regime, without such a birth's travail, would not have had that effect. Thus writers, studying the consequences of the Puritan Revolution, have attributed to Puritanism what were, rather, the consequences of Revolution.[79] A revolutionary movement against an existing church or society has to demand that degree of freedom necessary for it to receive a hearing from its contemporaries. Again, however, once the spirit of freedom has been released, it becomes difficult to contain it within planned strategic precincts. The Calvinist movement replaced the ecclesiastical hierarchy with self-governing congregations. The individual voice acquired a further sense of its own right to be heard. The domain for such democratic self-assertion was limited, but the wedge in the authoritarian structure was made which bolder individuals could widen. This democratic component, especially in the dissenting English Protestant sects, was far more significant for the growth of the scientific spirit than the so-called ascetic virtues of the Protestant ethic.[80] We might state the matter concisely by saying that it was the Protestant politic, not the Protestant ethic, which lent a helping hand to the scientific movement.

The Protestant standpoint contributed to the hedonist ethic in still another respect. It brought a higher degree of sexual freedom to the intellectual class. The philosophy of Aristotelian scholasticism was, we have seen, the product of celibate monks. Now Protestantism allowed marriage to its clergy. Thereby it at once raised marriage and sexual experience to a higher repute. In the minds of both the clergy and the laity, the Protestant Reformation signified at first a release from ascetic practices. As Roland H. Bainton tells the story, "in 1521 and 1522 one innovation followed another with disconcerting rapidity. Priests married, monks married, nuns married. Nuns and monks even married each other. The tonsured permitted their hair to grow. The wine in the mass was given to the laity. . . . Masses for the dead were discontinued. Vigils ceased. . . . Meat was eaten on fast days. . . . All this could not escape the eye of Hans and Gretel. Doctrine might go over their heads, but liturgy was a part of their daily religious life. They realized now that the reformation meant something, and this began to worry Luther. The glorious liberty of the sons of God was in danger of becoming a matter of clothes, diet, and haircuts." The abolition of the tonsure's mark and the regrowth of hair were symbols of the recovery of virility and the recognition of sexuality as, in itself, not necessarily evil. Carlstadt, Luther's collaborator, in his wedding announcement said that for lack of marriage "many priests have suffered in the dungeons of the Devil." Luther came to insist that sexual intercourse was a weapon against the Devil, for it was as necessary as eating and drinking; therefore to frustrate one's sexual desires was to weaken the body to the Devil's temptations. Marriage, he finally held, was a purer state than monastic celibacy, because the married were untormented by desire.[81]

The Protestant standpoint certainly had its own conception of the original sin of sexuality. At the same time, however, it removed the celibate nuns and priests from their status as ego ideals, and "downgraded" the cult of the Virgin Mary. The Protestant gibe at the "Mariolatry" of the Catholic Church is of great psychological significance. For it indicates the weakening of those mechanisms which reinforced the Oedipal complex. The sexual apathy induced by Catholic indoctrination was alleviated.[82] The changes, in other words, in the psychological structure of the Protestant family tended, despite the ascetic preaching of Protestant ministers, to promote a more worldly, hedonistic outlook.

A scientific movement, furthermore, cannot flourish where the social-religious system is such as to intensify the dependence-relations of the young on their priests, elders, or confessors. Dependence-relations are the counterpart of a strong authoritarian superego. They inhibit curiosity and they inhibit the senses. The confessional, as an institutionalized form of dependence-relationship, probably contributed more than any explicit theological doctrine toward retarding the diffusion of the scientific spirit among Roman Catholics. These dependence-relationships were uprooted by the individualistic component of the Protestant Reformation.

Calvinist asceticism, on the other hand, was the transient asceticism which characterized a class involved in a revolutionary transition; it was not their underlying philosophy. Even Calvin's Geneva was founded on a persistent substratum of pleasure-loving people. They became "Calvinists" only under the duress of historical crisis. The last free elections in 1538 to the City Council went against Calvin, who assailed the victorious party as "libertines." Geneva later submitted to the dictatorship against sin because Calvin, as Professor F. C. Palm has written, "was the one man who could unify them and thus save them from foreign intervention and internal chaos." Neither Calvin nor Robespierre represented the basic ethics of the bourgeoisie; both signified a terrorist reaction against fear and anxiety; both were persons who embodied defense mechanisms against transient insecurities. Calvin's classmates are said to have called him "the accusative case" because of his fault-finding disposition.[83] The bourgeois hedonists, like the proletarian ones, use this case only when the grammar of history requires it.

The Calvinist temper, moreover, hostile though it was to the scientific spirit, prepared the way for its diffusion by providing it with a literate, educated citizenry. In this fashion, the "theocratic democracy" of New England sowed the seeds of its own theocratic obsolescence. The New England divines believed in universal education, for in principle they held that every individual must arrive at his own commitment to God without the intervention of a priestly class. "But," as John Fiske long ago said, "in this energetic diffusion of knowledge they were unwittingly preparing the complete and irreparable destruction of the theocratic ideal of society which they had sought to realize by crossing the ocean and settling in New England." [84] The impulse to scientific questioning, however, was an illegitimate progeny of Calvinism. Its growth, even in its embryonic stage, tended to disrupt the enforced Calvinist stability of things. For again the scientific temper was linked with love for the body and its senses, love for things of this world in their fullness, love for the open expression of the individual and his liberation from the conscience's harsh censor. Hester Prynne, the heroine of Nathaniel Hawthorne's *The Scarlet Letter*, emerged to something like greatness because she became the spokswoman for the hedonistic, individualistic, inquiring spirit arising in the Puritan society against its censor's will. Hers was indeed, as Hawthorne described it, the ethic of science which the Protestant ethic could not contain:

> It was an age in which the human intellect, newly emancipated, had taken a more active and a wider range than for many centuries before. . . . Hester Prynne imbibed this spirit. She assumed a freedom of speculation, then common enough on the other side of the Atlantic, but which our forefathers, had they known it, would have held to be a deadlier crime than that stigmatized by the scarlet letter.

Protestant theology had its myths and its sense of sin, but its critique of the accumulated debris of centuries, with their saints' relics and miracles, thus liberated the sense of curiosity from a part of the repressive forces. The series of dissenting sects kept developing corollaries of liberation and discarding successive myths until by the end of the seventeenth century, in many places, both among scientists and common people, forms of deism and pantheism were widespread. The child's curiosity was no longer the sign of its original sin. To the degree that Protestantism became liberal—that is, to the degree that it was more hedonistic in its freedom from the sense of guilt and the so-called virtues of Protestant asceticism—the more productive it became of men with the scientific spirit.

NOTES

1. George Sarton, "Islamic Science," in *Near Eastern Culture and Society*, ed. T. Cuyler Young (Princeton, 1951), p. 86.

2. Ibn Khaldun, *The Muqaddimah: An Introduction to History*, trans. Franz Rosenthal (New York, 1958), Vol. III, p. 311. T. J. De Boer, *The History of Philosophy in Islam*, trans. Edward R. Jones (London, 1903), p. 3. George Sarton, *Introduction to the History of Science* (Baltimore, 1927), Vol. I, p. 523.

3. Aldo Mieli, *La Science Arabe et Son Rôle dans l'Evolution Scientifique Mondiale* (Leiden, 1938), pp. 51-2, 76. Alfred Guillaume, *Islam* (Harmondsworth, 1954), pp. 130-2. Gustave E. von Grünebaum, *Medieval Islam* (2nd ed., Chicago, 1953), pp. 34-7.

4. George Sarton, *op. cit.*, p. 524. G. Le Strange, *Baghdad During the Abbasid Caliphate* (Oxford, 1900), pp. 266, 272, 298. Philip K. Hitti, *History of the Arabs* (6th ed., London, 1956), pp. 301 ff. Edward G. Browne, *Arabian Medicine* (Cambridge, 1921), p. 5. Donald Campbell, *Arabian Medicine and Its Influence on the Middle Ages* (London, 1926), Vol. I, pp. 38-9.

5. José M. Millás Vallicrosa, *Estudios sobre Historia de la Ciencia Española* (Barcelona, 1949), pp. 16-17, 22-3. Yusef Salah El-Din Kotb, *Science and Science Education in Egyptian Society* (New York, 1951), pp. 60-1.

6. Ibn Khaldun, *op. cit.*, Vol. III, pp. 113-17.

7. E. Vacherot, *Histoire Critique de l'Ecole d'Alexandrie* (Paris, 1846), Tome I, pp. ii, iii, 100, 101, 111, 115. Also, Charles Kingsley, *Alexandria and her Schools* (Cambridge, 1854), pp. 19-20.

8. M. Rostovtzeff, *The Social and Economic History of the Hellenistic World* (Oxford, 1941), Vol. II, pp. 1084-85, 1095; Vol. I, pp. 411-15. With respect to the psychological roots of science in ancient Egypt, the statement of Otto Neugebauer is most significant: "Of all the civilizations of antiquity, the Egyptian seems to me to have been the most pleasant." Otto Neugebauer, *The Exact Sciences in Antiquity* (2nd ed., Providence, 1957), p. 71. As for the scientific creativity of the Greeks, Sir Thomas Heath notes, "It was a fortunate chance for the unhindered spiritual development of the Greek people that while their predecessors in civilization had an organized priesthood, the Greeks never had. To begin with, they could exercise with perfect freedom their power of unerring eclecticism in the assimilation of every kind of lore. . . . The

Greeks then, with their 'unclouded clearness of mind' and their freedom of thought, untrammeled by any 'Bible' or its equivalent, were alone capable of creating the sciences as they did create them. . . ." Sir Thomas Heath, *A History of Greek Mathematics* (Oxford, 1921), Vol. I, p. 9.

9. Arnold Reymond, *History of the Sciences in Greco-Roman Antiquity*, trans. Ruth Gheury de Bray (London, 1927), pp. 65-6. J. L. Heiberg, *Mathematics and Physical Science in Classical Antiquity*, trans. D. C. Macgregor (London, 1922), pp. 48 ff.

10. Erik Nordenskiöld, *The History of Biology*, trans. Leonard Bucknall Eyre (New York, 1932), p. 151.

11. William Bergin, "Aloscio (Luigi) Galvani (1737-1798) and Some Other Catholic Electricians," in *Twelve Catholic Men of Science*, ed. Sir Bertram Windle (London, 1912), pp. 69-87.

12. Américo Castro, *The Structure of Spanish History*, trans. Edmund L. King (Princeton, 1954), pp. 25, 44, 49, 59, 128, 451-2, 645-6, 648-9. Cf. J. B. Trend, *The Language and History of Spain* (London, 1953), pp. 115-22. José M. Millás Vallicrosa, *op. cit.*, pp. 22-3. José R. Carracido, *Estudios Histórico-Críticos de la Ciencia Española* (Madrid, 1917), pp. 32, 65-6. Cf. John David Hughey, Jr., *Religious Freedom in Spain: Its Ebb and Flow* (Nashville, 1955), pp. 44-5.

13. Santiago Ramón y Cajal, *Recollections of my Life*, trans. E. Horne Craigie, in *Memoirs of the American Philosophical Society* (Philadelphia, 1937), Vol. VIII, pp. 22-3, 36-41, 53-4, 71, 75, 104, 118, 131, 160, 193-4, 592. Harley Williams, *Don Quixote of the Microscope: An Interpretation of the Spanish Savant Santiago Ramón y Cajal* (London, 1954), pp. 146-7, 165-6.

14. John Smith, *Memoirs of the Marquis of Pombal* (London, 1843), Vol. I, pp. 64-5, 163-6, 222; Vol. II, pp. 101, 141, 165-8.

15. Thomas More, *Utopia*, in *Ideal Commonwealths*, ed. Henry Morley (London, 1885), pp. 115-18. Ernst Cassirer, *The Platonic Renaissance in England*, trans. James P. Pettegrove (Edinburgh, 1953), p. 109. There have been various interpretations of More's thought. The conservative view may be found in R. W. Chambers, *Thomas More* (London, 1935), pp. 131 ff. The pioneer radical interpretation was Karl Kautsky, *Thomas More and his Utopia*, trans. H. J. Stenning (London, 1927), which had a successor in Russell Ames, *Citizen Thomas More and his Utopia* (Princeton, 1949).

16. *The Works of Francis Bacon*, ed. Spedding, Ellis, and Heath (Boston, 1864), Vol. IX, pp. 206-7, 211. *Novum Organum*, Aph. XXXI.

17. Thomas Hobbes, *Leviathan* (Everyman's Library, New York, 1934), pp. 20, 22, 24-5, 40. *The Autobiography of Thomas Hobbes*,

trans. Benjamin Farrington, *The Rationalist Annual*, 1958, pp. 22-31.

18. John Locke, *An Essay Concerning Human Understanding* (new ed., London, 1909), pp. 181, 186, 549. Bk. II, Ch. XXI, Par. 41, 42, 50; Bk. IV, Ch. XII, Par. 11. Thomas Fowler, *Locke* (New York, 1880), p. 160. John Locke, "The Reasonableness of Christianity as delivered in the Scriptures," *The Works of John Locke* (12th ed., London, 1824), Vol. VI, p. 6. "Some Thoughts Concerning Education," Vol. VIII, pp. 6, 165, 194. "A Letter Concerning Toleration," Vol. V, pp. 45-6.

19. George Boas, *The Happy Beast in French Thought of the Seventeenth Century* (Baltimore, 1937), pp. 1-4, 93.

20. Harcourt Brown, *Scientific Organization in Seventeenth Century France (1620-1680)* (Baltimore, 1934), pp. 75, 213, 251. René Descartes, *The Passions of the Soul*, Art. XCI, CXLVIII, CCXII. *Discourse on the Method of Rightly Conducting the Reason and Seeking for Truth in the Sciences*, Pt. I, Par. 7; Pt. VI, Par. 2. *The Philosophical Works of Descartes*, trans. Elisabeth S. Haldane and G. R. T. Ross (Cambridge, 1931), Vol. I, pp. 84, 120, 372, 398-9, 427. Norman Kemp Smith, *New Studies in the Philosophy of Descartes* (London, 1952), p. 342. Leonora Cohen Rosenfield, *From Beast-Machine to Man-Machine* (New York, 1941), p. xxii.

21. R. W. Meyer, *Leibnitz and the Seventeenth-Century Revolution*, trans. J. P. Stern (Chicago, 1952), p. 87. Quoted from C. J. Gerhardt, *Die Philosophischen Schriften von Gottfried Wilhelm Leibniz* (Berlin, 1875-90), Vol. I, p. 57; Vol. VII, p. 185. *The Philosophical Works of Leibnitz*, trans. George Martin Duncan (New Haven, 1908), pp. 137-8.

22. *The Correspondence of Spinoza*, trans. A. Wolf (London, 1928), p. 290. Thomas Franklin Mayo, *Epicurus in England (1650-1725)* (Dallas, 1934), pp. 43, 51, 54. Clara Marburg, *Sir William Temple, A Seventeenth Century "Libertin"* (New Haven, 1932), pp. 22-3. *Works of Sir William Temple* (London, 1814), Vol. III, p. 203. Leonora Cohen Rosenfield, *op. cit.*, pp. xxv, 111. G. S. Brett, *The Philosophy of Gassendi* (London, 1908), pp. xliv, 185-6.

23. D. J. Struik, "Mathematics in the Netherlands during the First Half of the XVIth Century," *Isis*, XXV (1936), 46. George Sarton, "Simon Stevin of Bruges (1548-1620)," *Isis*, XXI (1934), 265.

24. George Sarton, "Simon Stevin of Bruges," pp. 247, 251. Hobbes, *Leviathan*, pp. 12, 40.

25. *Œuvres Complètes de Christiaan Huygens* (The Hague, 1950), Vol. XXII, pp. 14, 398, 766-7. In 1691, Huygens wrote, "*in metaphysicis . . . nec Existentiam Dei neque . . . umquam mihi demonstrasse visum.*" *Ibid.*, Vol. XXI, p. 342. Cf. Henri L. Brugmans, *Le Séjour de Christian*

Huygens à Paris (Paris, 1935), p. 104. A. E. Bell, *Christian Huygens and the Development of Science in the Seventeenth Century* (London, 1947), pp. 7, 97.

26. Christianus Huygens, *The Celestial Worlds Discover'd: or, Conjectures concerning the Inhabitants, Plants and Productions of the Worlds in the Planets* (2nd ed., London, 1722), pp. 40, 52-3, 70, 75, 80-1. Henri L. Brugmans, *op. cit.*, pp. 50, 52, 78-9, 85.

27. Phyllis Allen, "Scientific Studies in the English Universities of the Seventeenth Century," *Journal of the History of Ideas*, X (1949), 248. I. Todhunter, *A History of the Mathematical Theory of Probability* (London, 1865), pp. 38-9. James Geddes, *History of the Administration of John De Witt, Grand Pensionary of Holland* (New York, 1880), pp. 37, 302. Gustave Cohen, "Le Séjour de Saint-Evrémond en Hollande (1665-1670)," *Revue de Littérature Comparée*, XI (1926), 56-7, 73-5. Margaret Mann Phillips, "Erasmus and Propaganda," *Modern Language Review*, XXXVII (1942), 1, 5-7. Adriaan Jacob Barnouw, *Vondel* (New York, 1925), p. 36.

28. The courageous patrician, John Oldenbarnevelt, exemplified the emerging liberalism in the first part of the seventeenth century. John Lothrop Motley, *The Life and Death of John of Barneveld, Advocate of Holland* (New York, 1874), Vol. I, pp. 45, 346. Petrus Johannes Blok, *History of the People of the Netherlands*, trans. Ruth Putnam (New York, 1900), Vol. III, pp. 399, 428.

29. R. W. Innes Smith, *English-Speaking Students of Medicine at the University of Leyden* (Edinburgh, 1932), p. ix. W. De Sitter, *Short History of the Observatory of the University of Leiden, 1633-1933* (Haarlem, 1933), pp. 7-8.

30. Alphonse de Candolle, *Histoire des Sciences et des Savants depuis Deux Siècles* (2nd ed., Geneva-Basel, 1885), pp. 335-6, 419. Société d'Histoire et d'Archéologie de Genève, *Histoire de Genève des Origines à 1798* (Geneva, 1951), p. 391.

31. Adolphe Quetelet, *Histoire des Sciences Mathématiques* (Brussels, 1864), pp. 105-7.

32. Alphonse de Candolle, *op. cit.*, p. 425. Isidor Thorner, "Ascetic Protestantism and the Development of Science and Technology," *American Journal of Sociology*, LVIII (1952), 32-3.

33. *Time*, Dec. 30, 1957, p. 50.

34. Kurt B. Mayer, *The Population of Switzerland* (New York, 1952), pp. 154-5, 176-7, 246. E. Bonjour, H. S. Offler, and G. R. Potter, *A Short History of Switzerland* (Oxford, 1952), pp. 249 ff.

35. Isidor Thorner, *op. cit.*, p. 28.

36. Sydney E. Ahlstrom, "The Scottish Philosophy and American Theology," *Church History*, XXIV (1955), 257-8.

37. P. Hume Brown, *History of Scotland to the Present Time* (Cambridge, 1911), Vol. III, p. 289. John Ramsay, *Scotland and Scotsmen in the Eighteenth Century*, ed. Alexander Allardyce (Edinburgh, 1878), Vol. I, p. 60. Margaret Forbes, *Beattie and his Friends* (Westminster, 1904), p. 30.

38. Rev. Dr. Alexander Carlyle, *Autobiography* (Boston, 1861), p. 225.

39. Cf. Rev. Henry F. Henderson, *The Religious Controversies of Scotland* (Edinburgh, 1905), pp. 83-4.

40. John Ramsay, *op. cit.*, p. 471.

41. Adam Smith, *The Theory of Moral Sentiments*, ed. Dugald Stewart (New ed., London, 1853), pp. 3-5, xxx. David Hume, *An Enquiry Concerning the Principles of Morals* (reprinted, Chicago, 1912), pp. 79-80.

42. Adam Smith, *The Theory of Moral Sentiments*, pp. 180-1.

43. P. Hume Brown, *History of Scotland to the Present Time*, pp. 296-7. Henry Grey Graham, *The Social Life of Scotland in the Eighteenth Century* (London, 1937), p. 358. "In Scotland the 'Zeit Geist' was embodied in Mr. Hume." Margaret Forbes, *op. cit.*, p. 40.

44. Rev. Dr. Alexander Carlyle, *op. cit.*, p. 224.

45. Henry Grey Graham, *op. cit.*, pp. 353, 455, 463.

46. Rev. Dr. Alexander Carlyle, *op. cit.*, p. 71.

47. Sir Alexander Grant, *The Story of the University of Edinburgh* (London, 1884), Vol. II, p. 268.

48. Dugald Stewart, "An Account of His Life and Writings," *The Works of William Robertson* (London, 1817), Vol. I, pp. 10-11.

49. Cargill G. Knott, "Mathematics and Natural Philosophy," in *Edinburgh's Place in Scientific Progress* (Edinburgh, 1921), pp. 8-9.

50. H. Grey Graham, *op. cit.*, p. 536.

51. Dugald Stewart, "An Account of His Life and Writings," *op. cit.*, p. 53.

52. Adam Ferguson, "Minutes of the Life and Character of Joseph Black," August 3, 1801, *Transactions of the Royal Society of Edinburgh*, V (1805), 113.

53. Sir William Ramsay, *The Life and Letters of Joseph Black, M.D.* (London, 1918), p. 133.

54. John Playfair, "Biographical Account of the Late Dr. James Hutton," Jan. 10, 1803, *Transactions of the Royal Society of Edinburgh*, V (1805), 98.

55. *Ibid.*, pp. 41, 44-9, 91, 93-5, 98. Adam Ferguson, "Minutes of the Life and Character of Joseph Black," *op. cit.*, p. 116.

56. Cf. *The Works of Adam Smith* (London, 1811), Vol. V, pp. 51-2, 65, 89.

57. Herbert Westren Trumbull, *Bi-Centenary of the Death of Colin Maclaurin (1698-1746)* (Aberdeen, 1951), pp. 3-7. Charles Tweedie, *James Stirling* (Oxford, 1922), pp. 90-91.

58. Duncan K. Wilson, *The History of Mathematical Teaching in Scotland to the End of the Eighteenth Century* (London, 1935), pp. 57-8.

59. Ernest Campbell Mossner, *The Life of David Hume* (Austin, 1954), pp. 156-7, 247-50. J. Y. T. Greig, *David Hume* (London, 1931), pp. 131-2, 189. John Rae, *Life of Adam Smith* (London, 1895), pp. 47, 127. Cargill G. Knott, "Mathematics and Natural Philosophy," *op. cit.*, p. 15.

60. Dugald Stewart, James Mackintosh, John Playfair, and John Leslie, *Dissertations on the History of Metaphysical and Ethical, and of Mathematical and Physical Science* (Edinburgh, 1835), pp. 220, 249.

61. Sir William Ramsay, *op. cit.*, p. 5. Dugald Stewart, "An Account of His Life and Writings," *op. cit.*, p. 65.

62. Cargill G. Knott, *op. cit.*, pp. 5-6. Stewart, Mackintosh, *et al.*, *op. cit.*, p. 249. Charles Tweedie, *op. cit.*, pp. 12-13.

63. James Drever, "Educational Science," in *Edinburgh's Place in Scientific Progress*, p. 253. Henry Grey Graham, *op. cit.*, pp. 165, 180, 262, 456-7. John Hill Burton, *Life and Correspondence of David Hume* (Edinburgh, 1841), Vol. I, p. 198.

64. Sir William Ramsay, *op. cit.*, pp. 11, 350. Cf. William C. Lehmann, *John Millar of Glasgow 1735-1801* (Cambridge, 1960), pp. 3-4, 91-4.

65. W. A. Shenstone, *Justus von Liebig: His Life and Work* (London, 1901), p. 17.

66. *Swedish Men of Science: 1650-1950*, ed. Sten Lindroth (Stockholm, 1952), pp. 31-2.

67. Christen T. Jonassen, "The Protestant Ethic and the Spirit of Capitalism in Norway," *American Sociological Review*, XII (1947), 676-86.

68. *Swedish Men of Science: 1650-1950*, pp. 33, 42, 50, 59, 74, 81, 92, 105, 122, 160, 178, 193.

69. *Ibid.*, pp. 16, 17, 74. Carl Hallendorff and Adolf Schuck, *History of Sweden*, trans. Lajla Yapp (Stockholm, 1919), p. 328. Cf. Giovanni Bach, *et al.*, *The History of the Scandinavian Literatures*, ed. Frederica Blankner (New York, 1938), p. 94.

70. *Swedish Men of Science: 1650-1950*, pp. 15, 40, 43. Cf. Frederick Winkel Horn, *History of Literature of the Scandinavian North*, trans. Rasmus B. Anderson (Chicago, 1895), pp. 341-2.

71. *Swedish Men of Science: 1650-1950*, pp. 23, 24, 107. Cf. Frederik Winkel Horn, *op. cit.*, pp. 373-4. Nels F. S. Ferré, *Swedish Contributions to Modern Theology* (New York, 1939), p. 5.

72. Jöns Jacob Berzelius, *Autobiographical Notes*, trans. Olof Larsell (Baltimore, 1934), pp. 7-15, 22, 25-6. *Swedish Men of Science: 1650-1950*, p. 168.

73. George Sarton, *A Guide to the History of Science* (Waltham, 1952), p. 35. George Sarton, "The Artificial Fertilization of Date-palms in the time of Ashurnasirpal B.C. 885-860," *Isis*, XXI (1934), 13; "Additional Note on Date Culture in Ancient Babylonia," *Isis*, XXIII (1935), 251-2; Solomon Gandz, "Artificial Fertilization of Date-palms in Palestine and Arabia," *Isis*, XXIII (1935), 245-250. Julius von Sachs, *History of Botany*, (*1530-1860*), trans. Henry E. F. Garnsly (Oxford, 1890), pp. 388, 423.

74. Norah Gourlie, *The Prince of Botanists: Carl Linnaeus* (London, 1953), pp. 27-9. Benjamin Daydon Jackson, *Linnaeus* (London, 1923), p. 45. Nordenskiöld, *op. cit.*, pp. 207-13.

75. Knut Hagberg, *Carl Linnaeus*, trans. Alan Blair (London, 1952), pp. 64-5, 78, 86, 166, 169, 185.

76. *Ibid.*, pp. 186, 208, 41, 47, 232, 225-9, 242, 121, 174-5, 102-3, 233.

77. David Hume, *The History of England* (new ed., Boston, 1849), Vol. V, pp. 38, 411, 441-2, 484, 519-20, 528.

78. *The Philosophical Works of David Hume*, ed. T. H. Green and T. H. Grose (London, 1875), Vol. III, p. 183. *Bentham's Book of Fallacies*, ed. Harold A. Larrabee (Baltimore, 1952), p. 43 ff.

79. Ernst Cassirer, *op. cit.*, p. 74.

80. *The Philosophical Works of David Hume*, Vol. III, pp. 177, 187. Hume wrote pointedly: "Not to mention, that monarchies, receiving their chief stability from a superstitious reverence to priests and princes, have commonly abridged the liberty of reasoning, with regard to religion, and politics, and consequently metaphysics and morals." Spinoza paid a glowing tribute to the republican freedom of Amsterdam. *The Chief Works of Benedict de Spinoza*, trans. R. H. M. Elwes (London, 1883), Vol. I, p. 264.

81. Roland H. Bainton, *Here I Stand: A Life of Martin Luther* (New York, 1955), pp. 153-5. Preserved Smith, "Luther's Early Development in the Light of Psycho-Analysis," *American Journal of Psychology*, XXIV (1913), 364-5, 370.

82. For discussions of the sexual apathy induced by Catholic indoc-

trination, cf. *The Vanishing Irish*, ed. John A. O'Brien (New York, 1953).

83. George Macaulay Trevelyan, *England Under the Stuarts* (6th ed., London, 1914), p. 228. Franklin Charles Palm, *Calvinism and the Religious Wars* (New York, 1932), p. 30. R. N. Carew Hunt, *Calvin* (London, 1933), p. 20. "Geneva was a frontier state, a besieged garrison, in danger alike of falling under the physical control of Savoy and the spiritual control of Rome. Hence some of the restrictions. It must not be forgotten that neither good music, good cooking, nor good wine were prohibited. . . ." E. Bonjour, H. S. Offler, and G. R. Potter, *op. cit.*, p. 169.

84. John Fiske, *The Beginnings of New England* (Boston, 1898), pp. 160, 163, 165. G. P. Gooch, *The History of English Democratic Ideas in the Seventeenth Century* (Cambridge, 1898), pp. 7-9, 76-7.

VIII

The Masochist Mode of Perception in Asian Civilizations

◆§ The Stagnation of Science in China and Japan

WHY DID A SCIENTIFIC REVOLUTION OR A SUSTAINED SCIENtific movement fail to develop in China and Japan? This question has been a continuing challenge to students of Chinese and Japanese civilization. Various theories have been propounded, and in such a comprehensive work as Joseph Needham's *Science and Civilization in China* they appear in alternation side by side, almost as the author's particular mood at the time would prefer. Why did a movement of scientific intellectuals fail to arise in the highly stable, well-organized, and literate Chinese society? If our hypothesis of the causative role of the hedonist-libertarian ethic is sound, it should help answer this problem. For the touchstone of a sociological theory is in part its ability to explain negative instances.

Let us review the alternative theories that have been proposed to explain the absence of a scientific movement in China.

1. The real ruler of China through the ages, says Needham, "was, as it were, the Confucian Party." The ideology of Confucianism was unfortunately antagonistic to science. Its "intense concentration of interest upon human phenomena to the exclusion of non-human phenomena negatived all investigation of Things as opposed

to Affairs. Hence, not for the last time in history, not only in China, rationalism proved itself less favorable than mysticism to the progress of science." [1]

2. The mystical Taoist philosophers, says Needham, although they attacked "knowledge," were really attacking "Confucian scholastic knowledge of the ranks and observances of feudal society, not the true knowledge of the Tao of Nature. Confucian knowledge was masculine and managing; the Taoists condemned it and sought after a feminine and receptive knowledge which could arise only as the fruit of a passive and yielding attitude in the observation of Nature." The Taoists, according to Needham, despite their passive attitude, achieved the crucial step of transition to experimentation because their magicians believed that Nature could be mastered by manual operations.[2]

3. Nevertheless, the Taoist stimulus was insufficient to produce a sustained scientific movement, because Chinese society was not democratic—"there was no modern science in China because there was no democracy." For "modern science and modern democracy grew up together, as parts of that great movement in European development which included the Renaissance, the Reformation and the rise of capitalism." Chinese society was one of "bureaucratic feudalism"; although local, village democracy might persist under such conditions, they prevented the rise of a revolutionary, mercantile democracy. "Feudal bureaucratism" inhibited the rise of a scientific intellectual class in China. "No Renaissance awoke it from its 'empirical slumbers,'" because the suppression of the merchant class in China removed the social basis for a scientific awakening.[3]

4. Then again, Chinese thought lacked the stimulus of the theological belief in a personal God. According to Needham, the founders of modern science—Kepler, Descartes, Boyle, and Newton—were inspired to a quest for laws of nature because they conceived that these laws were "edicts which had been issued by a supra-personal supra-rational being." Whitehead's suggestion that the Christian medieval god prepared the way for science by bringing to European thought the idea of a law of nature is Needham's starting point. "Whatever may be the needs of mankind now, such a supreme God had inevitably to be personal then. This we do not find in Chinese thought. Even the present-day Chinese term for laws of Nature, *tzu-jan fa*, 'spontaneous law,' is a phrase which so

uncompromisingly retains the ancient Taoist denial of a personal God that it is almost a contradiction in terms." [4]

5. Insofar as a conception of a "law of nature" was adumbrated, it was understood by the Neo-Confucians in a Whiteheadian, organismic sense; law in the Newtonian sense was "completely absent." The Taoists meanwhile had been groping "after an Einsteinian world-picture, without having laid the foundations for a Newtonian one." The so-called Legalists, on the other hand, "made themselves the representatives of mechanistic materialism," and "failed to take account of the levels of organization in the universe." This was their "philosophical flaw." [5]

6. For the failure of a conception of "law of nature" to arise in Chinese thought, Needham proposes a political explanation in addition to the theological and economic. He follows an interesting line of speculation which the insightful Edgar Zilsel opened. According to Zilsel, the origin of the notion of "law of nature" was rooted in the rise of absolutist monarchies in the early modern history of Europe. With the decline of feudalism and the rise of capitalist economy, there ensued a great increase in the power of centralized royal authority. Royal absolutism made its appearance in Tudor England and the France of Louis XIII and XIV. "It is not a mere chance," said Zilsel, "that the Cartesian idea of God as the legislator of the universe, developed only forty years after Jean Bodin's theory of sovereignty." But then Needham is led into difficulties by the Zilsel hypothesis. For why did not the idea of "law of nature" arise in China, where " 'imperial absolutism' covered an even longer period" than in Western Europe?

7. To answer this question, Needham relies on the supposed influence of the conception of human law on that of law of nature. Although in Western Europe the conception of law of nature arose out of human, positive law, in China it did not develop from juristic theory and practice. Primarily this was because "the Chinese acquired a great distaste for abstractly codified law from their bad experiences with the Legalists during the period of transition from feudalism to bureaucratism." [6] Such is the final slender causal foundation in Needham's effort to explain the absence of the scientific standpoint in Chinese culture.

Analysis of Needham's Theories of Retardation of Science

NOW, THERE IS MUCH THAT IS SUGGESTIVE in the array of hypotheses which Needham proposes. But they oscillate so extremely, it seems to me, because they have no psychological mechanisms to which they are attached. Needham cannot decide whether to make rationalism or mysticism, democracy or absolutism, mechanism or organism into the sources or hindrances of a scientific movement. The evidence is confusing because, under some historical circumstances, rationalists, democrats, and mechanists have been proponents of a scientific movement, whereas under other circumstances they have been indifferent or hostile to the development of science. One must identify the actual psychological drives, the mental and physical sets, that make not only for scientific curiosity but for the determination to intervene with experiment and instrument in natural processes. Any philosophical standpoint or political form will contribute to a scientific movement insofar as, under the specific historical circumstances, it assists those psychological drives.

Confucianism, according to Needham, was so intensely concerned with human affairs that it ignored the world of non-human events; hence arose "its ambivalent attitude towards science." Certainly Confucius disliked speculations as to the supernatural. Asked about his duty to the spirits, he replied, "While still unable to do your duty to the living, how can you do your duty to the dead?" Asked about death, he said, "Not yet understanding life, how can you understand death?" [7] But an intense concern with human affairs does not necessarily engender a climate hostile to scientific study. Voltaire, the passionate social conscience of his time, was an equally passionate Newtonian; Diderot, D'Alembert, Adam Smith, David Hume, John Locke, Benjamin Franklin were all deeply involved with the social problems of their time, but their social interests fed rather than detracted from their interest in the natural sciences. The interest in nature can be stimulated and sustained by the desire to raise the level of human social existence; an interest in persons does not exclude an interest in things. But where the social aim is to inhibit human desires, the resultant psychological repression will produce a decline of interest in external objects. A social concern can be a repressive rather than expressive one, and Confucianism had a strong ingredient of such social repression. Clearly, some psychological ingredient other than the concern for human matters makes for the resistance to independent scientific inquiry.

It is tempting, of course, to link science with democracy, and to say that the rise of democracy brought forth the rise of science. One can then affirm with Needham that there was no scientific movement in China because there was no democracy. What this theory ignores, however, is that there is no intrinsic connection between science and democracy. The American democracy of the first half of the nineteenth century, as we shall see, did next to nothing to help the advancement of the sciences. The Congress of the United States was as stingy as any government could be in refusing to appropriate funds for scientific projects, and its democratic ideology was often intermixed with anti-intellectualism. The Napoleonic dictatorship, on the other hand, was the friendliest government to scientists that any nation has had. Moreover, one should not be misled by formulae such as "Oriental despotism" into overlooking the actual strength of village democracy in China. As two Chinese sociologists wrote in 1915:

> But in its actual working China is a huge republic within which are myriads of petty republics. For the village in China is an autonomous unit. Nominally it is governed by the central government through a hierarchical series of officials. . . . But actually with the exception of paying a nominal land-tax and in a few other cases, the village is as independent of the central government as any British self-governing colony. . . . This may sound strange, especially when it is remembered that the principles of government are those of unmixed despotism even under the present regime and its laws are enforced by such a minute gradation of ranks and subordination of officials that it partakes more of the nature of a military system than that of a civil government. Be this as it may, the village in China is less governed than any other in the world. In China the central government plays but an infinitesimally small part in the village life. The village has perfect freedom of industry and trade, of religion, and of everything that concerns the government, regulation, and protection of the locality. Whatever may be required for its well-being is supplied, not by Imperial

Edicts or any other kind of governmental interference, but by voluntary associations. Thus police, education, public health, public repairs of roads and canals, lighting, and innumerable other functions, are managed by the villagers themselves.[8]

The local village democracies in China were singularly untouched by the lines of authoritarian political power of the absolute monarchy. As the noted sociologist Hsiao-tung Fei said, "The court, except in the case of a few tyrants, did not interfere in the going concern of society. In general, a good monarch collected a definite amount of taxes and left the people alone." "We somehow managed to 'hang-up' the centralized power so that it did not reach to the ground. . . ."[9] The notion of "do-nothingism" became embedded in Chinese political philosophy; it provided the anti-authoritarian component in a society where scholar-administrators were the political elite, and it safeguarded the structure of village democracy.

But the village democracies were tradition-bound communities, following the ways of the past with peasant conservatism, holding fast to the past by the rituals and beliefs of ancestor-worship, a simple cult of the superego in which the individual's sense of his own reality was rendered dependent on his place within the family. Needham distinguishes the village democracy from the revolutionary mercantile democracy, which, in his view, was the real social basis for scientific movements. Certainly it is true that the relationship between the European towns, their merchant classes, and the support of scientific movements was a close one. The European towns, however, in which science flourished, were much more mercantile oligarchies, or mercantile aristocracies, than mercantile democracies. Venice for many centuries was renowned as the aristocratic republic in which merchants ruled, and such a Dutch town as Amsterdam was likewise a mercantile oligarchy.[10] Not the democratic principle as such but the philosophy of life found among the liberal merchants, their friendliness to the pleasures of the body, their respect for the body's senses, their aversion to asceticism and religious fanaticism, their attachment to numbers, rational calculation, and simple speech—all this made for a society in which a scientific movement could grow. Where a merchant class has for specific historical reasons come under the sway of Calvinism, it has not been the social mainstay of a scientific movement. Geneva, while it was under Calvinist hegemony, was not a scientific center; it became such when the liberal philosophy supplanted Calvinism. A revolutionary, democratic mercantile rule is thus no guarantee for a scientific movement; the mercantile class must be moved by a liberal hedonist ethic for it to be the social support of a class of scientific intellectuals.

Nor will it do to attribute the Chinese failure to develop a scientific movement to the hegemony of a "feudal bureaucratism." A controversy has raged among scholars as to the precise definition of the traditional Chinese society. Karl A. Wittfogel has with great forcefulness argued that China was a "hydraulic society," administered by agro-bureaucrats, who regulated the allocation of labor to the irrigation works, and kept the censuses, registers, and tax rolls. Chinese Communist writers, on the other hand, have maintained that, from the Han Dynasty on, China was a feudal society. According to Wittfogel, the "Oriental despotism atomized the non-bureaucratic groups and strata which, in feudal Europe and Japan, spearheaded the rise of commercial and industrial society." [11] Needham makes a syncretistic adjustment to this conflict of opinion; in the dispute as to whether the Chinese society was feudal or bureaucratic, he affirms it was a "bureaucratic feudalism." A syncretistic formula is too often a device for evading analysis; does "bureaucratic feudalism" or "feudal bureaucratism" have more significance than such phrases as "feudal capitalism" or "capitalist Socialism"? In any case, must we accept the view that it was the bureaucratic component in Chinese society which inhibited the rise of a scientific movement?

A bureaucracy as such need not be hostile to the spirit of scientific inquiry. Copernicus was a feudal ecclesiastical bureaucrat, and his bureaucratic setting and responsibilities in Poland were consistent with a devotion to science. The priest-bureaucrats of ancient Egypt were among the founders of science. When the Jesuits sought to show the superiority of Catholic Christendom to Confucianism in China, they adduced the European achievements in science, which they depicted as the offspring of Christendom. The Catholic managerialists were ready to enlist science for their own managerial ideology when it suited their purposes. But the Chinese bureaucracy was affected with a reverence for the past and an adherence to the ways of the ancestors. Although it was, in some measure, a bureaucracy open to talents, all its talents were molded in the image of loyalty to ancient ideas and practices. A perceptive sociologist has described how this gerontocratic factor in Chinese society operated to impede scientific and technological advance:

> In every traditional craft, the "old master" was most respected, not the brilliant and vigorous young worker. In agriculture his experience was similarly valued by the community. In 1949 the writer tried to introduce into a village an improved weeder which worked much more effectively than hand weeding or hoeing. The younger peasants tried it and liked it very much, but a few days later nobody wanted to use the new instrument because "the old people concluded that it will hurt the root system of the plant." The writer challenged the younger peasants to experiment with the instrument by offering to pay for any damage resulting from it, but to no avail. Confucius' advice of learning to farm from an "old farmer" still stood firm. . . . The old master taught and advised and laid down rules for the young to follow. He led the family and the community in economic matters.[12]

This pattern of psychological conditioning to self-abasement before the ways hallowed by ancestral authority is, indeed, typical of Asian civilizations. In India, where crafts and skills have been passed on as part of the caste mores, the independent innovator with a more scientific bent of mind finds himself confronted with the deep emotional resistance of the caste superego.

> It is no doubt this method of transmitting a craft which makes an innovation in method appear sometimes as if it were a sin against the craftsman's ancestors. Sonnerat found it useless to try to get Hindu carpenters to use improved methods of sawing wood, and a similar difficulty is still experienced in the hills of Assam, where the local inhabitant prefers the adze to the saw. . . .[13]

The harshness of the superego, the sense of guilt, the self-abnegation of the individual were all ingredients of the Chinese authoritarian ethic. The stability of the traditional Chinese family, writes Professor Yang, "was achieved at the price of strenuous repression of the young." "Legal and social pressures drove fear and feeling of rigid subordination deep into the mind of the young individual." "The status of the young man was indeed low, at times helpless. The authority of parents over child was absolute. Infanticide, approved by the community, was an expression of it; and even as the child grew older, the parents' threat against his life was by no means completely eliminated. The proverb 'The son must die if so demanded by the father' was a means of compelling obedience from the young in traditional China. . . ." [14] It was not until the fourth decade of one's life that a person would gain a respected status in the age hierarchy.

An ethic is not a liberal-hedonist one if it lacks a sense of individualism. For individualism implies a freedom from self-hatred, an absence of group or parental hostilities internalized against one's self. And the Chinese ethic always lacked the sense of individualism; its hedonism was always blended within a socially repressive framework. Traditional Chinese moral standards demanded the self-sacrifice of the individual; the Confucian ethic of self-cultivation looked to the individual's self-sacrifice as the means for preserving the social group.[15] Growing up "under the ancestor's shadow," observes Francis L. K. Hsu, the young Chinese acquired an "inability to create or to enter a new and untrod path." He possessed no psychological strength "for seriously challenging the existing scheme of things." His capacity for erotic life had usually been maimed to the requirements of filial piety, which imposed an estrangement of the sexes. Needham has remarked that "a certain heuristic naïveté" is helpful in the advancement of science. Such a naïveté could scarcely survive the gerontocratic discipline. The family revolution to which the Chinese Communist government has given its most vigorous support will probably release the most powerful energies for a scientific movement. Chinese Communism will have its bureaucracy, and its own ideological obstruction, but the psychological characteristics of the Communist techno-managerialists will differ radically from those of the Confucian scholar-administrators. The family revolution is hastening the psychological revolution in China, from which new economic and intellectual ways will derive their mainspring, and which will probably realize more fully the scientific revolution in China.

Now, Needham, in his theorizing concerning the failure of a scientific movement to arise in China, makes much use of Whitehead's theological interpretation of the origins of modern science. According to Whitehead, "the faith in the possibility of science, generated antecedently to the development of modern scientific theory, is an unconscious derivative from medieval theology." It was the "medieval insistence on the rationality of God," says Whitehead, which was the source of the belief that the search into nature would confirm that rationality. Medieval theology was thus held by Whitehead to have provided the scientist with the faith that there were laws of nature. Needham therefore doubts whether natural science "could ever have reached its present stage of development without passing through a theological stage." [16] A curious revival of the Comtist law of intellectual stages is thus under way; the theological stage is held to have been a necessary precursor to the scientific.

But it is against the evidence to assert that the scientific standpoint is "an unconscious derivative from medieval theology." Whitehead himself never gave any evidence for this piece of speculative history, and indeed it seems to partake of an autobiographical apology rather than an objective account of the history of science. Whitehead, brought up in a clergyman's home, was all but converted to Catholicism, as Bertrand Russell tells us. The experience of the founders of the modern scientific standpoint, as they themselves apprehended it, should guide our analysis; Bacon, Descartes, Spinoza, Boyle, Galileo all felt themselves to be squarely against the kind of "rationality" which the medieval Aristotelian philosophers demanded. The "order" and the "rationality" which the medieval God imposed was the "order" of a feudal monarch or absolute potentate who bound his subjects to fulfill his arbitrary will. Therefore, as Edgar Zilsel has observed, "The Middle Ages perceived the reign of God much more in miracles than in the ordinary course of nature. Comets and monsters were of greater moment to medieval piety than the daily sunrise and normal offspring." Only with the emergence of the new scientists did the idea of God's reign in the world shift from the exceptions in nature to the rules. The orders of nature that the scientists sought were mathematical uniformities, which expressed an impersonal sense of rationality rather than a personal one. In their self-awareness, the scientific thinkers of the seventeenth century saw themselves not as continuators of medievalism but as persons who had broken with it. The scientific revolution is misperceived when it is interpreted as an unconscious prolongation of tradition. Revolutionary changes do take place, and cannot be repressed from consciousness by *ad hoc* continuities. When medievalism prevailed in Europe, Jehovah's "rationality" held an ascendancy for a millennium, but science was virtually extinct.

The world that the Christian medieval thinkers conceived was one in which, as Charles Singer observed, the distinction between physical events and moral notions was lost. If this medievalism had really been a fructifying creed assisting scientists to a belief in laws of nature, one might have expected that the medieval thinkers themselves would have been led to some scientific observations. "Yet there is very little evidence of direct observation of nature in the great physical encyclopaedias of the thirteenth century, such as those of the Augustinian Alexander of Neckam (1157-1217), the Dominican Vincent de Beauvais (1190-1264), or the Franciscan Bartholomew of England (c. 1260)." Obsessed with the idea of the world as mortal, destructible, lowly, "the motive for detailed research, in our modern sense of the word, was hardly present." The dominant churchmen opposed Averroes and his heretical followers, who thought otherwise. "The Middle Ages begin, for science, at that period when the ancients ceased to make knowledge. . . . Mediaevalization, in our view, was a slow process under the action of which the human mind, failing to increase the stock of phenomenal knowledge, sank slowly into an increasing ineptitude."

This era coincides with the period of the high supremacy of the Christian God and his order. It was precisely the kind of "order" which made the scientific method a purposeless instrument—almost a blasphemy, since God's Order could be known from His Word. Originality of observation departed from the human mind, so that in the case of even the most learned medieval writers, such as Albertus Magnus, "it is possible, with sufficient application, to trace all the sources of his information."[17] It was the Arab influence, especially in the heretical, pantheistic Averroes, which imparted a new direction to European thought; "the important event in the history of science in the Middle Ages is the arrival of the Arabian learning." The later scientific revolutionists such as Kepler, Boyle, and Newton were Christians, but they all reconstructed God in their own image; they turned him into a Mechanician, Mathematician, or Watchmaker, and gave him a seventeenth-century impersonal rationality which the Christian feudal, personal

God never had. They carried through their labors despite, not because of, any medieval residues that may have persisted in their unconscious. The absence of a personal God in Chinese thought can therefore not be taken as an explanation for the absence of a scientific movement.

Similarly, the several legalistic, political, and linguistic hypotheses Needham also proposes do not withstand comparative analysis. The Chinese distaste for a systematic code of law can scarcely explain their failure to formulate a conception of a law of nature, because the English common law had an aversion to systems and codes which was just as great, yet Englishmen were in the forefront of scientific advance. The genius of the English common law has been precisely in its empirical groping from case to case, from precedent to precedent, without formulating in a comprehensive way a logical system of general principles. Bacon and Hobbes, students and theorists of the common law, were also molders of the conception of a "law of nature." The rise of absolute monarchies can likewise scarcely explain the genesis of the concept of a law of nature. Galileo's Venice, Huygens' Amsterdam, the Bernoullis' Basel were hardly instances of absolute monarchies, yet the Dutch and Italian Republicans were leaders in discovering the mathematical uniformities of nature. The use of the expression "law of nature," indeed, did not become widespread under the absolutist Tudors or Charles I; rather, it came to the fore under the Restoration monarch, Charles II, who was very much shorn of absolutist prerogatives and pretensions. It then appeared in the writings of Boyle, Hooke, Wallis, and Newton.[18] China, with its political absolutism on the other hand, never developed the theoretical notion of a mathematical law of nature.

Nor did a lack of the expression "law of nature" impede the investigations of such ancient scientists as Archimedes and the men of the Alexandrian school; instead, Galileo and Gilbert availed themselves of such terms as "principle" and "rule." Copernicus used no such terminology, while Kepler used the term "ratio" more frequently than "law."[19] The influence of Descartes and Newton spread the use of the expression "law of nature," but such thinkers as Spinoza and Boyle, while using it themselves, warned against allowing its teleological, purposive metaphor to be applied to physical objects. Clearly, the development of scientific culture had given rise to a need for an appropriate term to characterize a mathematical uniformity. The term "law" had a curious attraction for the philosophic revolutionary individualist Descartes, and for the men of liberal Restoration England. Robert Hooke, Curator of the Royal Society, was in 1678 the first one to use the expression "Law of Nature" to refer to a law he had himself discovered. Each great scientist of the seventeenth century could now become a discoverer of laws of nature which would forever be associated with his name. Antiquity in its science had an anonymous cast of mind. In the seventeenth century, however, science became markedly eponymous. The classical labor theory of value, which was outlined by John Locke in this early era of competitive capitalist civilization, was fully applied in scientific work; the scientist had a sense of ownership in the law he had discovered. It was not God the Lawgiver who came to fill the scientist's consciousness so much as Man the Law Discoverer, who had perceived an order where formerly disorder seemed to reign. The scientist's personality received an enlargement in the cosmos itself. The English society which began to speak of "laws of nature" was not one in which the theological impulse had grown stronger; rather, it was a time in which, according to Newton's correspondent Richard Bentley, atheism was rife in "taverns and coffee-houses, nay Westminster-hall and the very Churches." And when Newton was asked to confute the hypothesis of a non-supernatural mechanical cosmology, he replied that he had considered the matter "very little." Hedonist individualism, rather than a theological mainspring, was behind the new scientific spirit.

In itself, the absence of Chinese words for "law of nature" would have been no real obstacle to the development of a scientific movement. The Taoist pantheist associations with the expression *tzu-jan fa* could have been more of an asset to untrammeled scientific study than a hindrance. Cultural needs can help attach new senses to old words in order to achieve their expression. When a word to signify "idea" was needed by Confucian logicians, the word *hsiang*, which originally meant elephant, was co-opted to fulfill the new need. Since few people had seen an elephant, and therefore could only imagine one, *hsiang* came to designate whatever men conceived in the imagination.[20] That there were organismic overtones to the Chinese conception of a law of nature need not have inhibited a scientific development; Leibniz's notion of "mechanical laws of nature" as the "subordinate regulations" in the organic economy of the universe did not hinder the contributions of himself and such followers of his as Maupertuis to mechanics.[21] Similarly, the mechanistic outlook of the Legalists could, in principle, have been just as congenial to the advancement of science as the mechanical emphasis in the seventeenth century of such great scientists as Descartes, Boyle, and Borelli. If the Taoists were disqualified in science (according to Needham) by premature Einsteinian-Whiteheadian notions, then the Legalists should have been aided by their mechanical ones. Actually, neither philosophical school gave rise to a genuine scientific movement.

There is one linguistic fact, however, which goes to the heart of the problem as to why China and Japan developed no scientific movement, for it reaches into the whole underlying emotional foundation of Chinese and Japanese societies. " 'Love' plays no part in any Eastern philosophy (except perhaps in Islam and India in modern times); whenever this word is found in a Western translation of an ancient Eastern philosophical text, one may be sure that it is a case of Christian distortion." [22] There was an absence of intimacy, a reign of formalism, in the most personal relations of the Chinese family, and of men and women. As Marcel Granet has said, "The evolution of morals in China went on by way of progressive drying up, and . . . spontaneity saw its part reduced to nothing." Love was indeed the primary virtue in the philosophy of Chu Hsi (1131-1200 A.D.), but "*jen*," the word he used, signified benevolence, charity, agape, rather than Eros. It is in this repression of the emotional energies, this thwarting of the natural direction of sexuality, that the primary cause for the failure of Asian civilization to produce a sustained scientific movement will be found.

❧ The Masochist Repression of Science in China

THE SCIENTIFIC STANDPOINT IS BASED on a way of perceiving the world. The scientist from the seventeenth to the twentieth century could say with Bacon that knowledge brought power, and with the pragmatic Dewey that all perception is a stimulus to action. To "know" reality was equivalent to be able to change it. Perception, in the scientific mode, was the means for the mastery over nature, for the bringing of it under human control. Perception in the scientific mode was "realistic perception"; it conformed to the lines of fact, to the "reality principle." It was guided by an attitude which resolutely refused to misperceive the facts so as to make them more pleasing to human wishes, but which at the same time sought out every opportunity for intervening in the processes of nature so as to make them contribute more fully to human satisfaction. There are two other modes, however, in which nature can be perceived—the masochist and sadist modes of perception—and both of them are inimical to the development of science.

The masochist mode of perception has predominated in China and Japan, indeed throughout Asia. The sadist mode is characteristic of German metaphysics, and is exemplified by thinkers in the tradition of Fichte and Hegel. In the masochist mode, the subject-perceiver tries to identify himself through emotions of passivity and self-surrender with the object-perceived; every perception of nature, or a natural object, becomes an occasion for partial self-annihilation. In the sadistic mode, the subject-perceiver incorporates the object-perceived into his own ego, and regards the object as an "objectification" of the ego; the object's reality is derivative from the subject, and is indeed created or "posited" to satisfy the subject's needs. Every perception of nature, for the sadistic mode, becomes an occasion for ego-aggrandizement; the external object has no autonomous reality, but is completely subservient to the self.[23]

The pragmatic theory of knowledge erred when it said that all perception is a stimulus to action. This tends to be so under certain social and psychological conditions, but the generalization scarcely holds for all societies or historical eras. The happy confluence of circumstances since the scientific revolution has made realistic perception more characteristic of European and American civilization, but advocates of science from Bacon to Comte and Dewey, and the *philosophes* of the Encyclopédie, worked hard to rid the human psyche of the long-enduring tradition of the masochist mode of perception. The Enlightenment signified a psychological transformation which included the mode of perceiving the world.[24] Perception under favorable conditons can be a stimulus to action, but through much of history it has been, rather, a stimulus to inhibition. Throughout Asia, for many centuries, a felt desire tended to be accompanied by a partially repressive response. For Asians in their conditions of life learned early that a desire would almost inevitably be followed by its frustration. The longing for food, comfort, and sexual joy would only make more acute the sufferings of famine, lack of food, shelter, and deprivation of sexual choice. When desire is the signal for impending frustration rather than satisfaction, a deep pessimism is born. And the masochist mode of perception was linked to this pessimist standpoint. The Chinese mode of identifying man with nature was not the sort which could activate science.[25] The Confucian standpoint was "masculine and managing," to use Needham's description, insofar as social and political administration were concerned, but when it came to attitudes toward nature, the Taoist seeking after a "feminine and receptive knowledge" was typical of the Chinese. Man internalized within himself Nature's edicts, and made himself its passive instrument; thus he could partially conquer pain. He did not regard deprivation as a challenge to reconstruct the environment.

F. S. C. Northrop has said that the Asian formulates his concepts by "immediate apprehension," whereas the Westerner does so by "postulation"; the former he describes as characterized by the givenness of an "undifferentiated immediacy," by an "undifferentiated aesthetic continuum." This is a vague statement of the underlying distinction between the realistic and masochistic modes of perception. The masochist, merging his identity with the perceived objects, losing his sense of individuality, submerging his own personal needs, lends to his perceived field the quality of an "undifferentiated aesthetic continuum." For it is the awareness and expression of human need and preference which select objects in the perceptual field, emphasizing some, rejecting others, differentiating the important from the trivial. The person who wishes to repress his awareness of the future, because it portends only more suffering and insoluble problems, seeks an escape into an encompassing, undifferentiated present. Thus, in the masochist mode of perception, there is the effort to see things in an "undifferentiated immediacy."

The Taoist philosophy has often been described as naturalistic;

its naturalism, however, was thoroughly masochist. Its imagery was replete with symbols of feminine passivity and acquiescence; both its metaphysics and its ethical imperatives were masochist. The ultimate reality was void, and man's ethic was to seek emptiness; reality was nothingness, and the basic ethical principle was to nullify oneself. Why one should have to cultivate self-nullification when one was already null to begin with was never explained in this philosophy. The utility of things, says the *Tao Te Ching*, the classical source of Taoism, derives from the nothingness they contain; a wheel depends "on the space where there is nothing"; vessels, doors, and windows enclose nothingness. The Mysterious Female, the ultimate reality, with its fecund void, is symbolized by the Spirit of the Valley with its vaginal formation:

> The Valley Spirit never dies.
> It is named the Mysterious Female.
> And the Doorway of the Mysterious Female
> Is the base from which Heaven and Earth sprang.
> It is there within us all the while;
> Draw upon it as you will, it never runs dry.[26]

The Female Principle, according to Taoism, "conquers by being soft and weak, humble and low . . . so the Female conquers the Male by remaining passive in a lowly position." This is masochism exalted to the status of a metaphysics. This passive submission can promote a self-donation, a self-absorption into Nature, a merging of oneself, with identity extinguished, into the Maternal Source, an abrogation of all distinctions, differences, separations, and individualities. But this standpoint is not that of the scientist, who must handle natural objects, alter them, rearrange them, reconstruct them, compare them, contrast them, measure differences, evaluate different effects.

The masochist mode of perception pervaded the conception of the world as formed in the interaction of Yang and Yin, a concept which, says Fung Yu-Lan, "has remained dominant in Chinese cosmological speculation down to recent times." This cosmology arose in the earliest beginnings of Chinese thought, and its perdurance indicates how deep-seated were its sources in the conditions of Chinese life. Founded on the projection of the sexual relation upon all existence, its character is overlaid with masochist overtones. Yang is the male principle—noble, round, fecundating, the anterior; Yin is the female—square, passive, breeding. The heaven is male; it is hard and strong. The earth is female, soft and yielding. "One Yin and Yang, that is the fundamental principle. The passionate union of Yin and Yang and the copulation of husband and wife is the eternal rule of the universe." Thus, the Chinese cosmology cast the earth and its beings collectively in a female role of submissiveness. The earth, which to realistic perception is harder than the air of the skies, was transformed in the masochist mode to the feminine and yielding.[27]

All the classical schools of Chinese philosophy were affected by self-defeat and renunciation; all looked upon nature through the masochist mode of resignation. There were variations, to be sure, in the degree of this acknowledgment of self-defeat, but the general characterization holds, just as does the opposite for European-American thought from the seventeenth century on. The Confucian scholar-bureaucrats were not the bearers of an optimist, hedonist-libertarian ethic. Competing for place, they learned to live in an "atmosphere of rivalry and suspicion, of dramatic rise and fall of fortunes"; a "feeling of profound doubt and despair" entered and persisted in their writings.[28] Their poets mocked at the meaninglessness of their administrative careers. Su Tung-p'o reflected on the birth of his son:

> Families, when a child is born
> Want it to be intelligent.
> I, through intelligence,
> Having wrecked my whole life,
> Only hope the baby will prove
> Ignorant and stupid.
> That he will crown a tranquil life
> By becoming a Cabinet Minister.

The masochist mode of perception has its corresponding philosophy of history, which expresses the mode in which past, present, and future are to be perceived. "The everlasting law of the sequence of prosperity and decay," in Ssu-ma Ch'ien's words, was the immutable cycle of history. The sadistic mode of perception tends to see history as the field in which a particular nation or group realizes its supremacy; the Nazi philosophy, which raised to an extreme all the latent sadism in the German tradition, made history the vehicle for the expression of a racial soul, which could destroy other peoples to fulfill its aggressive compulsions, and which could bend all reality to its purpose. The realistic mode of perception conceives of universal progress as a genuine human possibility; it neither exalts nor denigrates any people; in its maturity, it sees progress as a humanly attainable achievement, not as a necessary law; it preaches neither emasculated submission nor sadistic dominance.

A cyclical philosophy of history, on the other hand, is always a projection of pessimism; it is the impotence of man perceived as the essence of history. Indeed, in the tragic life of the greatest Chinese historian, it projected a physical emasculation by an Imperial society, in which, as Ssu-ma Ch'ien described himself in self-crushing words, "I was nothing but a mere ant."[29]

The disbelief in progress, the perception of history as cycles of events that always returned to their starting point, was characteristic of Chinese thought. This view of history as an eternal oscillation inhibits the optimistic faith in the human intellect required to sustain an embryonic scientific movement. Ecclesiastes, reflecting that there is nothing new under the sun, but cynically observing that of the making of books there was no end, never inspired a scientific generation. Confucius, saying that the character of civilization, "even a hundred generations hence, can be known"; Mencius's summation of all human history as "consisting of alternating order and disorder"; Hsün Tzu's melancholy reflection that "past and present are the same," ruled by the "self-same principle" —all contribute to deflecting human energies from any mission seeking to increase the knowledge and mastery of the environment.[30] Chinese thinkers very often combined their cyclical philosophy of history with a belief in the Golden Age of the past, the era of the all-wise sage-rulers. The two doctrines were brought into a superficial consistency by the additional notion that society was now in the declining phase of a cycle. Francis Bacon found it necessary in his pleadings for science to lay hands on the myth of the Golden Age, on the reverence for antiquity. The Chinese philosophers, on the other hand, prevented the growth of scientific inquiry by exalting the cultural superego in their historical myth, and subduing the contemporary thinker's self-evaluation.

The purpose of the Chinese philosophers of history was to instill an acknowledgment of defeat into their contemporaries.

The pessimistic refusal to embark on scientific investigation was most clearly expressed in the philosophy of Hsün Tzu (c. 298-238 B.C.), who has been called both the "moulder of ancient Confucianism" and the "Aristotle of China." Man, said Hsün Tzu, should find his end in the Tao of the Sage-Kings; in the Tao there was not that unending incompleteness which frustrated scientific knowledge. Rather than delight in the search for and growth of knowledge, Hsün Tzu felt helpless before its beginnings. The would-be scientist would be wise to desist from a search that could never be consummated: "If he seeks to know the laws of the material world . . . there is nothing to hinder him; but in a lifetime he cannot go all over them. In studying these laws, although he lived a myriad years, it would not be enough for him to embrace the changes of all things—he would be the same as a stupid man. Though he studied until he was old and his children grown, he would be the same as a stupid man." Scientific knowledge was fruitless. Whatever the Tao was, it was incommensurable with scientific knowledge. Such was the philosophy of Hsün Tzu, who looked at human nature, and repeated, "Man by birth certainly is a small-minded man."[31]

It was the absence of a hedonistic-utilitarian standpoint which nullified scientific enterprise in China. Such was the conclusion of Fung Yu-Lan in a classical article he published in 1922, "Why China Has No Science—An Interpretation of the History and Consequences of Chinese Philosophy." Both Taoism and Confucianism, he observed, regarded physical goods as either inessential or inimical to man's welfare. The Taoist questioned the worthwhileness of scientific knowledge; to pursue the unlimited within a limited life seemed to him a perilous thing. The Confucian, too, felt that wisdom lay in diminishing human desires in order to recover the heavenly reason. Ascetic components were likewise dominant in the teaching of Mo Ti, the third of the classical Chinese thinkers. For though he was both an empiricist and a critic of the excessive Confucian rites of mourning, Mo Ti prescribed a stringency of poor food and coarse clothing, condemned music, and inculcated, as Hsün Tzu said, "anxiety undiluted with amusement."[32] The teaching of Mo Ti was part of that ascetic ethic which, writes Yi-Pao Mei, "is really the heart of the reason why science has not been developed in China." The Chinese mode of asceticism was as infertile for scientific seed as the European.

Mercantile, urban hedonism, moreover, failed to develop in China as it did in Western Europe. All the Chinese thinkers agreed in extolling the values of agricultural life. The bias of Chinese thought was definitely against the merchant, as corrupt, treacherous, and disobedient.[33] The brilliant achievements of Chinese inventors remained a series of isolated events; a Chinese scientific movement failed to develop until the nineteenth and twentieth centuries, when there began a revolt among the Chinese intellectuals against their philosophical form of masochist asceticism. Then came the beginnings of the Chinese Renaissance, which as Bertrand Russell wrote, reminded him constantly "of the renaissance spirit in fifteenth-century Italy." [34]

The Scientific Renaissance in China

THE CHINESE, LIKE THE JAPANESE, began to think of Western science seriously when they suffered the stimulus of military defeat. The rout of the Chinese forces in the Opium War of 1839 brought home the realization of the superiority of the guns and warships of the enemy. The realities were all too clear to be concealed with words. The structure of Chinese bureaucratic ideology was impaired by doubt and questioning as to its adequacy. The government began to promote the publication of scientific texts. Toward the end of the century, Liang Ch'i-ch'ao served China as its Francis Bacon; his message of the promise of science made thousands of students "burn with a sense of a new gospel."[35] The makers of rebellions in China have tended to be those scholars who, perhaps because of a strong emotional resistance, were unable to pass the examinations in the classics for the civil service. Liang, like the fomenters of the Taiping Rebellion, was one such unsuccessful scholar. Fortunately, he became the secretary of Dr. Timothy Richard, an English missionary who translated a book widely read in Chinese which vividly extolled the achievements of science. Liang imbibed the new scientific standpoint. He called

Bacon and Descartes the two heroes of modern times and ridiculed the traditionalists—"those who trumpet the words of a 'master' are like puppets on the stage."

The scientific renaissance in modern China became a psychological reality under the provocative auspices of a hedonist-libertarian ethic. Books such as John Stuart Mill's *On Liberty* and T. H. Huxley's *Evolution and Ethics,* translated at the end of the nineteenth century, and widely read, made a deep impression on Chinese intellectuals; Huxley's book, writes Hu Shih, "was a welcome stimulus to a nation suffering from age-long inertia and stagnation." Common-sense realism and utilitarianism came to be the dominant philosophy of the Chinese intellectuals. Numerous journals were founded, in the vernacular, which propagated the new philosophy; Hu and his schoolmates published one called *The Struggle,* a fitting title for the revolt against traditional attitudes of masochist submissiveness. Many people took new names, borrowed from the Darwinian theory of the struggle for existence, which indicated their casting off of masochist asceticism. Hu Shih took for himself the literary name Shih, which signified "fitness," derived from the phrase "survival of the fittest"; two of his schoolmates bore the names Natural Selection Yang and Struggle for Existence Sun. Many a Chinese student in America had probably the same experience Hu Shih recorded in his diary in 1914: " . . . the greatest thing I have learned since leaving China is this optimistic philosophy of life." The psychological revolution meanwhile was also undermining the emotional rigidities of the traditional family system. There was a sexual renaissance as "young China took to sex romance with an appetite as ardent as it was inexperienced." The literary renaissance, with its use of the vernacular to replace the classical idiom of the scholars, together with the efforts of such men as Y. R. Chao to alphabetize the Chinese language, was also part of this recovery of the fresh springs of emotion, a phenomenon of the hedonist-libertarian revolution.

There are those, like Bertrand Russell, who have loved China for its contemplative attitude and its freedom from any notion such as progress. But the same writer wished to see the scientific standpoint combined with the classical Chinese philosophy of life. "Although Chinese civilization has hitherto been deficient in science, it never contained anything hostile to science," says Russell. Thus the significant failure of science to take root in China is left by Russell as an inexplicable historical datum. However, precisely those components of passivity in contemplation, resignation of spirit, and callousness toward suffering, which Russell described as traits of the Chinese character, arose from an emotional foundation alien to the scientific spirit. The renaissance of Young China, like all renaissances, was rooted in the very ethic of progress and emotional self-assertion which Russell decried. Russell's admiration of the traditional Chinese passive ethic was far from the spirit of the young Chinese intellectuals of the May Fourth period, who sought a scientific and political awakening.

The rise of a scientific movement in China was thus contemporaneous with a basic psychological revolution, which manifested itself in changes in the rigid family structure, the demand for romantic marriages, political and civil rights, and a language revolution in favor of the vernacular.

The Masochist Mode of Perception in Japanese Civilization

THE MASOCHIST MODE OF PERCEPTION similarly pervaded Japanese life, and those who sought to introduce the scientific standpoint into Japan in the nineteenth century knew that it was their chief obstacle. "The attitudes of resignation and submission in every matter of life were imposed upon people under the feudal regime, since, it was told, everything was predetermined as the consequence to the causes in one's previous life." A mode of perception arose in which "the Japanese people seldom looked squarely at the objective reality as sharply distinguished from knowing subjects." [36] Their mode of "intuitive perception," as Hajime Nakamura writes, provided no basis for the rise of natural science. The phrase "intuitive perception" is itself a vague one, but as employed to characterize Asian experience, it signifies a mode of perception in which every tendency in the perceptual experience toward its functioning as a stimulus to active response, to active intervention or reconstruction of objects, has been repressed. "Intuitive perception" is indeed perception in the mashochist mode, "castrated" experience. The perceiver receives the perceived objects but does not react to them; instead of responding actively to assert his own needs among them, he identifies himself with their will. With his own self-denial of individuality, the perceived world relapses into an undifferentiated continuum of aesthetic immediacy.

Types of religious learning were pursued in the Buddhist temples of Japan, but the sciences were no part of them. "A crude theology, a purposeless logic, a feeble literature—these had some standing; but mathematics save for calendar purposes was ever an outcast in the temple. . . . In the period of the Ashikaga shoguns it is asserted that there hardly could be found in all Japan a man who was versed in the art of division."

The masochist mode of perception reaches deep into Japanese everyday life. Even today, for example, the *jidai-geki*—the contemporary Japanese "chase" film—has, despite its action, "something not found in the American film, namely a philosophy that life is a very fleeting thing and that it is idle to fret over it—a philosophy which is related to Buddhism. . . . The philosophy that life is a void is not, however, the exclusive philosophy of gangsters and lordless samurai. This philosophy is ingrained in Japanese society from top to bottom; it is, in fact, the philosophy of the people at large. Thus, so far as concerns philosophy, there is no substantial difference between the people who throng to see *jidai-geki* pictures and the intellectual devotees of Professor Nishida's philosophy." The tea ceremony was developed as a ritualistic form of the masochist mode of perception. Its foremost modern proponent wrote, "Teaism was Taoism in disguise." [37]

This sense of the void—of Being as non-Being, and of everybody as nothing—is linked in Asian thought with the emphasis on silence. It is a strange contrast between Asian and European-American thought that the former has been so much committed to an apotheosis of the values of silence, of the repression of speech, whereas the latter has sought rather to liberate speech and give it a sense of its own powers. Fung Yu-Lan completes his authoritative history of Chinese philosophy with the statement that the object of metaphysics is largely achieved "if one understands and realizes the meaning and significance of silence." Ch'anism, the Chinese form of Zen, which united Taoism with Buddhism, was above all a philosophy of silence. Its practitioners sought to extirpate purposeful response in human experience, and to reinforce the masochist mode of perception. They sought what the Taoists called *wu-wei* (non-action) and *wu-hsin* (no-mind).[38] Even one's most everyday actions—wearing clothes, eating meals—were supposed to be done with a completely non-purposeful mind, without any attachment. Such destruction of attachments, such a cultivation of detachment, was, in psychological terms, a withdrawal of emotion, of libidinal involvement with things.

Silence is a pervasive theme of Asian civilization; it is the verbal form of the masochist mode of perception, the word become non-word. It is the suicide of speech. The statement that "reality is inexpressible" projects the standpoint of the masochist mode of perception. For precisely the masochist who wishes to merge his self into an undifferentiated continuum of enveloping being wishes that it be impossible to articulate his experience, for such articulation, by lighting the distinctions between external things and the self, undoes the masochist submergence of the self. Japanese communication is a "closed communication," writes Kazuko Tsurumi; it tends to be more internalized as "self-conversation," to be intrapersonal rather than interpersonal. It is speech that has, in the masochist mode, lost confidence in itself because its words when spoken have been despised by those to whom they were addressed. It is the form of speech when speaking has been traumatized.[39]

At the Toshogu Shrine in Nikko, there is the famous painted design of the three monkeys, one holding its ears so as not to hear, another clasping its mouth so as not to speak, and the other holding its eyes so as not to see; the "see-no-evil monkey," the "say-no-evil monkey," and the "hear-no-evil monkey." Onlookers admire this expression of the Tokugawa philosophy. But how few people stop to reflect upon this assault against human speech. For instead of the hallowed admonition to silence, one might make the realistic translation: "Be silent" is more crudely "Shut up!" And the philosophy of silence is the ideology of "shut-uppism." It grew strong in feudal Japan, where the preachments of silence were designed to condition people to bear their sufferings mutely. The ideology of silence aimed at a socially induced mutism so that people would never voice their discontents but repress them. Thus there arose in Japan, as elsewhere in Asia, the voiceless man, so that books are written of the voiceless Far East. Thus, too, in demonstrations today in Japan, young radicals organize protest groups—"the voice for the voiceless"—and workingmen, farmers, and housewives gather in "life composition" circles to learn to speak about their inner experiences, a philosophy of free voice to undo feudal silence. This inhibition of speech reaction is part of the masochist mode of perception which is inimical to the scientific spirit.

The philosophy of silence is linked in Asian thought to the adoration of nothingness; the masochist self-extinction thus reaches its metaphysical apotheosis by making its nothingness into the highest reality. The destruction of the opposition between subject and object was not to be followed by a higher synthesis of being; the latter was the direction of the Fichtean-Hegelian dialectic. The masochist dialectic was, rather, suicidal; the abrogation of tension between subject and object brought nothingness. Thus Kitaro Nishida, whom many Japanese describe as their most representative philosopher, exalted "nothingness" as the transcendent unity of opposites; all being, he said, is a self-unfolding of nothingness, and its final phase is nothingness. Reality, which Nishida defined as the unification of subject and object, was identified with nothingness. Such metaphysics expressed the spirit of what has been called the Japanese "cult of tranquility"; in its aim to merge in a Great Oneness by diminishing the instinct of self-preservation, it endeavored to permeate life with a form of consciousness which can be called "death-consciousness." [40] Nature looms large in the Japanese consciousness, but it is nature as apprehended under the masochist mode of perception. In Japanese films today, as sociological critics have observed, nature is seen as the pervasive background of sorrow and sadness; nature in American motion pictures has, by contrast, the action-inspiring largeness that calls forth men's efforts—it is always potential with life. But in Japanese films the flowers, the birds, the moon all portend the transience of man, his essential nothingness. Thus the mood of feudal artists, who escaped the oppression of lords by attending to the moon and to the beauty of flowers, persists in the Japanese consciousness.

Nature, as Lovejoy and Boas have shown, is multifarious in its meanings; for the perceptions of men vary as do their political and moral standpoints.[41] Nature as perceived by the scientific revolutionists Kepler, Galileo, Newton, was a glorious world open to the understanding of man. Nature as perceived by the romantic poets Shelley and Wordsworth, inspired by the hopes of the French Revolution, was a liberating, surging force to which repressive social institutions were alien. Nature as perceived, however, under the Asian masochist mode of perception is the eternal master to whom the slave finally makes an everlasting obeisance.

The first significant breach in the Japanese masochist mode of perception came during the eighteenth century, when a handful of nonconformist intellectuals in Japan studied the Dutch language at the center of the Dutch Company in Nagasaki. Their precursors in the previous century had studied the Western sciences at the risk of their lives. Kichizaemon Hayashi was executed in 1646, while Oshinobu Kobayashi was cast into prison for twenty-one years. The fate of two Japanese who braved the law against emigration, and enrolled at the University of Leyden in 1654, is wrapped in mystery.[42] But from 1716 to 1745, the Shogun Yoshimune, reading the signs of the times, especially wished to promote astronomical knowledge and calendology among his countrymen. The Dutch language also opened the doors to advances in medicine, surgery, anatomy, navigation, and artillery. Dutch learning spread through various Japanese towns; captains of Dutch ships became the teachers of Japanese students. Thus the first fragile linkages of Japanese thinkers to the international community of scientific intellectuals were established. Medical science was, as almost always, because it dealt with the ultimate common denominators of life, health, and illness, the most effective in securing the reception of science: "The first introduction of Western knowledge," wrote Dairoku Kikuchi, "was almost entirely due to doctors of medicine." [43] The new practice of dissection was part of an intellectual unrest which led to the questioning of the old Chinese anatomical teaching. Ryotaku Mayeno (1723-1803), a physician at Yedo, found to his surprise that actual dissections confirmed his Dutch book of anatomy. He and a circle of seven thereupon toiled for three years to translate the first European book ever to be rendered into Japanese—the *Tabula Anatomica*, by Johann Adams Kulmus.

The masochist mode of perception, however, diffused as it was through Japanese society, from the military classes to the intellectuals, remained the formidable psychological barrier to science. The intellectuals of the late nineteenth century have been described as disinherited samurai. As Dr. Inazo Nitobe wrote, "Scratch a Japanese of the most advanced ideas, and he will show a samurai." [44]

The first intellectuals who spread the notion of the advancement of science—groups such as the Murokusha, men such as Arinori Mori, Sensai Nagayo, and Yukichi Fukuzawa—were but a generation removed from the sword-bearing samurai. Arinori Mori, on his return in 1873 from his diplomatic post in the United States, told of the learned societies in America where they "mutually study the arts and sciences," and expressed the desire to organize similar societies in Japan, where the "scholars are isolated and without mutual communication." Sensai Nagayo was inspired by the elements of the samurai's self-destructive ethic which he found in the scientist's readiness to sacrifice himself in the quest for scientific truth. When, as a student he heard how Pettenhofer had tested his hypothesis by drinking a solution containing cholera bacteria, he was much moved; he told his children that one must defend a scientific truth even at the risk of one's life. Yukichi Fukuzawa, the Bacon of the Japanese scientific movement, encountered all the resistance of family and tradition against the new Western learning. His father, a samurai of the lower ranks, objected vehemently to his son's learning arithmetic: "It is abominable," he exclaimed, "that innocent children should be taught to use numbers—the instrument of merchants. There is no telling what the teacher may do next." [45]

Thus, the new intellectuals emerged, warriors against the old samurai narrowness and intolerance, but themselves "rebellious, burning with hatred, possessed of a tragic sacrificial spirit." They could not look to the populace at large for support, for the masses had no sympathy for the alien scientific spirit. The people's uprisings often took on an intellectually reactionary character. The demands in a rice riot of 1873, for instance, called not only for the lowering of rice prices but also for the abolition of primary schools and the elimination of the Western, solar calendar.[46] The new, aspiring young intellectuals had, however, grasped a vision of a new freedom, in which science was to be an instrument to a more expressive life. Fukuzawa's father thought that his son's only avenue to social advancement lay through the priesthood, but the son would have none of it. He was drawn instead to the "strange letters written sideways," which nobody in his town understood. Fortunately for Fukuzawa, the coming of the American fleet under Commodore Perry, in 1854, created a crisis of national defense which opened partially the gateway to science—"the problem of national defense and the new art of warfare—the modern gunnery —had become the foremost interest of all the samurai." So he was permitted to go to Nagasaki to study the Dutch language, which would admit him to the new sciences. Underlying the desire for science, however, was the revolution in emotion which was beginning to take place in Japan, a psychological revolution whose basic direction was clear though it was overlaid with samurai overtones. Fukuzawa stated it plainly:

> The true reason why I went there was nothing more than to get away from Nikatsu. And so I would have been glad to study a foreign language or the military art or anything else if it only gave me the chance to go away. . . . I still remember how I swore to myself that like a bullet shot out of the gun's muzzle I would never come back. This was a happy day for me. I turned at the end of the town's street, spat on the ground, and walked quickly away.[47]

This was the act of revolt against the philosophy of quietism and self-abnegation which dominated the Japanese mentality. For a scientific movement to begin, a psychological revolution against this mentality was required. To the extent that this psychological revolution miscarried or was thwarted, to that extent the scientific standpoint remained fragile in Japanese life. For the self-destructive, masochist component was, despite the warrior's preeminence in Japanese society, deeply embedded in the Japanese character. Indeed, there was a curious combination of the militarist and the masochist, the warrior and the monk, in the Japanese psyche. The samurai's armor metamorphosed into the monk's garb, for each cloaked an inner sickness of self-destruction. "Zen Buddhism," writes Sir George Sansom, which was "taken up with enthusiasm by the military class in the Kamakura period, profited by their complete dominance in the next, and flourished under the patronage of the Shoguns and the great barons to such an extent that it might well be described as the official if not the state religion." [48] Young Japanese soldiers and sailors who were chosen in the Second World War to be sacrificed as human torpedoes comforted themselves with repeating the parables and sayings which reminded them that illumination comes when the strivings of life are gone. The warrior's ethic was imbued with the self-aggression characteristic of Buddhism. The self-aggression, and self-frustration characteristic of the monk and warrior gave rise also to a bitter aggression against the world as a whole. Because all external frustrations were internalized as one's own choice, there surged within the self-aggressor a tremendous repressed aggression against the external world. Such was the basis for the assault against the categories of everyday life, logic, and science.

Thus it was, therefore, that the first advocates in Japan of the scientific method, men such as Yukichi Fukuzawa, set themselves to criticize the ethic of self-aggression common to militarist and monk. Fukuzawa welcomed a law which aimed to disarm the samurai, and when the Shogunate fell, he renounced his rank and gave up wearing its two swords. When his friend Arinori Mori was married, the bride and bridegroom walked arm in arm—a demonstration of their belief in women's equality. Fukuzawa urged his belief that behind the West's supremacy in science was its "spirit of independence." Japanese must learn, he said to have the courage to doubt and to disenthrall themselves from the past: "For every one thing . . . the ancients knew, modern men know a hundred. . . . Progress in the future is beyond all imagining." Fukuzawa wrote many articles against the Japanese custom of concubinage.[43] He had perceived, indeed, that the scientific standpoint is based on a social psychological substratum. Aggression against self in Japanese society was periodically displaced by aggression against others in sexual relations; it expressed itself in the form of concubinage, in which the woman was humiliated and debased. The Japanese man acquired an incapacity for any relationship of love. The first scientific intellectuals in Japan divined that they must achieve a psychological revolution in order to liberate energies from self-aggression and repression into a living involvement in the world's existence and possibilities.

Their way, however, was to be a hard and largely unsuccessful one. The Japanese government, dominated by the traditional ethic, wished to select from Western civilization its science and technique, without borrowing those very psychological characteristics which were the source of the scientific spirit. The leaders of the Meiji Restoration consulted with Herbert Spencer, whose political conservatism they admired, but finally they had to reject his standpoint, for as one Japanese scholar put it, Spencer had "made an obvious mistake in considering the security and happiness of individuals as the ultimate ends."[50] The Japanese government by 1900 encouraged instead the adoption of German idealist metaphysics, in which the sado-masochist emotions might find a more congenial idiom. The scientific intellectuals in Japan had to wait for the Imperial defeat in 1945 and the total discrediting of the traditional ethics for their first historical opportunity to try to effect a nation-wide psychological revolution.

NOTES

1. Joseph Needham, *Science and Civilization in China* (Cambridge, 1956), Vol. II, p. 12. "The Past in China's Present," *Centennial Review*, IV (1960), 291.

2. Joseph Needham, *Science and Civilization in China*, Vol. II, pp. 33-4, 130.

3. Joseph Needham, "On Science and Social Change," *Science and Society*, X (1946), 250, 24. Joseph Needham, *Science and Civilization in China*, Vol. II, pp. 130, 518, 579, 573. Joseph Needham, "The Past in China's Present," p. 303.

4. Joseph Needham, *Science and Civilization in China*, Vol. II, pp. 564, 580. Also, Victor Purcell, *Problems of Chinese Education* (London, 1936), p. 126. L. G. Morgan, *The Teaching of Science to the Chinese* (Hong Kong, 1933), pp. 123-6.

5. Joseph Needham, *Science and Civilization in China*, Vol. II, pp. 542-3, 568, 210.

6. *Ibid.*, p. 582.

7. Confucius, *The Analects*, trans. William Edward Soothill (London, 1951), Bk. XI, Ch. XI, pp. 105-6. Joseph Needham, *Science and Civilization in China*, Vol. II, p. 12.

8. Y. K. Leong, and L. K. Tao, *Village and Town Life in China* (London, 1915), pp. 4-6.

9. Hsiao-tung Fei, *China's Gentry* (Chicago, 1953), pp. 69, 76, 79.

10. Cf. Lewis S. Feuer, *Spinoza and the Rise of Liberalism* (Boston, 1958), pp. 78, 166-7.

11. Karl A. Wittfogel, *Oriental Despotism* (New Haven, 1957), p. 8.

12. C. K. Yang, *The Chinese Family in the Communist Revolution* (Cambridge, 1959), p. 92. Cf. Lin Yueh-Hwa, *The Golden Wing: A Sociological Study of Chinese Familism* (London, 1947), pp. 73-4.

13. J. H. Hutton, *Caste in India* (Cambridge, 1946), p. 108. Cf. Prafulla Chandra Ray, *Autobiography of a Bengali Chemist* (Calcutta,

1958), pp. 416, 120, 121. The emergence of the scientific standpoint in India was preceded by a psychological revolution in which teachers seceded from their families and the caste system. *Ibid.*, pp. 32, 35.

14. C. K. Yang, *op. cit.*, pp. 92-3.

15. *Ibid.*, p. 172. Francis L. K. Hsu, *Under the Ancestor's Shadow: Chinese Culture and Personality* (New York, 1948), pp. 207, 236-7, 266. Theodore Hsi-en Chen, "Science, Scientists, and Politics," in *Sciences in Communist China*, ed. Sidney H. Gould (Washington, 1961), p. 95.

16. Alfred North Whitehead, *Science and the Modern World* (Penguin ed., Harmondsworth, 1938), pp. 23-4. Joseph Needham, *Science and Civilization in China*, Vol. I, p. 582.

17. Edgar Zilsel, "The Genesis of the Concept of Physical Law," *Philosophical Review*, LI (1942), 277. Charles Singer, *From Magic to Science* (New York, 1928), pp. xi, xiii, 61, 86, 89. Cf. Frederick Albert Lange, *History of Materialism*, trans. Ernest Chester Thomas (Boston, 1881), Vol. I, p. 219. Richard McKeon, "Averroes," *Encyclopaedia of the Social Sciences* (New York, 1935), Vol. II, p. 338.

18. "Law," *Oxford English Dictionary* (Oxford, 1933), Vol. VI, p. 115. Edgar Zilsel, *op. cit.*, pp. 271-3.

19. *Ibid.*, pp. 261-5. R. C. Jebb, *Bentley* (New York, 1882), pp. 21, 30.

20. Hu Shih, *The Development of the Logical Method in Ancient China* (Shanghai, 1922), p. 35.

21. Leibniz, *Discourse on Metaphysics*, trans. George R. Montgomery (Chicago, 1942), pp. 29-37.

22. P. Demiéville, "Fung Yu-lan, *A History of Chinese Philosophy*, Vol. II," *Pacific Affairs*, XXVIII (1955), 84-5. Marcel Granet, *Chinese Civilization*, trans. Kathleen E. Innes and Mabel R. Brailsford (New York, 1930), pp. 355-7, 416-17, 427-8. J. Percy Bruce, *Chu Hsi and his Masters* (London, 1923), pp. 263-7.

23. *Hegel's Philosophy of Right*, trans. T. M. Knox (Oxford, 1953), p. 236.

24. The League of Nations Educational Mission in 1931 said aptly to Chinese educators who were trying to introduce science and technology, "Modern science and technique did *not* give birth to present-day America and Europe; that, on the contrary, it is European and American mind which has engendered modern science and technique. . . . The era of development of the natural science and technique was preceded by another period . . . in which Europe awoke to its own possibilities. . . ." C. H. Becker, M. Falski, P. Langevin, and R. H. Tawney, *The Reorganisation of Education in China* (Paris, 1932), p. 27.

25. Hajime Nakamura, *The Ways of Thinking of Eastern Peoples* (Tokyo, 1960), p. 281. In India, health and vigor were not the aims of

medicine and alchemy; rather they were instruments for "pious exercise and austere discipline." Cf. *History of Chemistry in Ancient and Medieval India*, ed. P. Ray (Calcutta, 1956), pp. 113, 116.

26. Arthur Waley, *The Way and Its Powers: A Study of the Tao Te Ching* (London, 1942), pp. 149, 155. Liu Wu-Chi, *A Short History of Confucian Philosophy* (London, 1955), p. 42.

27. Fung Yu-Lan, *A Short History of Chinese Philosophy*, ed. Derk Bodde (New York, 1948), p. 138. Alfred Forke, *The World-Conception of the Chinese: Their Astronomical, Cosmological and Physico-Philosophical Speculations* (London, 1925), pp. 68, 55, 71-2, 194, 188, 167, 176, 47.

28. Burton Watson, *Ssu-Ma Ch'ien: Grand Historian of China* (New York, 1958), pp. 24, 44-5. *A Hundred and Seventy Chinese Poems*, trans. Arthur Waley (New York, 1929), pp. 151, 161-4, 201.

29. Burton Watson, *op. cit.*, pp. 63, 141-2. Herbert A. Giles, *A History of Chinese Literature* (New York, 1915), p. 105.

30. Derk Bodde, "Harmony and Conflict in Chinese Philosophy," in *Studies in Chinese Thought*, ed. Arthur F. Wright (Chicago, 1953), pp. 21, 28-9, 68.

31. *The Works of Hsüntze*, trans. Homer H. Dubs (London, 1938), pp. 8, 61, 276.

32. Fung Yu-Lan, "Why China Has No Science—An Interpretation of the History and Consequences of Chinese Philosophy," *International Journal of Ethics*, XXXII (1922), 261, 244. *The Ethical and Political Works of Motse*, trans. Yi-Pao Mei (London, 1929), p. 183, 187. Yi-Pao Mei, *Motse: The Neglected Rival of Confucius* (London, 1934), pp. 142, 181-4, 130-40, 173. Also, *Chinese Philosophy in Classical Times*, ed. and trans. E. R. Hughes (London, 1942), pp. 43, 53.

33. Fung Yu-Lan, *op. cit.*, pp. 18-19, 25-6. H. G. Creel, *Confucius: The Man and the Myth* (New York, 1949), pp. 177-8.

34. Bertrand Russell, *The Problem of China* (New York, 1922), p. 204. The Jesuit missionaries in the seventeenth century, like the Protestant ones in the nineteenth, failed to found a self-sustaining scientific movement. Cf. Cyrus H. Peake, "Some Aspects of the Introduction of Modern Science into China," *Isis*, XXII (1934), 174-176. *China in the Sixteenth Century: The Journals of Matthew Ricci, 1583-1610*, trans. Louis J. Gallagher (New York, 1953), p. 325. Pasquale M. D'Elia, S.J., *Galileo in China: Relations through the Roman College Between Galileo and the Jesuit Scientist-Missionaries (1610-1640)*, trans. Rufus Suter and Matthew Sciascia (Cambridge, 1960), pp. 5-6, 65, 33-4, 80. Kenneth Scott Latourette, *A History of Christian Missions in China* (New York, 1929), p. 236. Père Louis Van Hée, S.J., "The Ch'ou-Jen Chuan of

Yüan Yuan," *Isis*, VIII (1926), 106-7, 118. Paul A. Varg, *Missionaries, Chinese, and Diplomats: The American Protestant Missionary Movement in China, 1890-1952* (Princeton, 1958), pp. 87, 23-4, 17.

35. For the story of the coming of the scientific spirit to China, cf. E. R. Hughes, *The Invasion of China by the Western World* (London, 1937), pp. 212, 271. Joseph R. Levenson, *Liang Ch'i-Ch'ao and the Mind of Modern China* (Cambridge, 1953), p. 98. Hu Shih, in *Living Philosophies* (New York, 1931), pp. 248-251. Chow Tse-tung, *The May Fourth Movement: Intellectual Revolution in Modern China* (Cambridge, 1960), pp. 294, 312, 364. O. Brière, *Fifty Years of Chinese Philosophy*, trans. Laurence G. Thompson (London, 1956), pp. 19-20. John De Francis, *Nationalism and Language Reform in China* (Princeton, 1950), pp. 72 ff.

36. Hajime Nakamura, *op. cit.*, pp. 513, 546. David Eugene Smith and Yoshio Mikami, *A History of Japanese Mathematics* (Chicago, 1914), p. 15.

37. Taikei Imamura, "The Japanese Movie and Ways of Thinking," *The Science of Thought* (Tokyo, 1956), p. 7. Okahura Kakuzo, *The Book of Tea* (Edinburgh, 1919), p. 44.

38. Fung Yu-Lan, *op. cit.*, pp. 259, 341.

39. *Japanese Popular Culture*, ed. Hidetoshi Kato (Tokyo, 1959), pp. 32-3.

40. Kitaro Nishida, *Intelligibility and the Philosophy of Nothingness*, trans. Robert Schinzinger (Tokyo, 1958), pp. 30, 37, 51. Cf. Karlfried Graf von Dürckheim, *The Japanese Cult of Tranquillity*, trans. Eda O'Shiel (London, 1960), pp. 33-35, 43-5. Taihei Imamura, "The 'Japanese Spirit' as It Appears in Movies," in *Japanese Popular Culture*, pp. 142-5.

41. Arthur O. Lovejoy and George Boas, *Primitivism and Related Ideas in Antiquity* (Baltimore, 1935), pp. 447-56. J. Ingram Bryan, *The Interpretation of Nature in English Poetry* (Tokyo, 1932), pp. 13-14.

42. David Eugene Smith and Yoshio Miraki, *op. cit.*, pp. 134-5, 140-1.

43. Ayao Kuwaki, "Physical Sciences in Japan: From the Time of the First Contact with the Occident Until the Time of the Meiji Restoration," in *Scientific Japan: Past and Present* (Kyoto, 1926), pp. 246-8. Dairoku Kikuchi, "The Introduction of Western Learning into Japan," *Rice Institute Pamphlet*, II (1915), 64, 76. Yu Fujikawa, "A Brief Outline of the History of Medicine in Japan," *Scientific Japan: Past and Present*, pp. 235-238.

44. Inazo Nitobe, *Bushido: The Soul of Japan* (Philadelphia, 1900), p. 125.

45. Kosaka Masaaki, ed., *Japanese Thought in the Meiji Era*, trans.

David Abosch (Tokyo, 1958), pp. 61-4, 85-6. *The Autobiography of Fukuzawa Yukichi*, trans. Eüchi Kiyooka (Tokyo, 1948), p. 3.

46. *Japanese Thought in the Meiji Era*, p. 81.

47. *The Autobiography of Fukuzawa Yukichi*, p. 23.

48. G. B. Sansom, *Japan: A Short Cultural History* (New York, 1943), pp. 368-9, 337. Inazo Nitobe, *op. cit.*, pp. 9, 136. Daisetz Teitaro Suzuki, *An Introduction to Zen Buddhism* (Arrow Books, London, 1959), pp. 66-7, 95, 129.

49. *Autobiography of Fukuzawa Yukichi*, pp. 257-259. *Japanese Thought in the Meiji Era*, pp. 65, 74-5.

50. Michio Nagai, "Herbert Spencer in Early Meiji Japan," *Far Eastern Quarterly*, XIV (1954), 63.

IX

The French Revolutionary Ethic and Science

TOCQUEVILLE, NO FRIEND TO THE FRENCH REVOLUTION, WAS nonetheless compelled to acknowledge that it released the energies of scientific creativity among the people: "The French made surprising advances in the exact sciences at the very time at which they were finishing the destruction of the remains of their former feudal society; yet this sudden fecundity is not to be attributed to democracy, but to the unexampled revolution that attended its growth. What happened at that period was a special incident, and it would be unwise to regard it as the test of a general principle." [1] In our effort to understand history, however, we can scarcely accept the notion that the efflorescence which the French Revolution brought to the scientific movement was something so unique that it could not be explained by some general law. There was a general principle at work, one we have seen common to all scientific renaissances. Shelley's "Ode to the West Wind" caught its awakening spirit as it applied to Revolutionary France; our job will be to translate his ode into sociological prose.

The aftermath of the French Revolution called forth a pioneer essay in the sociology of science. It was a book by Charles Babbage, *Reflections on the Decline of Science in England and on Some of Its Causes*, published in London in 1830. Babbage, inventor of a precursor of the automatic computational machine, was—

as an English patriot and scientist—disturbed by the fact that the center of world science had moved from London to Paris. Just as the placing into orbit of the Sputnik by Soviet scientists in 1957 released varieties of soul-searching in American institutions, so did Babbage and his fellow-scientists brood upon the relative status of French and British science.

France in the early nineteenth century shone with the lustre of Laplace, Lagrange, Poncelet, Ampère, Fresnel, Monge, and Berthollet, whereas Britain seemed to be in the scientific doldrums. Now, the burst of scientific creativity in post-revolutionary France is scarcely to be explained by any theory making much of Protestant asceticism. For France remained, in a formal sense, Roman Catholic. What took place was a tremendous spread and encouragement, under the auspices of the ideology of the French Revolution, of the hedonist-libertarian ethic. The belief in secular happiness and human welfare opened up a new era in scientific education. The scientific intellectual in France assumed a position of eminence he had never known in any other country. In France, Babbage observed, "a knowledge of science is a recommendation to public appointments." In France, the scientific elite provided the cabinet ministers for the political elite; Lazare Carnot, the mathematician, brilliantly organized the armies under the Convention, and later served Napoleon as Minister of War; Chaptal, the chemist, Lavoisier's friend, was Minister of the Interior; Georges Cuvier, the renowned paleontologist, served as Minister of Public Instruction; Joseph Fourier was Prefect of L'Isère and Baron of the Empire; Lagrange was a Senator of France and a Count of the Empire, and the eminent Laplace was President of the Senate.

The French scientific intellectual, Babbage observed with melancholy, was also far more fittingly rewarded economically than his English colleagues. When the annual incomes of the six French scientists best known in Britain were compared with those of the six English scientists best known in France, the result was astonishing. The French scientists had an average income of nearly twelve hundred pounds a year, whereas the English scientists had an average income "very much smaller." The young scientist of talent, undertaking a scientific career in France, could look forward to the rewards of teaching at an Ecole Normale or Ecole Polytechnique, or the contentment of one of the provincial universities in the French national educational system. But in Britain, wrote Babbage, "there are no situations in the state; there is no position in society to which hope can point, to cheer him in his laborious path." The few chairs in science that did exist offered salaries that were insufficient for a family's needs. If the English scientist had no fortune, "the choice is taken away"; the young man must perforce renounce science. Perhaps he might try to remain faithful to his scientific calling with the help of a clerkship in the Board of Longitude; if so, he would soon find that a "high and independent spirit" was "incompatible with such appointments." [2] Babbage's own work on calculating engines evoked only the indifference of the English government. The English social environment moreover, with its snobbish insularity, could impede the advancement of science. As a student at Cambridge in 1812, Babbage, perceiving how English prejudice prevented the adoption of Leibniz's superior notation for the calculus, joined with Peacock and Herschel in a campaign for cosmopolitan objectivity.[3]

Apart from the English scientist's lower socio-economic status, the stifling hand of an entrenched bureaucracy among the scientists themselves was, according to Babbage, retarding the advancement of science in Britain. The Royal Society, jealously guarding its bureaucratic prerogatives, doggedly opposed the formation of, and even persecuted, such new groups as the Linnean Society, the Geological Society, and the Astronomical Society, which stood closer to the living scientific activities of Englishmen. The new societies nonetheless flourished, and deplored "with filial regret, the second childhood of their common parent, and the evil councils by which that sad event has been anticipated." Even the granting of medals and prizes by the Royal Society, it was alleged, had become, in large measure, the occasion for bureaucratic patronage and toadying.[4]

When François Arago, perpetual secretary of the Academy for Mathematical Sciences, asked why James Watt has not been elevated to the peerage, he was told that such dignities were reserved for military leaders and parliamentary orators, that it was not the fashion "to grant them to learned men, to literary men, to artists, to engineers"!

Even prior to the revolution, on its very eve, the perspicacious observer Arthur Young noted the superior social status in France of the scientific intellectual:

> The society for a man of letters, or who has any scientific pursuit, cannot be exceeded. . . . Persons of the highest rank pay an attention to science and literature, and emulate the character they confer. I should pity the man who expected, without other advantages of a very different nature, to be well received in a brilliant circle at London, because he was a fellow of the Royal Society. But this would not be the case with a member of the Academy of Sciences at Paris; he is sure of a good reception. Perhaps this contrast depends in a great measure on the difference of the governments of the two countries. Politics are too much attended to in England to allow a due respect to be paid in anything else; and should the French establish a freer government, academicians will not be held in such estimation, when rivalled in the public esteem by the orators who hold forth liberty and property in a free parliament.[5]

Young's prediction that the scientific intellectual would lose esteem in a more democratic society turned out to be erroneous. The high place which both French literary and scientific intellectuals enjoyed in social and governmental circles under the Third French Republic was not matched by any other nation. The French Revolution did indeed profoundly affect the status of the scientific intellectual; it lifted him in the social esteem of the community, and conferred upon him political prestige and administrative responsibility. The *ancien régime* had been a feudalism tempered with theocracy; the revolution created a France which—whether democracy, empire or constitutional monarchy—was tempered with *scientocracy*. Above all, however, the revolution opened the doors to scientific education to vast numbers of its citizens; a scientist's honors, a professorship at the Ecole Polytechnique became part of *la carrière ouverte aux talents*. If the young soldier-conscript carried in his knapsack a marshal's baton, the young French student might carry with his books a professional gown and the insignia of the Institut de France.

The French Revolution of 1789, like the Bolshevik Revolution of 1917, had a curiously ambivalent relationship toward the intellectual class. It exalted science and reason, and turned to its savants for the knowledge and invention with which it could hurl back the invader's armies. It also feared and was envious of the scientists. It unleashed especially a hatred on the part of people against intellectuals who had been associated in any way with the maintenance of the old order. The people's anti-intellectualism arose, as the old Babouvist, Buonarrotti, wrote, because it "feared that men, devoting themselves to the sciences, would imperceptibly form for themselves out of their acquirements, real or supposed claims to distinctions, to superiority, and to exemption from the common burdens"; and that in their vanity they would engage "in disastrous enterprises, against the rights of simple and less informed persons." Every popular revolution has an ingredient of fear that a new exploitative intellectual elite will arise. Every revolution, moreover, has tended to breed a certain kind of anti-intellectualism, for, willy-nilly, many of the leading intellectuals have often managed, by virtue of their abilities, to rise to important positions under the old order. In those who were members of the scientific institutions created by the kings, notes Joseph Fayet, the revolution saw only the privileged courtiers; "it went so far as to suspect scientists in general, science being considered in some way as a form of aristocracy, and genius as a kind of crime against equality." [6] During a revolution, also, the intellectuals of lesser stature have before them an opportunity for demagogically arousing hatred against those scientists of whose attainments they are envious. If there had been an English Revolution in the early eighteenth century, Isaac Newton, as Master of the Mint, might have suffered Lavoisier's fate for the reforms he instituted.

The upheaval of France's revolution gave an opportunity to embittered failures such as Jean Paul Marat to destroy those whose achievements they envied. Born to Calvinist parents, Marat had been frustrated in his scientific ambitions in his native Neuchâtel; he had tried without success to refute Newton's optics, had failed to become a member of the Academy of Sciences, and had suffered defeat in a competition for the prize of the Academy of Lyons. "From that instant, the pseudo-physicist became the bitter enemy of the scientific bodies of the whole universe, of whoever bore the title of an academician." [7] The revolution gave him leave to vent hatred upon Monge and Laplace, upon the great chemist Lavoisier, and the astronomer Bailly, Mayor of Paris. "Lavoisier," said

Marat, "the putative father of all discoveries which are noised abroad, having no ideas of his own, fastens on those of others"; Lavoisier was "this Corypheus of the Charlatans," this "son of a land-grabber." Thus Marat was able to revile the man who had ridiculed his own *Treatise on Fire*. A century and a half later, in the anxiety-ridden Soviet Union of Stalin's time, the plant physiologist Lysenko, who made up in fanaticism what he lacked in experimental rigor, was similarly able to call forth hatred against the geneticist Vavilov.

While the French Revolution in its permanent aspect helped open a new scientific era, it had a destructive phase in which its aggressions were released against the highest intelligence. "*La République n'a pas besoin de savants*" ("The Republic has no need of scientists"), allegedly remarked the miserable Coffinhal, president of the Revolutionary Tribunal, as he sentenced Lavoisier to death.[8] Lavoisier's atomic theory had initiated a chemical revolution even as political revolution was in gestation. He was of all scientists the one whose problems were most responsive to the urbanization which was a concomitant of the Industrial Revolution. We might call his work the new chemistry of the Urban Revolution.

If ever a republic needed scientists, it was the French Republic which was entering the Industrial Revolution. For the rise of crowded new cities produced a variety of problems which needed the chemist's aid. In 1767, for instance, the French Academy of Sciences offered a prize of two thousand livres for that essay which would tell how to light the streets of a large town at night most efficiently and cheaply. Lavoisier, then twenty-three years old, resolved to compete, studied various kinds of lamps, and won a gold medal from the king. Then there was the problem which arose from the shortage in the Paris water supply. Lavoisier was called on by the Academy to work on a project to make usable the waters of the Yvette River. He studied the chemistry of purification, and devised sensitive hydrometers for testing the purity of water by determining its density. The practicalities of water's purity provoked a problem of theoretical chemistry; was water a simple, stable substance, or was it convertible into earth? Would repeated distillations of water transmute it into earth? Lavoisier undertook such repeated distillations and showed that no transmutation of water took place. This scientist of the Urban Revolution, this collector of the king's taxes, was also the first man who applied the categories of accountancy to chemical reactions, and experimentally demonstrated the Law of Conservation of Mass—"Nothing is created in the operations either of art or of nature, and it can be taken as an axiom that in every operation an equal quantity of matter exists both before and after the operation. . . ." The balance sheet of nature's transactions gave it an equality of receipts and expenditures.

But Lavoisier, the father of the chemical revolution, was also one of the hated farmer-generals. As a young man of twenty-four, he had in 1768 entered the Ferme, a company of financiers that purchased for a fixed sum the privilege of collecting the national taxes, and which made its profit by a tax collection in excess of its purchase price. It was an association, says Douglas McKie, "which was ultimately to stink in the nostrils of his fellow-countrymen." [9] Lavoisier's own motives were not those of vulgar self-enrichment; he used his fortune to advance his experiments and to help younger scientists; he tried to lighten the burden of taxation on the poor. The Revolutionary Tribunal, however, fixedly saw only the agent of the exploiters, the functionary of the hated monarch.

But after its moment of aggressive destruction, after the hatred, born of a cumulated frustration, had spent its fury, the basic ethic of the French Revolution promoted a renaissance of the scientific spirit. For if, on the one hand, the democratic anti-intellectualism of Rousseau moved men like Robespierre, there was also the powerful current of thought and feeling that stemmed from Voltaire and the Encyclopedists, and which was finally the dominant one in shaping the relationship of the scientific intellectuals to French society. The Encyclopédie, especially—or as its subtitle reads, *A Reasoned Dictionary of the Sciences, Art, and Trades by the Society of Men of Letters*—embodied in its volumes the hedonist-libertarian ethic which was animating the developing scientific as well as much of the political movement. Diderot and his fellow-Encyclopedists maintained a ceaseless criticism of "the abuses," the legacy of Church and Christianity; prophets of the scientific movement, they heralded, in Diderot's words, the "general movement toward natural history, anatomy, chemistry, and experimental physics." "The sciences least common in the past century became the common ones from day to day." The Encyclopédie's article on

Faith was shorter than that on Furnaces, a blunt indication of an underlying change in basic values. The Encyclopédie, as Lynn Thorndike has said, was not dominated by some facile philosophy but was "permeated by a truly scientific spirit." Underlying that scientific spirit was the liberation of emotion which led Diderot to say, "I have always been the apologist of strong passions; they alone move me," and which inspired his stark self-insight into human nature—that the savage left to himself "would twist his father's neck and sleep with his mother." [10]

Diderot saw himself as the spokesman for the Baconian ethic in France. "I believe I have taught my fellow citizens," he wrote, "to appreciate and read Chancellor Bacon; they have read the pages of this profound writer more during the past five or six years than they ever have before." A scientific revolution, Diderot believed, would follow the psychological revolution then in the making; the most glorious moment for a work such as the Encyclopédie, he said, would be that which would follow immediately on "*quelque grande revolution*" ("some great revolution"). His collaborator, D'Alembert, the famous mathematical physicist of prerevolutionary France, in the "Discours préliminaire" of the Encyclopédie, wrote a kind of declaration of the new hedonist-libertarian ethic: Europe was leaving the stage of slavery, the long interval of ignorance into which it had been plunged. The revolution whose emotional foundations were being laid would come within a generation "because when once the barriers are broken, the human spirit often goes faster than it itself intends. . . ." D'Alembert looked to the new young generation of scientists, the "young professors full of knowledge, spirit and courage (for it is needed for innovations, even the most innocent)," who had dared to leave "*la route battue*" ("the beaten path") to create a new one.

Among the new generation of scientists was the Marquis de Condorcet, D'Alembert's close friend and later his biographer. Condorcet alone among the *philosophes* actually witnessed the revolution they had foretold. He transmitted to the Legislative Assembly in 1792 the heritage of the Encyclopedists' ethic in his famous *Report and Project of a Decree on the General Organization of Public Instruction*, in which he proposed a national system of education that would emphasize science from the elementary grades through the highest. "All errors in government and in society," he wrote, "are based on philosophic errors which, in turn, are derived from errors in natural science."

The cultivation of a libertarian outlook was a primary aim of Condorcet's plan of education. "Generally all authority, of whatever nature and in whatever hands and in whatever way it was acquired, is a natural enemy of enlightenment. . . . Everyone who makes it his business to seek the truth is odious to those who seek authority." And the test of human institutions was their contribution to human happiness. His *Sketch of the Intellectual Progress of Mankind*, a prose poem of the liberal philosophy of history, written while Condorcet, proscribed by the Convention, was hiding in a garret, is a vision of the deathless courage of man, overcoming superstition, ignorance, and self-hatred, until the day arrives when the sun "will shine only on free men who know no other master but their reason; when tyrants and slaves, priests and their stupid or hypocritical instruments will exist only in the works of history. . . ." [11] Condorcet's *Report* became the guiding document in the educational reconstruction of France which the Convention and Napoleon undertook. The Convention's Committee on Instruction conceived of itself as the heirs of the Encyclopedists' tradition, the fulfillers of the hopes of Diderot and D'Alembert.

The scientists' participation in the French Revolution finally proved a more effective, enduring force than the moments of anti-intellectualism. It should not be forgotten that scientists took leading parts in the Jacobin Club itself. Fourcroy, Lavoisier's co-worker, was for a while president of the Jacobins; Monge, the founder of descriptive geometry, which for fifteen years was guarded as a military secret, was their secretary and vice-president and, under the Convention, Minister of the Navy and the Colonies; the distinguished chemist Hassenfratz was a member; and all were faithful attendants at its meetings. The mathematician Lazare Carnot served throughout the Terror on the all-powerful Committee of Public Safety.[12]

The scientists have been ridiculed in our time for having placed themselves among the revolutionists. Monge and his fellow-scientists have been taken to task for not having recognized "that a mob which has once tasted blood is not satisfied till no more is forthcoming." [13] Monge, a peddler's son, is granted a partial extenuation because he had known through firsthand experience the corruption of the aristocrats and the economic deprivations of the masses, and was consequently a "natural revolutionist." We are compelled, however, to ask whether the revolution would have taken a happier course if the scientists had remained aloof. Can a democracy be raised to its highest potentialities if the scientists maintain the security of aloofness? At any rate, the French scientists were from the outset active participants in their society's struggles. They had imbibed from Voltaire the philosophy that it is the intellectual's duty to expose injustice and to elevate the people. They made their decision to place their philosophy to the test of action; they gave to the people's social revolution of 1789-94, the carrier wave of the movement, the harmonic wave of a "revolution of the intellectuals," and their achievements were tremendous.

The career of Gaspard Monge probably best illustrates the union of the motifs of science, revolution, and administration.[14] Monge was a scientific, revolutionary, and managerial intellectual, and represented the fullest synthesis of all the latent longings of Bacon's *New Atlantis*. An ardent member of the Jacobin Club, Monge, during the crisis of 1792 and 1793, was virtually in charge of the manufacture of armaments and ammunition in Paris. To introduce the artisans to the new technology, he gave them short "revolutionary courses" and wrote a manual, *Description de l'Art de Fabriquer les Canons*. The Ecole Polytechnique, for which he and Fourcroy drew up the first plans, later spread the taste for the study of the exact sciences throughout the republic, for it was a most powerful means "to advance with an equal step the perfection of the useful arts and that of the human reason." Then, in 1796, Monge became a member of the commission of scientific and artistic experts which joined Bonaparte's army in northern Italy; their purpose was to supervise the spoliation of artistic and scientific treasures from the conquered area. "With prodigious feats we have conquered, defended and made triumph our liberty," Monge wrote to his son-in-law. As a scientific ambassador of liberty, he was appalled by the backwardness of the Roman people:

> . . . so brutalized, so ignorant, that the pity which it inspires at first changes after a certain time to repugnance. There is no street

corner where there hasn't been a Madonna who has done the miracle, of raising her eyes as a sign of protection for the poor imbeciles who today still spend the whole evening looking at these miserable crusts to see the miracle. When we arrived, it was after daily processions of 30,000 persons, barefoot, had been going for a month from church to church to pray against the French. It seemed to us we were living among sleepwalkers.

During the Napoleonic era, Monge, as a managerial scientific intellectual, served for two years as president of the Senate. The old Jacobin became Count of Péluse. When Napoleon was defeated at Waterloo, Monge had to go into hiding for several months. He was expelled from the Institute of France. When he died in 1818, there was no official homage, but Berthollet, Chaptal, and Laplace led the mourning of their fellow-scientists. The song Monge loved passionately till his end was the *Marseillaise*.

Among the revolutionists, the scientists found their principal friend in Joseph Lakanal, a professor of philosophy at Moulins who was elected deputy to the National Convention from Ariège. Lakanal, a militant Jacobin, became the revolution's organizer of science. From his vantage point as President of the Committee on Public Instruction, he was the prime mover in establishing the Primary and Central Schools, and above all the Ecole Normale, with its celebrated faculty. The Museum of Natural History and the Bureau of Longitudes were likewise among his creations. The Restoration, years later, ended his career as Inspector-General of the metric system. Then, for twenty-two years, he lived in self-imposed exile in America, where he served several unappreciated years as president of the College of New Orleans.[15] When he returned to Paris many years later, in 1837, the professors of the Museum of Natural History, in remembrance of his services to science during the revolutionary era, gave the old *conventionnel* a key to the Jardin des Plantes. During the revolutionary era, he was pre-eminently the managerial intellectual of the scientific community.

A variety of problems in applied science first engaged the interest of the French revolutionists. By its decree of September 11, 1793, the Committee of Public Safety gathered together, in its Commission on Weights and Measures, an illustrious group of scientists: Monge, Borda, Lagrange, Laplace, Delambre, Coulomb,

Berthollet, and the ill-fated Lavoisier himself. The metric system was the contribution of the Year II of the Revolution, a year that has been called one of the truly important dates in the history of science. Though Vendémiaire, Fructidor, and Thermidor were a calendar of progress which failed to supersede the Christian reckoning, the grams and meters did become part of science's nomenclature. Curiously, the promulgation of the metric system was related to the hedonist-libertarian ethic of the Revolution. For the metric system was the outcome of a quest for "natural" units in physical science, just as the republic was an attempt to realize the most "natural" form in politics.[16] The multiplicity of weights and measures in different localities before the revolution was a challenge to scientists to find those units most grounded in the intrinsic nature of things, and free from the superimpositions, distortions, and encumbrances of local custom.

Above all, however, the French Revolution transformed the character of scientific activity as a social institution. The French Revolution broke the tendency toward the monopoly of science by the leisured aristocracy. Lazare Carnot, a military organizer as well as the mathematician who helped inspire Poncelet's projective geometry with his own *Geometry of Position*, could be admitted to the school of Mézières in 1771 only by supplying documents to show that "neither his family nor his mother had endeavored to enrich their family and their country by commerce or by manual labor." Fourcroy, the son of an impoverished pharmacist who had been deprived of his right to practice by the Paris corporation of apothecaries, knew hunger at first hand, and was saved for a scientific career only by a benefactor. Science was still largely bound to the *salon*. "It was a fashionable pursuit, a luxury of the great," in Merz's words. Now, however, the Ecole Normale and the Ecole Polytechnique opened the highest scientific education to those with the greatest talents. They preached a religion of science for its own sake, and linked their work to the industrial and military needs of the nation as well. The government which had begun by closing the existing academies and colleges because they ministered to "*les messieurs*" ended by creating the most advanced educational system for its people which the world had yet seen.[17] The creation of the Ecole Polytechnique, as Joseph Fayet says, was an event of the first importance in the history of French science. Born of a national military emergency, its very first graduates included such distinguished names as Biot, Poinsot, Poisson, Gay-Lussac, Dulong, and Poncelet. The most illustrious scientific names of nineteenth-century France were old *polytechniciens*—Sadi Carnot, Fresnel, Arago, Becquerel, Le Verrier, Poincaré.

A new conception of scientific teaching arose. Hitherto, the original investigator of nature would not have wished to demean himself by teaching his science. To teach was equivalent to being a practitioner of a trade, which was beneath a gentleman's status. The Convention, however,

> . . . by appointing the first geometers, the first philosophers, and the first naturalists of the world to be professors . . . threw new lustre upon the profession of teaching, the advantageous influence which is felt to the present day. In the opinion of the public at large a title which a Lagrange, a Laplace, a Monge, a Berthollet, had borne, became a proper match to the finest titles.[18]

This the Convention accomplished a few months after the Ninth of Thermidor. It brought fifteen hundred students from all parts of France to listen to the great professors of the Ecole Normale. Among them, for instance, was Joseph Fourier, an eager pupil who was later to open a new branch of physics and analysis with his *Théorie Analytique de la Chaleur*. Fourier, a tailor's son, orphaned at the age of eight, had managed to secure admission into a military school run by Benedictine monks. He wished to be a soldier, but the minister said, "Fourier not being noble, could not enter the artillery, although he were a second Newton." Thereupon, Fourier decided to become a monk. The Revolution of 1789 opened new doors to him before he had yet taken any vows. Nine years later, he left his professorship at the Ecole Polytechnique to serve with Napoleon in Egypt as head of a scientific mission. In this fashion, the revolution opened up new vistas of scientific life to French youth. The priest's habit and cell could be exchanged for the professor's robes and laboratory; science replaced theology, and revelation gave way to empirical evidence.

Then, too, the revolution altered the very style of teaching itself. In the "ancient great colleges," the professors read their discourses, the same each year, while the students dozed indifferently. The authorities now, however, exacted a promise from the scientist-professors of the Ecole Normale that they would never recite memorized lectures. "From that time, the chair has become a tribune where the professor, identified, so to speak, with his audience, sees in their looks, in their gestures, in their countenance, sometimes the necessity" for retracing his steps, illustrating them, or "of clothing in a new form the thought which, when first expressed, had left some doubts in the minds of his audience." [19] The lectures were taken down by the state's reporters, and sent to the students, to the members of the Convention, and to representatives abroad. These lectures on science were becoming adventures in research on which the French nation prided itself.

The wars which Revolutionary France waged against the invading Prussian and Austrian armies diverted its scientific resources from what would have been their normal direction. The *Annales de Chimie*, for instance, ceased publication in July, 1793, with its eighteenth volume. The nineteenth was delayed until three years later, but when it appeared, the foreword, which was signed, among others, by Monge, Berthollet, Fourcroy, and Chaptal, bore no rebuke for the revolution. On the contrary, it spoke of the necessity of defending the republic, and the public duties of the revolution, which had caused the journal's temporary suspension.

The revolution meanwhile had broken the monopolistic status which the Academy of Sciences had enjoyed in prerevolutionary years. The Convention, however, with its creation of the Institut de France and the new Ecoles, opened new channels for organization and recognition among scientists. Naturalists such as Lamarck who had been discriminated against in the *ancien régime* found unwonted recognition.[20]

England, engaged for a generation in suppressing its radicals and their societies, saw its science languish. Humphry Davy noted that the English aristocracy had lost its scientific élan:

> In looking back to the history of the last five reigns in England, we find Boyles, Cavendishes, and Howards, who rendered these great names more illustrious by their scientific honors; but we may in vain search the aristocracy now for philosophers. . . .[21]

The same Davy, however, evidently corrupted by his own desire to win plaudits in the *salons* of nobility, resigned his professorship at the Royal Institution and frittered away his energies in seeking the approbation of titled fools. Sir David Brewster, writing in the *Quarterly Review*, likewise found English science in decline. Unlike the Ecole Normale and the Ecole Polytechnique, the English colleges and universities were scarcely, as Brewster appraised them, havens for scientific research. The great inventions and discoveries which had been made in the last century, wrote Brewster, were made outside the academic halls:

> In proof of this, we have only to recall the labors of Bradley, Dollond, Priestley, Cavendish, Maskelyne, Rumford, Watt, Wollaston, Young, Davy, and Chenevix; and among the living, to mention the names of Dalton, Ivory, Brown, Hatchett, Pond, Herschel, Babbage, Henry, Barlow, South, Faraday, Murdock and Christie; nor need we have any hesitation in adding, that within the last fifteen years not a single discovery or invention, or prominent interest, has been made in our colleges, and that there is not one man in all the eight universities of Great Britain who is at present known to be engaged in any train of original research.

Brewster proposed that Britain create scientific institutions on the model of the French. He urged the establishment of research professorships at the universities, and high economic rewards and social status for scientists. "And why does England thus persecute the votaries of her science? Why does she depress them to the level of her hewers of wood and her drawers of water? It is because science flatters no courtier, mingles in no political strife. . . . Can we behold unmoved the science of England, the vital principle of her arts, struggling for existence, the meek and unarmed victim of political strife?" This was the England which allowed John Dalton, its greatest chemist, "to spend the flower of his days in the drudgery of teaching the elements of mathematics at Manchester," and which never conferred on him a single mark of national recognition. This was the England which nominated to its technical boards not a single man of science but filled its posts with incompetent aristocrats and clergymen. This was the England in which not a single scientist bore even the lowest title, received a pension or grant, or in any way enjoyed "the favor of his sovereign or the friendship of his ministers!" [22]

Very different was the self-image of the scientist in France. Georges Cuvier, as Secretary of the Section of Physical and Mathematical Sciences of the Institute, addressed to his Majesty the Emperor Napoleon I his famous *Rapport Historique sur le Progrès des Sciences Naturelles depuis 1789, et Sur Leur Etat Actuel* (*Historical Report on the Progress of the Natural Sciences since 1789, and on their Present State*). The Emperor ordered its printing, for it was indeed the noblest testimony to the glory of his reign. Cuvier stated proudly the ethics of the French scientists among whom His Majesty was numbered:

> To lead the human mind to its noble destination, the knowledge of truth; to spread sound ideas even among the least educated classes of the people; to draw men away from the empire of prejudice and passions; to make reason the arbiter and supreme guide of public opinion, that is the essential object of the sciences, that is how they cooperate to advance civilization. . . .[23]

Condorcet's vision and the hopes of the Encyclopedists were written into national policy.

The French scientists, Cuvier also boasted, were complete empiricists. They did not pursue the phantoms of German *Naturphilosophie;* they took no part in disputation as to whether the phenomenal world was an adjective of the ego, or an emanation from spiritual substance. The German nature-philosophers, said Cuvier, apply moral terms to physical phenomena, and employ metaphor rather than argument. The French scientists, on the other hand, were in healthy contact with positive facts. Science was making life more salubrious for the people, was benefiting their clothing, their lodgings, their food, their freedom from epidemic and disease; "whoever will compare with a little care and impartiality our private life with that which we led thirty years ago, will not fail to recognize its advantages." The advance in the medical sciences and public health in France had surpassed that of other European countries. Its botanical collections were the richest. French chemists had adopted and extended Lavoisier's theories of combustion and oxygen, so that the new ideas became known throughout Europe as the *chimie française*.

The anti-intellectualism of the French Revolution, with respect to its scientists, was thus a transitory phase. The Convention had soon seen that its armament and armies required scientists and surgeons. As it battled the European monarchs, it perceived that its "arsenals were empty, steel was no longer imported from abroad, saltpetre came not from India." It required powder, cannon, food. Fourcroy taught them new chemical methods for extracting saltpetre, Berthollet a better method for making gunpowder. Monge explained the arts of casting and boring cannon. "In the space of a few years science had become a necessity to society at large." [24] But in one significant respect, the new Napoleonic society remained hostile to intellectuals. It did its utmost to repress the social sciences; its philo-intellectualism extended solely to the physical and biological sciences.

The Napoleonic dictatorship was much like its Soviet counterpart more than a century later. Each opened the doors of scientific institutions to new classes of its citizens, and each honored the men of the scientific academies and research institutes; each admired the mathematical view of the universe, and each was keenly aware of the potential military power in scientific discoveries. Each wanted the use of science to better the material welfare of its citizens. But Napoleon, like the Soviet leaders, disliked the social sciences. In 1803, he dissolved that part of the Institute of France which was concerned with the study of the moral and political sciences. For Napoleon hated the *idéologues*, those like Condorcet, Turgot, Condillac, and Montesquieu, who aimed to apply the scientific method to the study of society. He could not use them; he jeered at them. The ideological intellectual is never a favorite of a dictatorial regime; the technical intellectual often is. And both Napoleon and the Soviet government valued the scientific intellectuals as technical men, but feared the never-ending critique of the ideological intellectuals. The positivism of Saint-Simon and Auguste Comte, with their managerial emphases, was the kind of philosophy which expressed the spirit of the Napoleonic dictatorship.[25] So Saint-Simon in 1808 could behold in Napoleon the scientific leader of humanity:

> On one hand he holds the infallible compass; in the other the exterminating sword against the opponents of the progress of knowledge. About his throne the most illustrious scientists of the earth should group themselves, even as the most valiant captains.

It was a compromise version between the hedonist-libertarian ethic and the principle of political authoritarianism. It gave a tremendous impetus to scientific work, but always with a latent anxiety. For it is hard to contain the method of science within fixed domains, and one was always uncertain that some issue might not arise to transform the technical intellectual into an ideological one.

The Napoleonic anti-intellectualism was, it must be emphasized, a new variant; it was a managerial anti-intellectualism, not the democratic anti-intellectualism of the Revolutionary Tribunal against Lavoisier. Despite its political authoritarianism, however, the French society had made a great step of advancement in diffusing more of the hedonist-libertarian ethic than had ever obtained among all classes of the French people. And the consequence was the most remarkable scientific movement in the Europe of its day.

Never perhaps in the history of civilization have natural scientists and mathematicians enjoyed a more honored place than the one they held in the first years of Napoleon's rule, when the impress of the revolution's ideals was still strong. The friendship between Monge and Napoleon was so close that Napoleon remarked, "Monge loved me as one loves a mistress." The Marquis de Laplace dedicated two great works to Napoleon. When General Bonaparte received a volume of the *Mécanique Céleste*, he wrote to its author, "The first six months which I shall have at my disposal will be employed in reading your beautiful work." After he had read several chapters, he said he regretted that "circumstances had directed him into a career which removed him from the pursuit of science." He wished future generations to know the "esteem and friendship" he had had for its author. And in the midst of the Russian campaign of 1812, when he received Laplace's *Traité du Calcul des Probabilités*, he regretted not being able to read it, but welcomed its contribution to "the most important of the sciences" and "the glory of the nation." "The advancement and the improvement of mathematical science are connected with the prosperity of the state."

Napoleon is said to have asked Laplace what place God had in the system of *Mécanique Céleste*. "*Je n'avais pas besoin de cette hypothèse-là*" ("I had no need of that hypothesis"), replied Laplace, a disbeliever in miracles and theological mysteries. The prefatory and culminatory passages of theology with which Catholic and Protestant scientists were wont to embellish their works had vanished. Laplace wrote openly of the "gradual enfeeblement of the proofs of the Christian religion," and advocated a system of education which, free from "religious prejudices," would encourage the "progress of human reason." [26] The hedonist-libertarian ethic stood out unadorned in this era as the philosophy of the scientific movement.

The philosophy of the French Revolution did not, however, impose ideological requirements on science. What is an ideology as distinct from philosophy? An ideology insists that the laws of nature must conform to a model set by a political form or hope; the Marxist ideology, for instance, insists that the laws of nature must show the same pattern of abrupt, discontinuous change which they take to be the law of social evolution. In this sense, the science of the French Revolution was unfettered and free from ideological intrusion. The word "revolution" did acquire a vogue, and there was a tendency to think of change as revolutionary and catastrophic. Cuvier entitled his work *Révolutions de la Surface du Globe*.[27] But revolution was not imposed upon the universe as the canonical law of change. Laplace, living in an era of revolutionary instability, achieved his famous demonstration of the stability of the solar system. Astronomers had wondered whether the mean distance of Jupiter from the sun would continue to grow smaller until it fell into the sun. Such a cosmological conclusion might very well have harmonized with the collapse of the *ancien régime;* if the philosophy of the French Revolution were to have provided a model for physical systems based on its political experience, it would have found altogether congenial the notion that the solar system was as unstable as social systems. Instead, Laplace proved that the planetary changes were not cumulative but periodic, and showed, at least on the basis of the facts then known, that an astronomical revolution was not pending.

There have been cases where scientific discoveries have been influenced by analogies drawn from the contemporary social setting. Both Darwin and Wallace, to mention the most famous examples, were predisposed in part toward a theory of natural selection by their reading of Malthus's description of the competitive human struggle for existence. But there have been numerous discoveries in science which were out of phase with the dominant social analogy, and Laplace's was one of them. Nor should it be forgotten that social analogies can mislead the scientist; the stimulus, for example, to Lamarck's theory that the needs of living creatures created new organs to satisfy them may very well have come from the revolutionary situation at the end of the eighteenth century, when new social organs were being founded to meet social needs.[28] Biological science has not, however, sustained Lamarck's theory. The basic influence of the hedonist-libertarian ethic was not ideological. Rather, it liberated the imagination, and gave a charter to perception as the agency for acquiring knowledge. It enabled men to recapture an undistorted approach to natural phenomena; it did not, however, prescribe, in a new authoritarian fashion, the outlines of a system of the universe.

NOTES

1. Alexis de Tocqueville, *Democracy in America*, trans. Henry Reeve and Francis Bowen, ed. Phillips Bradley (New York, 1953), Vol. II, pp. 42-3.

2. Charles Babbage, *Reflections on the Decline of Science in England and on Some of Its Causes* (London, 1830), pp. 26-7, 35-8.

3. Charles Babbage, *Passages from the Life of a Philosopher* (London, 1864), pp. 38-9, 105.

4. Charles Babbage, *Reflections on the Decline of Science in England*, pp. 41-2. Goethe similarly expressed the envy of the "miserable isolated" German scientists for their French colleagues. Cf. George Ellery Hale, "The Intellectual Inspiration of Paris," in American Scholars, *Science and Learning in France* (Chicago, 1917), p. 7.

5. Arthur Young, *Travels during the Years 1787, 1788, and 1789. Undertaken more particularly with a view of ascertaining the Cultivation, Wealth, Resources, and National Prosperity, of the Kingdom of France* (London, 1792), p. 71.

6. Filippo M. Buonarroti, *History of Babeuf's Conspiracy of Equality*, trans. Bronterre (London, 1836), p. 211. Joseph Fayet, *La Révolution Française et la Science 1789-1795* (Paris, 1960), p. 473. Fayet's important book came into my hands too late for me to use it fully.

7. François Arago, *Biographies of Distinguished Scientific Men*, trans. Admiral W. H. Smyth, Rev. Baden Powell, and Robert Grant (Boston, 1859), First Series, p. 187. Louis R. Gottschalk, *Jean Paul Marat: A Study in Radicalism* (New York, 1927), pp. 24-31. T. E. Thorpe, *Es-*

says in Historical Chemistry (London, 1902), pp. 139-40. Joseph Fayet, *op. cit.*, pp. 31-8.

8. Douglas McKie, *Antoine Lavoisier* (Philadelphia, 1936), pp. 297-8. Cf. Henry Guerlac, "Lavoisier and His Biographers," *Isis*, XLV (1954), 61.

9. Douglas McKie, *op. cit.*, p. 37. G. Pouchet, *Les Sciences Pendant la Terreur* (Paris, 1896), pp. 41-3.

10. Joseph Fayet, *op. cit.*, p. 474. Lynn Thorndike, "L'Encyclopédie and the History of Science," *Isis*, VI (1924), 365. M. de Voltaire, *Elémens de Philosophie tirez de Newton* (Nouvelle Edition, Dresde, 1749), pp. 42-4. Lester G. Crocker, *The Embattled Philosopher: A Biography of Denis Diderot* (East Lansing, Mich., 1954), pp. 59, 278. "Encyclopédie," "Expérimental," *Encyclopédie, ou Dictionnaire Raisonné des Sciences, des Arts, et des Métiers* (3rd ed., Geneva, 1778), Tome XII, pp. 369, 405; Tome XIII, p. 629.

11. J. Salwyn Schapiro, *Condorcet and the Rise of Liberalism* (New York, 1934), p. 198. John Theodore Merz, *A History of European Thought in the Nineteenth Century* (Edinburgh, 1896), Vol. I, pp. 109-10. Antoine Nicolas de Condorcet, *Sketch for a Historical Picture of the Progress of the Human Mind*, trans. June Barraclough (New York, 1955), pp. 179, 201. G. Pouchet, *Les Sciences Pendant La Terreur*, p. 21.

12. G. Pouchet, *op. cit.*, p. 23.

13. E. T. Bell, *Men of Mathematics* (New York, 1937), p. 188.

14. René Taton, *L'Œuvre Scientifique de Monge* (Paris, 1951), pp. 36-8. Louis de Launay, *Monge, Fondateur de l'Ecole Polytechnique* (Paris, 1933), p. 115. Paul V. Aubrey, *Monge: Le Savant Ami de Napoleon Bonaparte* (Paris, 1954), pp. 166, 177.

15. Charlotte H. Boatner, "Certain Unpublished Letters from French Scientists of the Revolutionary Period Taken from the Files of Joseph Lakanal," *Osiris*, I (1936), 173-183. Joseph Fayet, *op. cit.*, pp. 110, 119, 157.

16. Henri Sée, *Economic and Social Conditions in France During the Eighteenth Century*, trans. E. H. Zeydel (New York, 1927), p. 11. Norman Campbell, *Physics: The Elements* (Cambridge, 1920), p. 395.

17. François Arago, *op. cit.*, Second Series, p. 8. John Theodore Merz, *op. cit.*, pp. 109, 143. Joseph Fayet, *op. cit.*, pp. 68, 280-1.

18. François Arago, *op. cit.*, pp. 389, 401.

19. *Ibid.*, pp. 398-90. Cf. L. Pearce Williams, "Science, Education and the French Revolution," *Isis*, XLIV (1953), 311-30.

20. G. Pouchet, *op. cit.*, p. 34. Henry Guerlac, "Some Aspects of

Science during the French Revolution," *Scientific Monthly*, LXXX (1955), 97-100.

21. Sir Humphry Davy, *Consolations in Travel, or The Last Days of a Philosopher* (London, 1830), p. 226. Jöns Jacob Berzelius, *Autobiographical Notes*, trans. Olof Larsell (Baltimore, 1934), pp. 79-80. T. E. Thorpe, *Humphry Davy, Poet and Philosopher* (London, 1896), pp. 219-20. George A. Foote, "Sir Humphry Davy and his Audience at the Royal Institution," *Isis*, XLIII (1952), 10.

22. Sir David Brewster, "Reflexions on the Decline of Science in England, and on some of its Causes, by Charles Babbage," *Quarterly Review*, XLIII (1830), 320, 323-4, 331, 341. Bernard H. Becker, *Scientific London* (New York, 1875), pp. 272-4.

23. Georges Cuvier, *Rapport Historique sur les Progrès des Sciences Naturelles depuis 1789, et sur leur Etat Actuel* (Paris, 1810), pp. 387, 234-5, 363, 360, 267, 79.

24. Cf. John T. Merz, *op. cit.*, p. 148.

25. George Boas, *French Philosophies of the Romantic Period* (Baltimore, 1925), pp. 19, 254. Frank E. Manuel, *The New World of Henri Saint-Simon* (Cambridge, 1956), pp. 60, 139.

26. François Arago, *op. cit.*, Second Series, pp. 365-6. Cf. Sir Edmund Whittaker, "Laplace," *American Mathematical Monthly*, LVI (1949), 369. Roger Hahn, "Laplace's Religious Views," *Archives Internationales d'Histoire des Sciences*, XXXIV (1955), 38-9. Jean Pelseneer, "La Religion de Laplace," *Isis*, XXXVI (1946), 159.

27. Jules Marcou, *Life, Letters, and Works of Louis Agassiz* (New York, 1896), Vol. II, p. 115.

28. Jean Jaurès, *Bernstein et l'évolution de la Méthode Socialiste* (2nd ed., Paris, 1931), p. 10.

X

The Scientific Revolution Among the Jews

By the end of the seventeenth century, the scientific leadership of the world had passed from Italy to Britain—from a Catholic to a Protestant country. Toward the end of the eighteenth century, revolutionary France became the center of European science. The Jews meanwhile had been little involved in the rise of the scientific movement. Throughout Europe, they were confined to narrow, stuffy, and mind-constraining ghettos; their tradition and respect for learning had degenerated into sterile commentary on the Talmud. Then, at the end of the eighteenth century, a momentous change began. The collapse of the ghettos' walls breached the dams that had contained Jewish intellect and feeling. A fresh breath was felt throughout all the Jewish communities. It moved wherever the spirit of freedom touched—from Germany to Poland to Russia. Despite all difficulties, the greatest scientific movement that has ever seized and transformed a people began. For the psychological revolution among the Jews in the nineteenth century was the most rapid and thoroughgoing emotional revolution the world has ever seen. It bore no relation to the Protestant ethic. It was a leap, within a generation, from feudal and pre-feudal Talmudism to the most advanced scientific thought of the day. It was a transition from a religious to a hedonist-libertarian ethic. It produced conflict and excommunication within

Jewish communities, but always the issue was clear: the younger generation was choosing secularism, science, and the liberal ethic.

> To the lover of mankind the history of the Russo-Jewish renaissance is an encouraging and inspiring phenomenon [wrote Jacob S. Raisin]. Seldom has a people made such rapid strides forward as the Russian Jews. . . . From the darkness of the Middle Ages in which they were steeped until the time of Alexander II, they emerged suddenly into the life and light of the West. . . . Destitute of everything that makes for enlightenment, and under the dominion of a Government which sought to extinguish the few rushlights that scattered the shadows around them, they nevertheless snatched victory from defeat, sloughed off medieval superstition. . . .[1]

When Czar Alexander I, in 1811, opened the schools and colleges to them, many young Jews came to seek the secular knowledge. This was the dawn of the so-called Haskalah movement—the enlightenment—which moved the Jewish people into the swift, dangerous stream of European history. The Haskalah movement, in Israel Friedlaender's words, undertook "a mental revolution, less extensive but not less radical than the one which is associated with the name of Copernicus."[2] Wherever the emotion of Haskalah was felt, Talmudical studies declined. German Jewry had seen its impact during the preceding generation, when Moses Mendelssohn led an exodus into the *Aufklärung*, and was welcomed as a modern Socrates by Immanuel Kant. The venerable Talmudical academies in Metz, Frankfurt, Hamburg, Fürth, and Halberstadt were soon bereft of students and closed their doors.

The rumor of the new liberal science infiltrated slowly into the ghetto villages of Poland and Russia. In a Polish settlement, Solomon Maimon painfully learned the Roman alphabet from the transliteration of titles on pages in Talmudical works, a Rosetta Stone for his passage from an ancient to the modern era; Dr. Behr learned his letters in Wolff's *Mathematics*. The leaders of orthodox Jewry were dismayed when Russian institutions offered the new sciences to the Jewish youth. In their eyes, Haskalah became "synonymous with apostasy or licentiousness"; nothing like it had been seen among the Jews since "the Hellenistic craze" during the Judaean Commonwealth of two thousand years before. But "Russian Jewry was astir with a new life. In many places secular education was divorced for the first time from rabbinical speculations." In Odessa, St. Petersburg, and Moscow, young Jews flocked to the high schools and universities in numbers far exceeding their proportion in the population. "What Maimon said of a few, could now be applied to hundreds and thousands, they were 'like starving persons suddenly treated to a delicious meal.' " Once upon a time, a rich man would have wanted as his prospective son-in-law a young scholar learned in the Law, but now he sought the uniformed university student. The "yeshivah bachur" yielded to the gymnasiast. The orthodox bravely and tragically resisted the new secular learning, especially during the 1840's. When Rabbi Israel Salanter learned that his son had gone to Berlin to study medicine, he removed his shoes and sat down on the ground for seven days to mourn his son as dead. To be seen reading a pamphlet of the Haskalah was to be accursed with the mark of an *epikoros* (a heretic). Within the synagogues and yeshivahs themselves, however, "Buckle and Spencer, Turgeniev and Tolstoi were secretly passed from hand to hand, and read and studied with avidity." [3]

The Czarist governments soon inaugurated determined measures to end the Jewish exodus into the promised land of science and freedom. In 1875, a law was enacted withholding stipends from Jewish students; in 1882, their number in the Military Academy of Medicine was reduced to 5 per cent, and later to zero. Four hundred Jews passed their matriculation examination for the university in 1887-88; three hundred and twenty-six were denied admission. Jewish students had carried off far too many honors, and were filled with too much enthusiasm for science and learning. Emancipated from the "trammels of rabbinism," they "had transferred their extraordinary devotion from the Talmud to secular studies." Pobyedonostzev, Procurator of the Czar's Holy Synod, was ready to do all to stem them: "These Jews have the audacity to excel us pure Russians." The repressive measures made those who would have been scientific intellectuals into revolutionary intellectuals. Young Jews, denied admission to the Russian universities, frustrated in their intellectual hopes, became idealist revolutionaries; the frustrated would-be scientists became "scientific" Socialists, and joined the numerous political societies that sprang up in the towns, villages, and hamlets of Russia. Often they journeyed to foreign universities to continue their studies, to cities such as Bern and Zurich, which became centers of Russian revolutionary activity.[4]

> An immense host of young men and women [wrote the distinguished historian Dubnow], who found their way blocked to the higher educational institutions in Russia went abroad, flocking to foreign universities and higher professional schools, where they learned to estimate at its full value, a regime which in their own country denied them the advantages granted to them outside it. A large number of these college youths returned home permeated with revolutionary ideas—living witnesses to the sagacity of a government which saw its reason for existence in the suppression of all revolutionary stirrings.[5]

The greatest number of Jews lived in Russia, but the same drama of liberation took place in the smaller national communities. The Italian Jewish community, for instance, was one of the smallest in Europe; at the time of the *risorgimento,* in the nineteenth century, it consisted of only forty thousand persons. But with the advent of freedom, there was no country of Europe "where the Jewish contribution was proportionately so great." To science it gave Levi Civita, creator of the tensor calculus; Peano, pioneer in the foundations of mathematics; Vito Volterra, analyst of hysteresis; and Federigo Enriques, philosopher of science.

> Released from the Ghetto [writes Cecil Roth], Jewish genius became apparent in every aspect of Italian life. . . . It was unnecessary for the Italian Jews, as it was for some of their coreligionists beyond the Alps, to become assimilated to the ruling culture before they could contribute to it. Their Italianità was already so complete that the period of transition was reduced to almost nothing. . . . It was like a tree-trunk, held artificially below the water, and forcing its way irresistibly to the surface once the obstacles are broken.[6]

During the Italian Renaissance, there had been every prospect that the small Jewish communities of the Italian towns would join fully in the life of science. Vesalius, in his *De Humani Corporis Fabrica*, for instance, speaks of two Jews who helped him on his book; one of them, Lazzaro de Frigiis, he called his intimate friend. Padua, in Vesalius's time, with its six to seven hundred Jews, benefited from their high scientific contribution.[7] Then, however, commenced the era of the repression of Italian Jewry. The Catholic Church, confronted by the Protestant challenge, closed ranks, stamped out disagreement, insisted on total unity and discipline. The Popes ceased to be the patrons of arts and sciences, for they could no longer brook the dangers of free thought to total dogmatic commitment. Cardinal Caraffa, an exponent of the Inquisition, became Pope Paul IV on May 23, 1555; fifty days later, he promulgated the Bull which segregated the Jews of Rome into a ghetto. Jewish physicians had always been the leading advocates of the scientific standpoint. Another Papal Bull of 1581 forbade them to have Christian patients. Henceforth, though there were noted individual Jewish physicians, "the golden age of Jewish medicine in Italy was at an end." Italy and the Papacy, which had hitherto been "synonymous in Jewish history with an easygoing tolerance, became associated for three centuries with the darkest reaction. . . ." There were brief interludes of freedom during Napoleon's hegemony and the Revolution of 1848, when the ghetto was abolished only to be re-established with the restoration of papal civil power. As late as 1870, the Jews of Rome addressed a petition to the Pope that the ghetto be abrogated. They pleaded with the Most Holy Father to be mindful of

> . . . the insalubrity of the old Jewish dwellings; the direct and indirect obstacles to the free pursuit of the trades, the fine arts and the larger number of industries . . . the inability to take energetic measures for the better education of the greatly increasing poorer classes. . . .[8]

Their freedom, however, came not from a papal decree but with the triumph of Victor Emmanuel and the advent of Italian unification.

Jewish eminence in scientific achievement soon reflected itself in their frequent honors as Nobel Prize laureates. The percentage of Jews among the laureates has been far greater than their proportion among the European and American populations. The first Nobel Prizes were awarded in the year 1901. There were 128 laureates in the sciences from that year up to 1940, embracing the fields of physics, chemistry, and medicine and physiology. Of that number, 17 were classified as Jews; in physics, Albert Abraham Michelson, Gabriel Lippmann, Albert Einstein, Otto Meyerhof, Niels Bohr, James Franck, Gustav Hertz; in chemistry, Adolf von Baeyer, Otto Wallach, Richard Willstatter, Fritz Haber;[9] in medicine and physiology, Paul Ehrlich, Elie Metchnikoff, Robert Barany, Karl Landsteiner, Otto Warburg, Otto Loewi. Four of the laureates were "half-Jews," by virtue of their Jewish mothers. If we take the count of 17 laureates of Jewish descent, then in terms of percentages slightly more than 13 per cent of the Nobel Prize winners were Jews. With respect to the particular fields, there were 6 Jews among the 46 laureates in physics, 4 Jews out of 40 laureates in chemistry, and 7 Jews out of 42 laureates in medicine. In terms of percentages, 13 per cent of the physics awards were given to Jews, 10 per cent in chemistry, and more than 16 per cent in medicine and physiology. The Jewish population in Europe and the United States was during this period about 2.4 per cent, its proportion of the world's population about 1 per cent. Germany during this time received 40 Nobel awards, but of that number 12 were Jews—that is, about 33 per cent. The Jewish population in Germany prior to the Nazi rule was less then 1 per cent of the total population.[10]

It is perhaps an indication of the dominance of the secular, libertarian ethic among scientists that the most thorough accounts of the lives and work of the Nobel Prize winners completely omit any reference to their religious background, descent, or education.[11] Nobel Prizes are not awarded for achievements in pure mathematics, but we can mention one simple measure of the Jewish achievement in this field which was an outcome of the psychological revolution in the nineteenth century. *Men of Mathematics*, the brilliant book of E. T. Bell on the lives of mathematicians, chooses for its later chapters the names of sixteen great mathematicians who were born in the nineteenth century. Of these sixteen, four were Jews—Jacobi, Sylvester, Kronecker, and Cantor. The relationship of three of them to formal Judaism had become latent, for the enlightenment in Germany was followed quickly by the conversion of many middle-class Jewish families to Christianity. The Voltairean father of Karl Marx, for example, had his children and himself baptized in order to promote his legal career and their professional and social lives. The banker's son, Karl Gustav Jacob Jacobi, was thus Jacques Simon before his conversion;[12] Leopold Kronecker—liberal in his youth, later successful in business, a cynical realist in politics—embraced Christianity in his last years; George Cantor, the master of the transfinites, was also of Jewish descent, but his father had been converted to Protestantism and his mother was baptized a Roman Catholic. The "leading woman mathematician of our time," Emmy Noether, "the most creative abstract algebraist in the world," Bell notes, was also Jewish.[13]

There have been various theories to account for Jewish eminence in the sciences beginning in the nineteenth century. One oft-held theory emphasizes the social inheritance of the respect for learning, especially as found in the Talmudical tradition. Chaim Weizmann, a noted chemist himself, held to a variant of this theory:

> Our great men were always a product of symbiosis between the ancient, traditional Talmudical learning in which our ancestors were steeped in the Polish or Galician ghettos, or even in Spain, and the modern Western universities with which their children came in contact. There is often as not a long list of Talmudic scholars and Rabbis in the pedigrees of our modern scientists. In many cases they themselves have come from Talmudic schools, breaking away in their twenties and struggling through to Paris or Zurich or Princeton. It is this extraordinary phenomenon—a great tradition of learning fructified by modern methods—which has given us both first-class scientists and competent men in every branch of academic activity, out of all relation to our numbers.[14]

That the Jews respected learning through the Middle Ages is true; that they sharpened their intellect in the "dialectical training school" is also true;[15] but it was equally true that this sterile type of "learning" and disputation was an obstacle to the development of science among the Jews, a hurdle they had to surmount. This was the experience of Spinoza, the first great Jew to make the solitary perilous journey from the Talmudic dialectic to the free air of direct, straightforward Cartesian doubt and demonstration. Solomon Maimon, in an eighteenth-century Polish village, recorded his search for scientific knowledge in an atmosphere of obscurantism:

> But how was I to begin? To learn Polish or Latin with a Catholic teacher was for me impossible, on the one hand because the prejudices of my own people prohibited to me all languages but Hebrew, and all sciences but the Talmud and the vast array of its commentators, on the other hand because the prejudices of Cath-

olics would not allow them to give instruction in these matters to a Jew.

When, having learned the Latin and German characters through a painful deciphering, he searched for German books on the sciences, the question anew was:

> . . . but where was I to obtain German books in Lithuania? Fortunately for me I learned that the chief rabbi of a neighboring town, who in his youth had lived for a while in Germany, and learned the German language there, and made himself in some measure acquainted with the sciences, continued still, though in secret, to work at the sciences and had a fair library of German books.[16]

The Talmudical tradition, like Catholic scholasticism and Protestant fundamentalism, could make of science an underground pursuit. In Frankfurt, for instance, at the end of the eighteenth century, the leaders of the Jewish community fought against the introduction of secular studies. They "wished to live and think in accordance with the traditions of their ancestors, not altering a jot or tittle." They feared the whole structure would tumble down if the old girders were replaced. Their spiritual head, Rabbi Pinkes Hurwitz, inveighed from his pulpit against Moses Mendelssohn's translation of the Bible into German. The *cheder*, the traditional Jewish school, had its life-destroying, curiosity-crushing aspect. Simon Dubnow described it with some bitterness in 1884: "The entire pale is filled with thousands of children's prisons. These children are criminally tortured both in spirit and body. They know nothing of childhood, fields, meadows or blue skies. . . . An enormous Babylonian storehouse of wisdom is forcibly injected into the brains of these youngsters. They are told nothing about the real world, about nature and life, but only about the next world and about death." [17] Ghetto Judaism, indeed, was Judaism which had become contaminated with strong ingredients of masochist asceticism.

Subject to the depredations of mobs, the exactions of governmental officers, the always potential outbreak of lynching parties, the hatred of priests, peasants, peers, and proletarians, the ghetto Jew tended to mock both the Gentile world and himself. "It was only after the expulsion from Spain," wrote the noted Ahad Ha'am, that the Jews, in despair, succumbed to the alien influences of asceticism; "hatred and contempt for the flesh" had not been the standpoint of Maimonides.[18] In the ghetto, the Jew tended to level all human existence to a common denominator of meaninglessness; he hated society for its contempt of him, and he hated his defenseless, cringing self for what it had become. He knew a respite from a hostile world only in his family and synagogue. There was nothing to do but submit. His intellectual life lost the zest of adventures. His ideas congealed into a routine of words. Spinoza, precursor-rebel against ghetto Jewry and the spokesman for the coming age of the scientific intellectuals, voiced the criticism of the hedonist-libertarian ethic against ghetto masochistic asceticism. "The foundations of their religion," Spinoza wrote, may have "emasculated their minds," but not to such an extent, he hoped, as to preclude their national renaissance.[19] "*Effeminare*" ("to make feminine") was the vivid word Spinoza used to characterize the masochism of the ghetto.

Talmudical-Cabalist ways of thought were an expression of people living in perpetual anxiety, living as far as they could in self-contained communities, with their own courts and political structure, trying to have as little to do as they possibly could with the treacherous, hostile environment. The Talmudical preoccupation represented a clinging to the familiar warmth of tradition; its rote repetition meant emotional security, and one could joust with friends and neighbors in scholastic distinctions and debate. The world of things, action, and discovery was closed off to the Jews; therefore they cultivated a bygone world of words. Those who were discontent with verbal formalism turned to Cabalist mysticism, a "madness according to method," as Maimon described it, which claimed to bring man into direct communion with God, and to render all other sciences unnecessary.[20]

In the spring of 1950, I visited a Talmudical Academy in Safed, a town famous in Palestine as the center of Jewish mysticism for many centuries. I talked with a young student, thin, pale, with forelocks, dressed in a black caftan, a replica of his ancestors of three centuries ago, who disputed in the dank basements of their synagogues in Polish villages. It was a warm spring day in Israel, and on the farming settlements there was gaiety and dancing. The girls and boys were dressed in light, colorful clothes. But here in Safed, defying the sunshine and the green hills, was this young museum piece of ghetto learning. I asked him whether they studied any sciences or history or sociology. He looked at me reproachfully, and spoke curt words to rebuke my pagan intrusion: "*Rak limuday kodesh*" ("Only holy studies"). This was no dwelling place for the scientific spirit of free inquiry, and I could appreciate the measure of revolt which the youth of the Haskalah and the enlightenment undertook.

As a persecuted minority in late-medieval and Renaissance Europe, the intellectual culture of the Jews congealed, and became, in the absence of challenge and problems, repetitive and rigid. "In the sixteenth to eighteenth centuries," says Israel Abrahams, "the Jews fell under a subservience to Rabbinical authority and custom which can only be described as medieval. . . ." Medieval Spain had produced a Maimonides; now Judaism, cut off from the new worlds of science and exploration, "became more mystical as Europe became more rational, it clasped its cloak tighter as the sun burned warmer," and the seventeenth century was the gloomiest in the era before emancipation.[21] The nineteenth century brought a revival of the "old cosmopolitanism," speaking in natural accents of freedom which had long been repressed. But the traditional Jewish learning did not animate the scientific revival; Spinoza's earlier experience had been of rebellion and excommunication, not of continuity and growth from a vitalizing Jewish tradition. His was the prototypical experience of the Jewish scientific intellectual. Nonetheless, it is still true that the underlying ethic of Judaism remained one of a rational, moderate hedonism.[22] But the Talmudical-Cabalist era distorted this underlying philosophy in response to external pressures. When the Talmudist-Cabalist defense mechanism had outlived its purpose, the underlying hedonist ethic was released in full vigor. Einstein exemplified the hedonist-libertarian standpoint of the emergent Jewish scientist. As a believer in individual liberty, he refused to join in campaigns against Sabbath amusements and the indulgence in tobacco. "He was always more inclined to rely on the natural instincts" than on abstract ethical principles. "Ascetic instincts were foreign to him." [23]

Probably the best-known of the theories that have been advanced to account for the high Jewish contribution to science is the one Thorstein Veblen set forth in his essay "The Intellectual Pre-eminence of Jews in Modern Europe." In essence, Veblen argues that the fertility of Jewish science rests on the fact that the

Jew is what is called today an "alienated" intellectual. To preserve the high level of Jewish contribution, therefore, the Jew must be preserved in his state of alienation. According to Veblen, the young Jew is doubly alienated; he has surrendered his own archaic, "thearchic" culture, but at the same time he has found no "secure place in the scheme of gentile conventions into which he is thrown." Consequently, "he becomes a disturber of the intellectual peace . . . an intellectual wayfaring man, a wanderer in the intellectual no man's land, seeking another place to rest, farther along the road, somewhere over the horizon." [24] The Jew's alienation, says Veblen, turns him into a skeptic, a dispassionate inquirer, a complete follower of scientific method, which he turns freely on all things and institutions, without inner compunction.

Does Veblen's drama of the Jewish scientific intellectual really conform to the facts? No doubt it conveyed the drive of his own life's labors, the Norwegian-American boy never at home in American "pecuniary" culture, "interned" in American society. But it scarcely explains the fecundity of Jewish scientific work. The least "alienated" Jewish community in Europe, the Italian, was proportionately the most vigorous in its scientific contribution. The Italian Jewish scientists mixed most freely in all walks of Italian life; freedom and identification with the dominant secularism stimulated its work, not a sense of alienation.[25] Perhaps, it might be said, Veblen's theory is intended primarily to explain the contribution of Jews to social science; here, their sense of alienation from any culture, their rootlessness and belonginglessness make them the most dispassionate and detached of social analysts. Presumably the Jewish social scientists have less inner resistances to overcome as they analyze the dominant society. Again, however, the theory of inspiration through alienation does not altogether gibe with salient facts. The most noted group of Jewish social scientists came into being in France with the work of Emile Durkheim and Lucien Lévy-Bruhl. Durkheim, the scion of a rabbinical family, was the first to teach sociology in France; the courses he instituted at Bordeaux in 1887 marked the beginning of the French sociological school. His masterly analyses of "anomie" and "collective representations" in religious life are part of the permanent heritage of social science. Yet this student of "anomie," of alienation, was himself a person who experienced a fullness of identification with French life. His theorizing on the value of ceremonies, rites, emblems, holidays, and meetings was born of his own intense emotional experience. "During the anniversary of the fall of the Bastille on July 14, 1880, Durkheim spent the whole day in the streets for sheer joy of basking in the popular enthusiasm which this fete evoked." *La patrie* was to him a social group of higher order than the family; despite the anti-Semitism of the Dreyfusard years, "he was a soulful French patriot." In his words, "*La patrie, la Révolution française, Jeanne d'Arc, etc. sont pour nous des choses sacrées auxquelles nous ne permettons pas qu'on touche*" ("The nation, the French Revolution, Joan of Arc, are for us sacred objects which we will not allow anyone to touch").[26]

Greatness in social science can be linked either to the thinker's alienation from *or* his identification with social realities. Marx's critique of capitalist society was certainly born out of a profound disaffection with its ways, but the Jewish chemists, physicists, and mathematicians were, in large measure, persons who sought an identification with the prevailing host societies. The large number of converts to Christianity in the nineteenth century, among the German group especially, testified to an increasing identification with German liberal culture.

It is possible, however, that the Jewish reverence for learning tended through the centuries to result in a genetic selection which favored the reinforcement of intelligence. Well-to-do Jewish fathers would seek young scholars as their sons-in-law, and support them for years, often with a dowry which made them permanent fellows on a "foundation grant"; in many cases, young women married and supported scholars because they deemed it to be a reflected glory to have a husband devoted to the Law. Monastic celibacy among the Catholics tended to terminate genetic lines of high intelligence; perhaps the Jewish marriage preferences tended to strengthen them. Perhaps the more intelligent men had larger families and were more frequently married than the less intelligent. This theory is supported by Norbert Wiener and J. B. S. Haldane.[27] But to verify it would require historical data that are simply not available.

The Jewish experience of leaping within a generation from the religious to the scientific stages of thought, of telescoping within a few years a process which took Western European thinkers two centuries, resulted, however, in the creation of one science which was distinctively Jewish—psychoanalysis. Sigmund Freud and almost all of his co-workers were Jewish: Alfred Adler, Otto Rank, Hanns Sachs, Wilhelm Stekel, Sandor Ferenczi, A. A. Brill, Karl Abraham, Theodor Reik. This fact evidently weighed on Freud's mind; he always resented the suggestion that there was something uniquely Jewish in the discovery of psychoanalysis. When the French psychologist Pierre Janet attributed the origin of psychoanalysis to the peculiarities of the city of Vienna, with its "atmosphere of sensuality and immorality," Freud intimated that the idea was "so nonsensical" that he was inclined to take "the reproaching of the Vienna spirit" as a "euphemistic substitution for another one which one did not care to bring up publicly"—that is, the Jewish spirit.[28] Freud himself was, however, clearly troubled by the obvious linkage of psychoanalysis to a circle of Jewish intellectuals. He welcomed the tall, blond, Protestant, "Aryan" Carl Gustav Jung for the respectability he brought to the pariah among the sciences. In 1910, when Freud planned the founding of an International Psychoanalytic Association, he proposed that Jung be its first president. His Viennese Jewish co-workers were recalcitrant to the idea. Freud stormed at them:

> Most of you are Jews and therefore you are incompetent to win friends for the new teaching. Jews must be content with the modest role of preparing the ground. It is absolutely essential that I should form ties in the world of general science. . . . We are all in danger. . . . The Swiss will save us—will save me and all of you as well.[29]

Every revolution, however, as Freud later observed sadly, had its "epigones, reactions, and restorations," and Jung soon was heading a major revolt against psychoanalysis. Jung later wrote, in 1934:

> The Aryan unconscious has a higher potential than the Jewish and this is the advantage and also the disadvantage of a young people close to the barbarian. The Jewish psychology cannot understand this and considers it nonsensical.

Freud and his followers, said Jung, had failed to comprehend the German psyche, and were being taught a lesson by Nazism, "a movement which pervades a whole people and is manifest in every German individual." [30]

That Freud and his psychoanalytical school underestimated the savagery latent in German culture is no doubt true, but this was an optimistic error which they shared with all the world's civilized people. And Freud's analysis of aggression and civilization made his margin of error, in this respect, much less than that of any other contemporary social scientist. We must, however, clarify the sense in which we are able to say that psychoanalysis was very largely a Jewish science. It is the sense in which Pierre Duhem was able to say that chemistry was a French science, and in which it could be said after 1880 that seismology, the study of earthquakes, was a Japanese science.[31] There were social circumstances, such as the rapid urbanization of France at the end of the eighteenth century, which contributed to the direction of scientific talent toward important chemical problems; the frequent occurrence of severe earthquakes in Japan was a similar challenge to many of its young scientists who hoped to predict them or, in any case, to devise measures which would reduce the damage they inflicted. The intensity with which certain problems are experienced is the primary factor in explaining the relative allocations of scientific intelligence in those directions. Similarly, the social situation and experience of the Jews in the latter part of the nineteenth century made them especially sensitive to psychoanalytical insights. It was not, perhaps, "entirely a matter of chance," wrote Freud, "that the first advocate of psychoanalysis was a Jew." [32]

What then were the social circumstances which account in large part for the Jewish origins of psychoanalysis? In the first place, it must be borne in mind that the largest proportion of Jewish scientific intelligence tended to go into the medical profession. In part, this was the outcome of the high traditional Jewish regard for the medical art, but there were still more important causes involved. A young Jew with scientific powers could not realistically aspire to a career in teaching or research at a university laboratory. "Jews," writes Max Grunwald, "were particularly numerous in the medical profession because other occupations were closed to them." [33]

A doctor could practice his profession as an individual entrepreneur; he was the petty bourgeois among scientists, dependent to a minimum on the good will or facilities of institutions. Especially was this the case with the doctor who undertook psychiatric practice. In other branches of medicine, the question of hospital appointments and the use of laboratory and surgical resources was crucial. Jewish doctors encountered an anti-Semitism in hospital appointments which was only a little less than that in the universities. The healer of mental anxieties, however, needed no physical equipment; his capital investment was zero. He worked with intuition and imagination. For such reasons, there was a revival in the nineteenth century of the medieval Jewish figure of the physician-philosopher.

Second, the Jewish doctor in the nineteenth century tended to acquire the authority which had once been the prerogative of the rabbi. The latter's prestige had been inordinate in the scattered communities of Europe; the Jewish people were ruled, as Maimon said, by "a perpetual aristocracy under the appearance of a theocracy." [34] During the nineteenth century, however, hundreds of thousands of Jews made their way from the villages to the cities. Ancient roots were torn asunder. The rabbi, the village theocrat, was in little evidence in the big city. In America, the editor of the *Jewish Daily Forward* became the familiar adviser to thousands of immigrants in a celebrated column, the "Bintl Brief"; it would have been pointless to ask a rabbi's advice on the new questions, for he was even more at sea in the new civilization than the layman.[35] It was above all the doctor to whom the Jew went with his problems. The physician would listen to all the troubles and tribulations, and he had the mastery of the new sciences in his possession. Roman Catholics had their priests for confessional; the Jewish doctor could not absolve, but he became the greatest listener in the world. Freud himself explicitly conceived of the psychoanalyst as a "secular spiritual guide." "These words," he wrote, " 'a secular spiritual guide,' might well serve as a general formula for describing a function which the analyst . . . has to perform in his relation to the public." He could not bring relief to the patient "by receiving him into the Catholic, protestant or socialist community." [36] The omission of "Jewish community" is striking. For he was indeed a secular rabbi, a secular guide for the perplexed.

Third, during the nineteenth century the Jews experienced an extremely sharp rise in sexual repression. In the early eighteen-hundreds, a young Jew living in an Austrian or Polish village was apt to get married at the age of fourteen or fifteen. Maimon had his first child when he was in his fourteenth year.[37] The phenomenon of postponed sexual satisfaction was relatively unknown. As the Jews, however, migrated to the urban centers, and their sons undertook to rise from a commercial lower middle class and working class to the professional class, their mode of existence altered. Young Jews with ambitions to become lawyers and doctors were compelled, as Freud was, to postpone marriage for many years. A genre of Viennese literature developed which, as in Schnitzler's plays, dealt with problems that arose from the frustrated sexuality of young middle-class men. Thus, the rapid evolution of the Jews in Europe during the nineteenth century tended to expose to view the role of sexuality in the causation of neurosis.

In the fourth place, the scientific revolution among the Jews produced a greater conflict and tension within families than had been the case with any other people; it thereby brought to the surface the operations of all the mechanisms of the superego, the force of early upbringing, the hostilities between fathers and sons. "In the de-Judaized intellectual of Jewish origin," writes Horace Kallen, "the pretense of scientific impartiality and intellectual detachment is all too often a screen for a seething of passion and prejudice. . . ." For among the Jews the scientific revolution went hand in hand with a cultural revolution; the revolt against traditional religious ideas took a tremendous emotional toll from the younger generation. The revolt against the superego was the dominant emotional episode in thousands of Jewish homes. In Minsk at the end of the nineteenth century, Jewish students, wrote Shymarya Levin, "spoke with bitterness of the years they had given to Jewish lore. . . . They considered them a complete waste; it was as if they now saw the light of the world for the first time." They wished to wipe out their own past.[38]

The dynamics of psychoanalysis caught the drama of the emotional-intellectual conflict of Jewish generations. The Protestant Reformation had riven section against section, country against country, and even class against class; but never did it divide families in the fashion that the coming of secularism and science did among the Jews. Here one could see clearly into the workings of the unconscious. More than a hundred years ago a bullet wound tore open the intestinal wall of a French Canadian fur trapper; he survived, and his physician was enabled to peer into the hitherto concealed digestive operations. Thus it was among the Jews. Their scientific revolution was founded on so rapid and violent a psychological revolution that the operations of the unconscious stood closer to the introspective view than they ever had before. The Jewish psychologist was almost inevitably a psychoanalyst.

Lastly, there was among Jewish scientists the phenomenon which we can call the "vigor of skipped stages." The young Jews stepped from orthodox religious homes into the most advanced scientific circles. Orthodox religion was hopelessly more intellectually irrelevant than the various Protestant compromises. The Jewish scientists usually became freethinkers and agnostics; they did not pause in a metaphysical stage. The Darwinian controversy scarcely created a ripple among Jewish scientists; they straightway became Darwinians, because they had virtually thrown aside all their religious baggage and had no pillboxes of emotional resistance to the most advanced scientific theories. They moved to the forefront of scientific speculation. They had to undo three centuries of retardation, and they wasted no time on intervening doubts and hesitations. As Morris R. Cohen remarked:

> A gas that has just been taken away from some compound and liberated combines more rapidly with new elements. So the Jews being in a nascent or transitional stage, are eager, and have the zest or spirit of adventure essential for modern science.[39]

The Viennese psychoanalytical society will take its place in the annals of science with the little invisible college group out of which grew the Royal Society with its "new philosophy." [40] The circumstances were not too dissimilar. Psychoanalysis in the twentieth century could not find a home in the established universities and curricula. Its practitioners were not allied to any religious orthodoxy, and they proposed to apply the scientific method to the deepest concerns of the human being. Barred from universities and laboratories, they set up their own society, and research and training programs, and built a science devoted to problems which the existing institutions preferred not to see.

The young Jewish scientific intellectuals experienced all manner of anti-Semitic rebuffs. To experiences of this kind, as to anxieties generally, there are three kinds of responses. One can take human aggression and guilt as virtual constants, and seek to alleviate a world of constant evil through understanding and assimilating it. Or one can refuse to accept the constancy of people's behavior, and seek, by immersing oneself in social movements, to alter institutions, to bring about a changed world. Or one can seek the resolution of problems by recourse to the divine, to religion and its world beyond earthly things. The Jewish scientific intellectuals took the first two directions. The religious adaptation of psychoanalysis was something not found among Jewish scientific intellectuals till after the nightmares of the death camps.

Freud himself, pursuing the first course of understanding and adaptation, prudently limited the orbit of his moral advice. "Be abstinent, but under protest," he told young students in a famous lecture.

> He felt that it was imperative to keep alive the inner protest against a social order which prevented mature young men from fulfilling a normal instinctual need. He drew parallels between this attitude and that of the French Encyclopedists of the eighteenth century who, though submissive outwardly to the power of the Church which ruled their age, dedicated themselves to tireless protest against its overwhelming and unbearable force.[41]

There was a melancholy in Freud that always warned him to limit his hopes; he had no high expectations for even his own therapy, and he seemed to see himself as a Moses who had brought wisdom from on high to humanity only to see them persist in worshiping false gods. Deep within himself, he looked upon Europeans as the persecutors of his own, as the humiliators of his father, and he idealized Hannibal, the Semitic general who had sworn eternal hostility against the Romans. He could assign to the European masses no historic mission to save civilization; what salvation there was was in the hands of a small intellectual elite. He seems to have conceived himself in a curious rivalry with the founder of Austrian Socialism, Victor Adler, for the Socialist movement, like Zionism, competed in Vienna for the emotional loyalties of Jewish scientific intellectuals who had sustained the impact of anti-Semitism.[42] The Jewish youth of Vienna, writes Grunwald, were for

> . . . lack of an ideal . . . in the throes of conflicting mental complexes. It is no accident that Vienna was the place where Adler

hit upon the idea of fighting the inferiority complex by means of individual psychology.

And here, too, Theodor Herzl promulgated his vision of a Jewish state. Freud dreamed one night of Herzl, pale and sad-eyed, explaining to him "the necessity of immediate action if the Jewish people was to be saved." [43] The revolt against the masochist asceticism of ghetto Judaism took many forms—psychoanalysis, Zionism, Socialism. All these modes of thought were linked, however, with the common denominator of the hedonist-libertarian ethic, which in its variant forms was the philosophy of the Jewish renaissance, the philosophy of the Jewish scientific intellectuals.

NOTES

1. Jacob S. Raisin, *The Haskalah Movement in Russia* (Philadelphia, 1913), p. 11.

2. Israel Friedlaender, *The Jews of Russia and Poland* (New York, 1915), p. 198. Cf. Israel Cohen, *History of Jews in Vilna* (Philadelphia, 1943), pp. 310-11.

3. Jacob S. Raisin, *op. cit.*, pp. 131, 167, 239-40, 245. Professor Louis Ginzberg, however, describes the opposition of Salanter and many of his party to Haskalah as "not the result of hostility to secular knowledge" but rather as based on the conviction that the Czarist government was furthering secular knowledge among the Jews in order to destroy Judaism. However, the Russian government soon dropped its educational plans for the Jews, and tried to suppress the spread of scientific interests. The Jewish youth itself clearly longed for scientific studies, and every village knew the conflict between orthodoxy and secularism. Cf. Louis Ginzberg, *Students, Scholars, and Saints* (Philadelphia, 1928), p. 156.

4. Jacob S. Raisin, *op. cit.*, p. 273. Shmarya Levin, *Youth in Revolt*, trans. Maurice Samuel (New York, 1930), pp. 279-80. Louis Greenberg, *The Jews In Russia* (New Haven, 1944), Vol. I, pp. 149 ff.

5. S. M. Dubnow, *History of the Jews in Russia and Poland*, trans. I. Friedlaender (Philadelphia, 1920), Vol. III, p. 31.

6. Cecil Roth, *The History of the Jews of Italy* (Philadelphia, 1946), pp. 479, 501. Louis Gershenfeld, *The Jew in Science* (Philadelphia, 1934), p. 146.

7. M. Roth, *Andreas Versalius Bruxellensis* (Berlin, 1892), pp. 117,

119, 364. Cf. Moses A. Shulvass, "The Jewish Population in Renaissance Italy," *Jewish Social Studies*, XIII (1951), 15.

8. Cecil Roth, *op. cit.*, p. 296, 316-17. Louis Wirth, *The Ghetto* (Chicago, 1928), pp. 113-14. Also cf. Cecil Roth, *The Jews in the Renaissance* (Philadelphia, 1959), pp. 37-40, 80, 112, 213-14, 229.

9. For the last years of Willstatter and Haber, cf. Chaim Weizmann, *Trial and Error* (New York, 1949), pp. 350-4.

10. Abraham Shinedling, "Jewish Nobel Prize Winners," *Universal Jewish Encyclopedia* (New York, 1942), Vol. VIII, pp. 228-9. Flora Kaplan, *Nobel Prize Winners: Charts-Indexes, Sketches* (Chicago, 1939), pp. 142-3. Cf. Cecil Roth, *The Jewish Contribution to Civilisation* (London, 1938), p. 173. Cf. Tina Levitan, *The Laureates: Jewish Winners of the Nobel Prize* (New York, 1960), pp. 20-21.

11. Niels H. de V. Heathcote, *Nobel Prize Winners in Physics: 1901-1950* (New York, 1953); Lloyd G. Stevenson, *Nobel Prize Winners in Medicine and Physiology: 1901-1950* (New York, 1953); Eduard Farber, *Nobel Prize Winners in Chemistry: 1901-1950* (New York, 1954). Cf. Benjamin Harrow, "Jews in the Field of Science," *Menorah Journal*, VI (1920), 95-108.

12. Louis Gershenfeld, *op. cit.*, p. 147; "Carl Gustav Jacob Jacobi," *Universal Jewish Encyclopedia*, Vol. VI, p. 15. E. T. Bell's account *Men of Mathematics* (New York, 1937) does not mention the fact that Jacobi's first academic appointment followed his conversion to Christianity. Nor is it discussed in Leo Koenigsberger, *Carl Gustav Jacob Jacobi* (Leipzig, 1904). According to Shmarya Levin, Kronecker paid his dues from 1883 to 1891 to the Jewish community, "but he had privately accepted the Protestant faith, and had been ashamed to make it known. He paid for his professorship with his Jewishness, and for his Protestantism with his taxes to the Jewish community." Shmarya Levin, *op. cit.*, p. 263.

13. E. T. Bell, *op. cit.*, p. 261.

14. Chaim Weizmann, *op. cit.*, p. 356.

15. Louis Wirth, *op. cit.*, pp. 80-2.

16. Solomon Maimon, *An Autobiography*, trans. J. Clark Murray (London, 1888), pp. 89-90, 106-7.

17. A. Freimann and F. Kracauer, *History of Jews in Frankfurt*, trans. Bertha Szold Levin (Philadelphia, 1929), pp. 182-3, 217-18. Simon Dubnow, *Nationalism and History*, ed. Koppel S. Pinson (Philadelphia, 1958), pp. 9-10.

18. Ahad Ha'am, *Selected Essays*, trans. Leon Simon (Philadelphia, 1912), pp. 141, 151.

19. *The Chief Works of Benedict de Spinoza*, trans. R. H. M. Elwes

(London, 1883), Vol. I, p. 56. The contrast with the Spanish Jewish culture of the twelfth century was striking. Cf. Israel Abrahams, *Jewish Life in the Middle Ages*, ed. Cecil Roth (London, 1932), pp. 389-90.

20. Solomon Maimon, *op. cit.*, p. 95.

21. Israel Abrahams, *op. cit.*, pp. 2, 6, 11, 176.

22. Cf. Simon Bernfeld, *The Foundations of Jewish Ethics*, trans. A. H. Koller (New York, 1929), pp. 187-224.

23. Philipp Frank, *Einstein: His Life and Times*, trans. George Rosen (New York, 1947), pp. 186-7.

24. Thorstein Veblen, *Essays in Our Changing Order*, ed. Leon Ardzrooni (New York, 1934), p. 227-8. Cf. Lewis S. Feuer, "Thorstein Veblen: The Metaphysics of the Interned Immigrant," *American Quarterly*, V (1953), 99-112.

25. Cf. Laura Fermi, *Atoms in the Family: My Life with Enrico Fermi* (Chicago, 1954), p. 118.

26. M. Marion Mitchell, "Emile Durkheim and the Philosophy of Nationalism," *Political Science Quarterly*, XLVI (1931), 100, 105. Emile Durkheim, "De la Définition des Phénomènes Réligieux," *L'Année Sociologique*, II (1898), 20.

27. Norbert Wiener, *Ex-Prodigy: My Childhood and Youth* (New York, 1953), pp. 11-12. Cf. pp. 154-6, 297.

28. Sigmund Freud, *The History of the Psychoanalytic Movement*, in *The Basic Writings of Sigmund Freud*, trans. A. A. Brill (New York, 1938), pp. 956-7.

29. Fritz Wittels, *Sigmund Freud*, trans. Eden and Cedar Paul (New York, 1924), p. 140. Ernest Jones, *The Life and Work of Sigmund Freud* (New York, 1955), Vol. II, p. 69.

30. S. S. Feldman, "Dr. C. G. Jung and National Socialism," *The American Journal of Psychiatry*, CII (1945), 263. Also, Edward Glover, *Freud or Jung?* (New York, 1956), pp. 151-2.

31. Pierre Duhem, *La Chimie, Est Elle une Science Française?* (Paris, 1916), pp. 1, 186. Torahiko Terada and Takeo Matuzawa, "A Historical Sketch of the Development of Seismology in Japan," in *Scientific Japan: Past and Present*, ed. Joji Sakurai (Kyoto, 1926), pp. 252-5. Charles Davison, *The Founders of Seismology* (Cambridge, 1927), pp. 181-2.

32. Sigmund Freud, *Collected Papers*, ed. James Strachey (London, 1950), Vol. V, p. 174.

33. Max Grunwald, *History of Jews in Vienna* (Philadelphia, 1936), p. 518. Also Arthur Ruppin, *The Jews in the Modern World* (London, 1934), p. 218. Shmarya Levin, *op. cit.*, p. 227. Arnold Merzbach, "Jewish Physicians in Central Europe During the Transitional Period from Ghetto to Emancipation," *Archives Internationales d'Histoire des Sci-*

ences, XXXIII (1954), 172. For the medieval period, cf. Max Meyerhof, "Medieval Jewish Physicians in the Near East from Arabic Sources," *Isis*, XXVIII (1938), 432-60. Raphael Mahler, "Jews in Public Service and the Liberal Professions in Poland, 1918-39," *Jewish Social Studies*, VI (1944), 327, 337.

34. Solomon Maimon, *op. cit.*, p. 285.

35. Marvin Bressler, "Selected Family Patterns in W. I. Thomas' Unfinished Study of the Bintl Brief," *American Sociological Review*, XVII (1952), 565.

36. Sigmund Freud, *Collected Papers*, Vol. V, pp. 210-11.

37. Solomon Maimon, *op. cit.*, p. 79.

38. Horace M. Kallen, *Of Them Which Say They Are Jews*, ed. Judah Pilch (New York, 1954), p. 162. Shmarya Levin, *op. cit.*, pp. 100-101. The youthful Morris R. Cohen depicted the conflict of the generations on the East Side of New York. Cf. *Memorials of Thomas Davidson*, ed. William Knight (Boston, 1907), p. 87.

39. Morris R. Cohen, "The Jew in Science," *Reflections of a Wondering Jew* (Boston, 1950), p. 100.

40. *The Basic Writings of Sigmund Freud*, p. 973.

41. Theodor Reik, *From Thirty Years with Freud* (New York, 1940), p. 15.

42. Sigmund Freud, "The Moses of Michelangelo," in *On Creativity and the Unconscious*," ed. Benjamin N. Nelson (New York, 1958), p. 37. Martin Grotjahn, "A Letter by Sigmund Freud with Recollections of his Adolescence," *Journal of the American Psychoanalytic Association*, IV (1956), 647-9, 651-2.

43. Max Grunwald, *op. cit.*, p. 456. Leo Goldhammer, "Herzl and Freud," in *Herzl Year Book*, ed. Raphael Patai (New York, 1958), Vol. I, pp. 194-6.

XI

The Scientific Intellectual in the United States

I

The Scientists of Colonial America

THE ACHIEVEMENTS OF AMERICAN CIVILIZATION HAVE ALWAYS been associated with the qualities of character referred to under the name "Protestant ethic." Whatever the causal circumstances for the rise of scientific movements in Catholic Italy or Eastern European Jewry or revolutionary France, the American scientist, like the American businessman, seems to many persons the product of the Protestant outlook. America, with its fresh culture, in large part self-formed, without the impediments of a feudal past, is therefore a unique test case in our effort to find the psychological conditions that make for the emergence of the scientific intellectual.

◆§ The Decline of the Spanish-American Universities

IT SEEMED FOR A WHILE in the seventeenth century that a scientific movement might flourish in Catholic Spanish America rather than in the Protestant English colonies. Samuel Eliot Morison, devoted historian of his Puritan forebears, actually states, "The scientific production of colonial New England was negligible compared with that of Mexico." [1] The Catholic city of Mexico externally had seemed to promise to become a cultural beacon for the Western Hemisphere. Its Royal University had twenty-three chairs. Its professor of mathematics from 1637 to 1668, Don Diego Rodriguez, wrote treatises on logarithms, speculative geometry, and algebra, while in 1681 Don Carlos de Sigüenza, a Cartesian scientist who broke away from the Jesuit order, published a rationalist pamphlet, *Philosophical Manifest against Comets stripped of their dominion over the timid.*[2]

But no Padua was to emerge in Mexico or elsewhere in Spanish America. Every professor in the University of Mexico had to subscribe to the dogma of the Immaculate Conception of the Virgin Mary, and take an oath to defend its integrity.[3] The masochist asceticism which prevailed in Spanish Catholicism stamped out the sources of the scientific intelligence. As Henry Bamford Parkes writes:

> The religion of the Spaniards, like that of the Aztecs, was dualistic, requiring not only pageantry and *fiestas* but also the infliction and the suffering of pain. In every church there was an image of the bleeding Christ. Down to the nineteenth century there were convents where nuns, who had dedicated themselves from childhood to be his brides, wore crowns of thorns and slept on boards studded with iron spikes. Annually, during the season known as the *desogravios*, a similar acknowledgement of the sinfulness of human flesh was expected of the laity, and at nighttime, in darkened churches, after a priest had described how Christ had been scourged, congregations lashed themselves until the floor was wet with blood.[4]

To this religion of fanatical self-aggression, "heresy was the only unpardonable sin." As late as the beginning of the nineteenth century, a questioning spirit, Fray Servando de Teresa y Mier, was deported to Spain because he denied the miraculous origin of the picture of the Virgin of Guadalupe. The doctrine of the Mexican church, says Professor Parkes, bore no kinship with "the more elevated forms of Catholicism in Europe." Its clergy sought "a despotic government, a privileged priesthood, and an ignorant laity." In Spanish America, the command to believe was a command to ignorance and self-hatred. Although more than twenty universities were founded in Spanish America before July 4, 1776, their intellectual careers were stifled by the same forces that crushed the Galileisti in Italy. Scholastic theology ruled in the Spanish American universities. The chairs of theology commanded the highest salaries, and the higher degrees in theology were most numerous. Of the 2,510 degrees granted at Guatemala by the year 1821, few were in medicine—only thirty bachelors, twelve licentiates, and twelve doctors.[5] The Spanish American students evidently grew restless with the enforced scholastic mode of thought. The medical students especially exhibited a ribaldry which outraged the authorities. Bishops dealt with disciplinary cases in which, for instance, "the student took a light view of the cloth." There was a "growing levity and restlessness" on the part of the students and some of the professors in the second half of the eighteenth century. When the circumstances suggested overt heresy, as in the case of Gil Rodriguez in 1795, the powers of the Inquisition were invoked. The hedonist-libertarian ethic was the philosophy of these first Spanish-American student movements. As Professor John Tate Lanning writes, "A certain vague resentment of sameness expressed itself at first in sheer deviltry and then revealed overtones of 'Enlightenment' and political unrest." [6]

The Spanish-American universities and libraries had more books than those of the English colonies. The largest college library in New England in the eighteenth century was approximately the size of that of San Carlos in Guatemala. But books of experimental science were scarce among the Spanish Americans. Agriculture and commerce languished, university chairs were not filled for lack of funds, intellectuals became frustrated and embittered. The

Aristotelian texts, expounded in Latin, remained as the heart of the curriculum until the end of the eighteenth century, and their professors were chosen, in medieval fashion, through contests of syllogistic jousts. This situation endured in Mexico until after the middle of the nineteenth century, when Benito Juárez and his Comtist advisers came to power.[7]

The Growth of the Merchant Aristocracy in New England

THE EARLY GOVERNMENT of the Massachusetts Bay Colony has been well described as a "Puritan oligarchy," a government of the elect, by the elect, and for the elect.[8] As the colony, however, matured, various factors tended to diminish the social and intellectual hegemony of the Puritan clergy. The scientific movement in colonial New England was not the outcome of the Puritan philosophy; rather, it was tied to the liberal protest which by the end of the seventeenth century succeeded in basically transforming the character of Puritan society.

The economic development of Massachusetts undermined the sway of the Puritan divines. During the first thirty years of its life, the unified economy of the agricultural village was being supplanted rapidly by far-flung communities of dispersed farms. The Puritan clergyman could no longer oversee easily the deeds of his flock. The influx of strangers, of non-members of the Congregationalist churches, became considerable. Meanwhile, by 1664, the merchant fleet of Boston grew to no less than three hundred vessels. Boston was becoming known as "the mart town of the West Indians."[9] A merchant aristocracy came into being, wealthy, powerful, with a love for fine furniture and silver, and with leanings toward a rational empiricist outlook. They ignored the disapproval of the divines, and allowed their mansions to shelter such pursuits as dancing, even "mixed" dancing. In vain, the Boston ministers published in 1684 a pamphlet entitled *An Arrow against Profane and Promiscuous Dancing*. They were unable to prevent the installation of dancing masters. The well-to-do, furthermore, began toward the century's end to wear wigs, the fashion of the Cavaliers, in contravention of the ministers' warnings against the "pride of hair" which was a sign of "spiritual decay."

The Boston merchants early found themselves at odds with the strict Puritan ideology. In 1645, they petitioned for the abrogation of laws which restricted the entertainment of strangers and banished Anabaptists. Puritan clergymen exhorted them to "remember that originally they are a plantation religious, not a plantation of trade." Their economic experience, however, was impressing the merchant class with a rationalistic spirit. This matter-of-fact standpoint was spreading among the lowly classes as well. When a Massachusetts minister bade his congregation in a fishing village to remain steadfast to religion, since it had been the main end of their migration to America, "a well-known person there in the assembly cried out, 'Sir, you are mistaken—our main end was to catch fish.' "

The Puritan divines brooded over the rising tide of liberal rationalism. The terrible delusion of witchcraft which spread through the Colony in 1692 was in large part the outcome of their desire to strike a blow at the scientific philosophy. To have proved the reality of witches would have been a devastating blow against the new rationalism. In 1681, a group of New England ministers, after considering earnestly the mounting dangers to religion, decided to gather proofs of the supernatural, to gather and publish all instances of "divine judgments, tempests, floods, earthquakes, thunders as are unusual, strange apparitions . . . witchcrafts, diabolical possessions. . . ." Increase Mather in 1684 raised fears of magicians and witches among the populace in his *An Essay for the Recording of Illustrious Providences.* He and his son Cotton regarded the "facts" of witchcraft as most important evidence against "Sadduceeism," which in the seventeenth century comprised all rationalist, deistic tendencies.

According to Raymond P. Stearns, there was no "war" between science and religion in seventeenth-century New England.[10] Actually, however, within the setting of Puritan Massachusetts, the conflict between the hedonist-libertarian and the authoritarian-ascetic ethic ranged over a series of questions: liberal education, witchcraft, smallpox inoculation. The Puritan standpoint led to no natural alliance with the scientific spirit. "Though the Puritans lived in the presence of the great scientific revolution," writes Perry Miller, "the first consideration for them was that it should not sweep their feet off the ground of religious orthodoxy."[11] Their suspicion of the scientific intellectual never vanished.

It is striking, moreover, that Puritan asceticism led to a revival of philosophical realism and an extreme hostility to nominalism. The close correlation we observed in medieval Europe between sexual repression and philosophical realism held in colonial America as well. The Puritans became intensely attached to the formulations of the Protestant logician Petrus Ramus (martyred in Paris during St. Bartholomew's Massacre), according to which concepts denote objective, Platonic essences.

> The appeal of this logic to the Puritan mind [says Perry Miller], resulted from its satisfying one of the deepest desires of that mind. . . . Puritanism's need for a stick to beat the dog of nominalism was desperate, as is shown by the recurrence throughout the literature of New England Puritanism in sermons, theological arguments, and above all in the treatises of ecclesiastical polity, of the insistence that universals are objectively real.[12]

The Puritan divines are said to have counted that day lost in which they did not spend ten or twelve hours in their studies. Their Puritan discipline, however, sundered their sense of reality. John Cotton, the leading spokesman of American Puritanism, energetically insisted that the Bible was the authority for settling any question whatsoever. If on occasion some remarks of Jesus on the weather led Cotton to the hesitant inference that "it is not utterly unlawful for men to make observation of the estate of the weather," he still took the meteorology of Ecclesiastes as the touchstone for sound explanation. Natural philosophy remained under a cloud as a source of vexation for the human spirit.[13]

Almanacs were the first American secular publications of popular science; they met the needs of farmers and fishermen in the most practical way, with a minimum of theology. As early as 1659, young Harvard graduates who compiled the New England almanacs were expounding the Copernican hypothesis. One of them, Samuel Cheever, even undertook to reconcile the Copernican system with original sin; fallen man was left so ignorant by "his dim Intellectual eye" and "dark medium of the body" that it took the accretions of knowledge through the ages to undo his ignorance. The almanacs were, indeed, "the most widely diffused form of literature, and the only periodical literature, in New England." Although they were published by the Cambridge printer in the college yard, it cannot be said, as Samuel Eliot Morison does, that the Puritan clergy "were the chief patrons and promoters of the new astronomy, and of other scientific discoveries, in New England." [14] For the almanac makers were the new young generation, moved—as we shall see in the case of William Brattle's almanac—by a philosophy very different from that of the leading Puritan divines. John Cotton, however, the dominant Puritan divine from 1633 until his death in 1652, with "an ascendancy more sovereign" than any other American clergyman ever reached, rejected the Copernican hypothesis as contrary to Scriptural authority.[15] The Puritan divines were not the promoters of the Copernican cosmology and science; their reception of science always partook of a rear-guard action.

The power of the merchant community was brought to bear decisively against the Puritan theocrats when the hysterical accusation of witchcraft touched persons close to themselves—the wives of a magistrate, the leading merchant of Salem, and, last, the Governor himself. A lay intellectual elite became influential in Massachusetts toward the end of the seventeenth century. They clashed with the Puritan theocrats. They refused to be subservient to orthodoxy. The new elite opened the doors of Harvard to some of the newer ideas which were arousing Europe. As Morison states, "There was just enough notion of academic freedom to give Harvard a bad name among strict Calvinists." [16]

The advent of the Restoration strengthened the liberal development of the Massachusetts colony. In 1662, King Charles II directed the colony to grant the franchise to all freeholders of competent estates, whether members or not of a Congregational Church. The Puritan oligarchy resisted for years with all its devices of delay and evasion. Increase Mather called upon them to yield nothing of what their fathers had wrought so dearly. But he himself bowed to the times in 1689, when he accepted a charter which enfranchised all freeholders with a specified income. The Puritan theocracy gave way to a liberal commercial elite.

☙ The Brothers Brattle and John Leverett

THE COLONIAL FELLOWS OF THE ROYAL SOCIETY were predominantly drawn from the ranks of the newly formed liberal American elite. Let us review their lives and characters briefly, and see what manner of men they were. Thomas Brattle, prosperous merchant and scientist, was an embodiment of this new liberal temper. He combined the hedonistic ethics with a scientific outlook, and he worked to shape policy at Harvard in a liberal direction. Brattle was elected to the Royal Society in 1692. His observations on the comet of 1680 were used by Halley, Flamsteed, and Newton, and he contributed articles on the solar eclipses of 1692, 1703, and 1707 to the *Philosophical Transactions*. He took a justifiable pride in the fact that Newton had regarded his observations of the comet of 1680 as among the better ones.

During the frenzy of the witchcraft hysteria, Brattle's voice was raised courageously in protest. He circulated in 1692 a paper entitled, *A Full and Candid Account of the Delusion Called Witchcraft Which Prevailed in New England*, in which he wrote forthrightly:

> This Salem philosophy some men call the new philosophy, but I think it rather deserves the name of Salem superstition and sorcery, and it is not fit to be named in a land of such light as New-England is.

Brattle further outraged the Puritan divines when he provided the land in 1699 for the founding of the Brattle Street Church, a new group, which dispensed with public confessions and gave to non-communicant members a share in church government. Increase Mather published a tract against the tenets of these innovating liberals. In 1711, Brattle imported an organ for his and his friends' enjoyment. He bequeathed it to the new church, but liberal ideas had not reached a stage of advancement sufficient for its acceptance.

From 1693 until his death, Thomas Brattle was Treasurer of Harvard College. As his family history says, he endured "great opposition and enmity in his public and private life from the closer adherents to the popular theology of the day." In 1699, "owing to his liberality in religious views," he was excluded, together with John Leverett, from his seat in the Harvard Corporation, but was reinstated in 1703. Four years later, Brattle helped to turn the tables against the Mathers. In 1707, the Harvard Corporation selected John Leverett as president of its college. He was the first layman to hold that office. His inauguration was a true celebration of victory; the liberal party had come to power.[17]

William Brattle, brother of Thomas, was elected to the Royal Society in 1713. Curiously, he declined, according to the Society's minutes, to "accept of the Title of member of the Society as unqualified." He was not an empirical scientist like his brother, but he performed the great service of introducing the new scientific philosophy into Harvard in 1690. William wrote the first book on logic ever published in the colonies—an adaptation of Descartes' *Compendium Logicae. A Compendium of Logick* was the breach in the orthodox Ramist teaching at Harvard. Under William Brattle's influence, a candidate for the Master's degree at Harvard dared argue an affirmative answer to the question: "Is doubt the beginning of all indubitable philosophy?" Calvinist theology was largely a scholatic system; William Brattle had set out in new directions. At his ordination, "he gave evidence of his intention to cast loose from some of the established customs of the New England churches," and he, too, was for a while excluded from the Harvard Corporation in 1700 because of his liberal views. "It is largely owing to Brattle as tutor and Leverett both as tutor and President," says Professor Morison, "that Harvard was saved from becoming a sectarian institution. . . ."[18] Religious liberalism was simply the dilution of received creeds with hedonistic and scientific ideas; religious liberalism was, above all, opposed to the typical Calvinist ideas—election, predestination, asceticism. It was the product of man's ease of spirit, not of a sense of guilt.

William Brattle's own philosophy was colorfully expressed in a publication of his in 1682 which was a blend between an essay in astronomy and a farmers' almanac. It was entitled *An Ephemeris of Caelestial Motions, Aspects, Eclipses, etc., for the Year of the Christian Era 1682;* an "ephemeris," Brattle explained, was a set of astronomical tables fitted to a certain place for a certain time. Each month was assigned its page of prognoses, and each month was celebrated with verse. Again what strikes one is the total absence of a theological note in Brattle's calendar verse. He is a secular-minded hedonist delighting in each month's offerings. Several of the scientist-versifier's stanzas convey the joyous mood:

March heralds spring's rebirth:

> The Vernal Rams-horn shall no sooner sound
> But lifeless Beings Latent in the ground
> Shall pierce the clodded earth, Spring up and thrive,
> Till at the height of Nature they arrive.

April celebrates sexual passion:

> The Rusticks, now the Flesh to satisfie,
> Will not obscene, and dirty acts defie;
> With sweat they toil in th' earth, and do expect
> Seed by their Mother to erect.
> But, if the heavens do from sweat abstain
> The Rusticks sweat will wholly be in vain.

May brings a warning against superstition:

> Hundreds of Apes almost everywhere
> Will now appear with wings flying in th' Air. . . .
> But (Friends) Fear not, the news it doth portend.
> No harm at all, but sweet things in the End.

July is the month for young manhood:

> Young Blades with beards (this month) there will appear
> Whom for to shave, the Country men won't fear;
> Crookt rasors, and course hones are brought, and they
> The Barbers trade don't blush to steal away. . . .

August brings its seasonal change:

> Now Sol to Virgo goes, and there does stay
> Till that his Heat does very much Decay.

September's haying season draws its comment:

> Young Folks in Fields so Wanton now appear,
> That some Poor men will lose their Ears, I fear.

Brattle's *Ephemeris*, no doubt, was perused with pleasure in many a Massachusetts home. Brattle explained in his latter pages that his book was designed so "that even men of mean capacities" might come to know the reason for many things of which they were ignorant. He was bringing popular science to replace popular ignorance; men, said Brattle, are "potentially rational" even when they are irrational.[19]

John Leverett, also elected to the Royal Society in 1713, made no contributions to science, and possibly was chosen because he was president of Harvard College. He resolutely opposed those who sought to give "a more sectarian tone" to Harvard, and even neglected the exposition of Scripture.[20] In so doing, he incurred the special animosity of Cotton Mather. There was something about Leverett which smacked of the deviationist. He had begun his career as a minister, but for unknown reasons had left that calling for the law. He made his distinguished contribution to liberalism at Harvard at a personal cost. The sectarians harassed him, the legislature never raised his salary, and he was driven into debt.

Roger Williams and John Winthrop, Jr.

THE BROTHERS BRATTLE AND JOHN LEVERETT were elected to the Royal Society more than half a century after its inception. Were those, however, who were elected to the Royal Society in its earlier, formative period representatives of the Puritan spirit, or were they persons who could be regarded as rebels against that philosophy?

Roger Williams and John Winthrop, Jr., were among the fellows of the Royal Society elected to membership in its first year's choices in 1663 and 1664.[21]

Williams is, of course, the prophet of freedom of thought in America. He began as a Puritan, but his deviations were so deep-seated as to bring about his banishment from the Massachusetts Bay Colony in 1635. Williams contended that the civil magistrates had no right to enforce the decisions of churches; he advocated, in other words, the separation of church and state. In particular, he said that no magistrate had the right to punish breaches of the first five commandments, which embraced the injunctions against profanity and Sabbath-breaking. He protested against the "oath of fidelity," which the General Court exacted of freemen.

Calvinist philosophy divides the world into the elect and the damned. Puritan thinkers naturally tended to regard the American Indians as among the damned, for these red men dared to fight against God's own commonwealth. Roger Williams was the first American to rise above racial provincialism. He outraged the colony's leaders by writing a pamphlet in which he said that the King of England had no right to give them their lands because all

New England belonged to the Indians. Williams went among the Indians to study their way of life. "God was pleased to give me a painful patient spirit," he wrote, "to lodge with them in their filthy smoke holes, (even while I lived in Plymouth and Salem) to gain their tongue." He published in 1643 the first anthropological treatise in colonial America, *A Key Into the Language of America*.[22] This work, primarily an analysis of the vocabulary of an Indian language, also contained chapters on Indian government, marriage, sports, trade, painting. It saw the Indians' language as an expression of their cultural needs. Williams' appreciation of the Indian mode of existence is memorable:

> I could never discerne that excesse of scandalous sins amongst them, which Europe aboundeth with. Drunkenness and gluttony, generally they know not what sinnes they be; and although they have not so much to restraine them (both in respect of knowledge of God and Lawes of Men) as the English have, yet a man shall never heare of such crimes amongst them of robberies, murthers, adulteries, etc. as amongst the English. . . .

Here was no discourse on the Indian sunk in original sin, no Calvinist dissertation on their predestined fate, their sloth and idleness. When the Royal Society chose Roger Williams among its original fellows, it was choosing a New England man who was about as far from the Puritan philosophy as it could find.

The views of Roger Williams were shared by John Winthrop, Jr., a mutation from the Puritan stock. His father had been a grim governor of Massachusetts, ruling in the manner of Calvin in Geneva. The colony for Winthrop, Sr., was a refuge from Europe whose true churches were being "brought to desolation" by Catholic victories. He was elected governor after a stormy contest in 1637, in which conservatives triumphed over liberals. Governor Winthrop drove the heretical mystic Anne Hutchinson from the colony, and was apotheosized by Cotton Mather as "a lawgiver as patient as Lycurgus, but not admitting any of his criminal disorders. . . ." But the son was not cast in the father's stern mold. He was kindly, tolerant, with no inclination to persecute. He resisted the judicial murder of Quakers in Massachusetts. As Roger Williams said, "You have always been noted for tenderness toward mens soules, especially for consciences sake to God. You have been noted for tenderness toward the bodies and infirmities of poor mortalls."

John Winthrop, Jr., had come a long way from Puritanism. He was educated at Trinity College, Dublin, traveled widely, spent several months at Constantinople and Padua, became the good friend of the Cavalier Sir Robert Moray. Science was the consuming interest of his life. To do scientific work, he would have preferred to remain in England; only respect for his father induced him to stay in the colonies. In 1663, Winthrop, Jr., brought to Connecticut its first telescope. His observations were used by Isaac Newton. He sent communications to the *Philosophical Transactions*, and corresponded with many European scientists. Henry Oldenburg, the indefatigable secretary of the Royal Society, urged him several times to "season and possesse the youth of New England" with "this reall Experimentall way of acquiring knowledge" rather than the "notional and disputacious School philosophy." Winthrop took Oldenburg's advice, and gave Harvard its first telescope in 1672. The three Harvard tutors and almanac-compilers acknowledged Winthrop's gift with enthusiasm, "as a sure witnesse of your unfeigned Love to Learning; and a clear Demonstration of your hearty desire, eminently to promote the same in this schoole of the prophetes." They promised "to employ it shortly in the service of Urania." As New England's first chemist and metallurgist, moreover, Winthrop wrote papers on a variety of practical subjects—the making of pitch, the refining of gold, the brewing of beer. His own extensive economic interests included iron works, lead, copper, and tin mines; he served for many years as Governor of Connecticut. For the Royal Society, Winthrop, Jr., represented a liberal, post-Puritan personality, a fitting choice, from their Restoration standpoint, for membership in their group, their counterpart in America.[23]

The so-called Puritan virtues of frugality and hard work were, indeed, the most suited to the severe conditions of pioneer life. There was no real alternative to the Puritan philosophy, says Samuel Eliot Morison, "and for a very good reason, that the mere physical labor of getting a living in a virgin country is so great as to exhaust and stultify the human spirit, unless it have some great emotional drive." [24] Puritanism throve under conditions of rigor, hardship, and isolation. However, the rise of science in colonial

New England came with more settled conditions of life. As existence became secure and prosperous, there were less of those frustrations which make one prone to hate oneself and the world; there was a longing for a more human and pleasurable life. The scientific spirit was associated with a liberation from the Puritan ethics.

William Byrd II and Colonial America's First Professors of Science

EIGHT BONA-FIDE SCIENTIFIC FELLOWS were elected to the Royal Society from Massachusetts during the colonial period, two from Connecticut, two from Pennsylvania, three from Virginia, and one each from Rhode Island, New Hampshire, South Carolina, and New York.[25] The high proportion of Massachusetts men cannot be attributed to the influence of the Puritan ethics.[26] Actually, the Massachusetts colony had the initial advantage of an exceedingly high number of university-trained men. In 1645, this colony of 25,000 persons included as many as 130 alumni of English universities.[27] The Quakers of Pennsylvania, indeed, adhered to an ethic not less suited for the development of science than the Puritan. But they generally came from a poorer class of the population, and lacked persons of academic and scientific training. As for Virginia, its gentlemen were certainly hedonistic, but a plantation economy has never provided the stimulus to a scientific movement which arises in a commercial and industrial center.

William Byrd II, elected to the Royal Society in 1696, one of its first ten American fellows, was a typical Virginian. He had been educated in England by Sir Robert Southwell, in the circle of Sir William Petty, and when he studied law in London, he enjoyed "back slidings" with "naughty Jades" for which later "Matrimony has atoned sufficiently." Through Southwell's influence, he was, at the age of twenty-two, elected to the Royal Society, and presented it with a paper born of the plantation background, "An Account of a Negro Boy that is dappled in Several Places of his Body with White Spots." He returned to Virginia, where he was much occupied with the economic and medical uses of its plants and minerals. He encouraged the importation of books, scientific instruments, pictures, and music. Byrd was "gay and fun-loving," fond of dancing, skating, and billiards. He has been characterized as a "staunch Anglican," "a typical eighteenth century rationalist," and "Virginia's most polished and ornamental gentleman." [28]

In Virginia, also, at the College of William and Mary, there was appointed the first man to hold a chair of science in any American college. Mr. Le Fevre in 1711 was nominated professor of natural philosophy and mathematics. Le Fevre's hedonism, however, was excessive even by the generous Virginian standards; his tenure as professor was brief. He got into trouble, according to Governor Spotswood, because of "an idle hussy he brought over with him" from London. The lady in question was promptly deported to England; the unfortunate Le Fevre sought solace in drink. His "irregularities" and neglect of duties led to his discharge in 1712.[29] Under such hedonistic auspices, the teaching of science in America was inaugurated.

Harvard's first Hollis Professor in Mathematics and Natural Philosophy, Isaac Greenwood, was also led into misfortune by hedonistic errantries. Greenwood, appointed to the new chair in 1727, had the distinction of being the first American to publish an arithmetic. Moreover, he spread the knowledge of Newton's theories among his students. But Greenwood incurred debts, which he neglected to pay, over such luxuries as pearl-colored stockings. "A ramble of a few weeks" in London did not help matters. Greenwood managed to hold his post for ten years; finally, he was removed for intemperance.

◆§ Cotton Mather, Zabdiel Boylston, and Thomas Robie

ALONE AMONG THE MASSACHUSETTS FELLOWS of the Royal Society, Cotton Mather was the one unequivocal Puritan in ethics and theology. English scientists were, however, unconcerned with the fulminations on original sin of this guilt-smitten divine. Rather, they read the thirteen letters he sent them during November, 1712, on "Curiosa Americana"—such subjects as American plants and birds, Indian cures, monstrous births, remedies revealed in dreams, remarkable recoveries, the Indian measure of time, the rattlesnake, dream telepathy, thunder, lightning, and the bones of a giant found near Albany ("There were giants in the earth in those days").

Even in the stern Cotton Mather, the Puritan ethics ran afoul of the scientific temper. This was evident in the critical incidents of 1721. Boston, since its foundation, had been afflicted by six epidemics of smallpox. In May, 1721, that dread disease struck the city again. Cotton Mather feared for the lives of his children. He recalled a notice he had read in the *Philosophical Transactions of the Royal Society* concerning a method of inoculation. He remembered a Negro slave who had told him how African tribes practiced inoculation. Cotton Mather had for many years, together with most Puritan leaders, regarded "the spreading of that infectious disease of the smallpox" as the just chastisement of "the threatening hand of God." The world of natural phenomena was to his mind an everlasting witness of the wrath of God. "When I see a comet blazing and rolling about the immeasurable ether," he wrote, "I will think, who can tell but I now see a wicked world made a fiery oven in the time of the anger of God." [30] But the lives of his own children were at stake, and Calvinist doctrine suddenly dropped from Mather's action. He went before the physicians of Boston to urge them to inoculate and save lives. The sense of guilt, the acquiescence in God's awful punishment, left him. He wished to save lives and spare sorrow. A clamor broke out against Mather. He was denounced for the violation of Calvinist principles; Puritan superstition was this time (as he wrote) "with infinite prejudices against me and my ministry." And Mather's answer had all the accents of the liberal utilitarian: "The cursed clamour of a people strangely and fiercely possessed of the Devil will probably prevent my saving the Lives of my Two Children from the Small-pox in the way of Transplantation." Finally, Cotton Mather had his own son inoculated. The boy lived. The triumph of inoculation had begun. But an angry mob menaced the lives of Mather and the physician Zabdiel Boylston, and a bomb was thrown into Mather's study.

Zabdiel Boylston was the first physician in Boston who responded to Mather's call for inoculation. Largely self-educated, he managed somehow to escape the Puritan philosophy. Within a few months after the first successful experiments, Boylston inoculated two hundred forty-one persons, of whom only six died. Reports of his work were published in the *Philosophical Transactions*, and during his visit to London in 1726, Boylston was honored with election as a Fellow of the Royal Society. His work had a great influence on British medical opinion.[31]

During the smallpox epidemic, another physician ranged him self by the side of the harassed Zabdiel Boylston; he was Dr. Thomas Robie (1689-1729), then a librarian and tutor at Harvard College but shortly afterward, in 1723, to leave Harvard in order to practice medicine in Salem. Dr. Robie was going through an unusual intellectual development at this time. Later he became known as "the most famous New Englander in science in his day"; in his early manhood, however, he seriously considered entering the ministry, and filled his commonplace book with notes on predestination and the ethics of sexual relationships. He finally decided, however, to become a physician, somehow acquired a medical education, and began to practice in Cambridge. During the smallpox outbreak, Robie inoculated eleven persons. He stood resolutely by Boylston's side. When the Boston selectmen compelled six people whom Boylston had inoculated to go into isolation on Spectacle Island, Robie went to take care of them. He stayed with them for two weeks, and wrote in his journal of "the fury of the Boston mob." His was a "courageous and intelligent part," writes Frederick G. Kilgour, in the battle for smallpox inoculation against the vast majority of physicians and laymen, who bitterly opposed it.

"The Thomas Robie who left Harvard in 1723 was a different man from the one who had received his A.B. there in 1708. During the fifteen years which followed his graduation he underwent a truly remarkable scientific evolution." He became a skilled scientist for love of science, and he used scientific knowledge to dispel the gloomy world-view of Calvinism and superstition. In 1722, with the new twenty-four-foot telescope, which Thomas Hollis had given Harvard, Robie prepared to observe the solar eclipse of November 27th. He educated the people of the colony as to the significance of this event with an article published in two Boston newspapers, aptly entitled "For the Entertainment of the Country and the Promoting of Knowledge." Instead of the fear of cosmological portents, Robie substituted the "knowledge" which was "entertainment." His first scientific paper (other than several notes for the *Philosophical Transactions*) was a pamphlet of eight pages on the natural causes of a meteor which appeared on the night of December 11, 1719. Robie refused to interpret the awesome red apparition as a manifestation of divinity. Rather, he tried to explain it as a chemical phenomenon arising from the ignition of particles vaporized from the earth. "No man should fright himself by supposing that dreadful things will follow," he wrote. He left Harvard for Salem shortly after his marriage in 1723, but continued his scientific work. Late in October of that year, he observed the transit of Mercury with a nine-foot telescope, trying to determine whether there was an atmosphere around that planet. He was elected a Fellow of the Royal Society in 1725. Robie's commonplace book began with notes on Calvin, but these gave way to abstracts and copies of Newtonian works and papers. The scientist's world-view supplanted the theologian's; dread gave way to entertainment, suffering to the conquest of illness, in the ethic of this colonial scientific intellectual.[32]

☙ Paul Dudley and the Two John Winthrops

AMONG THE OTHER NEW ENGLANDERS who were elected to the Royal Society during the colonial period were Paul Dudley and two John Winthrops. None of them can be regarded as protagonists of the Puritan philosophy. All that we know of them would place them among the liberal philosophers.

Paul Dudley, later Chief Justice of Massachusetts, was taken into the fellowship of the Royal Society in 1721. When he was dying, Justice Dudley asked that his memorial sermon emphasize the liberality of his religion. A participant at the funeral "thought him too liberal and indifferent about the Puritan tenets and dogmas." He was reckoned among the king's party in Massachusetts. His father, Governor Joseph Dudley, had defeated Cotton Mather's design to become president of Harvard, and persuaded the liberal Leverett to take the post. Christianity, Dudley had written Mather, should have more of a "spirit of meekness," and less of reviling, stigmatizing, bitter admonishing, evil surmising, vilifying, fear, and jealousy; "your wrath against me is cruel," he said. The son, Paul Dudley, sent the Royal Society about twenty-five papers, on such homely subjects as the making of maple sugar, molasses, and cider, the planting of vegetables, and the location of beehives. An enthusiastic naturalist, he made accurate observations on the rattlesnake and moose deer, and foreshadowed Melville with *An Essay upon the Natural History of the Whales.* His sole foray into theology was a polemic in 1731 against the Roman Catholic Church for its "merchandizing" of men's bodies and souls, and despoiling them "of their Civil Rights and Properties." [33]

A second John Winthrop was elected to the Royal Society in 1734. He was an indefatigable collector of geological and natural specimens, and presented the Society with six hundred of them. Little is known concerning his philosophical outlook. One fact, however, is noteworthy. A legal question of inheritance took him from Connecticut to England. He never returned to America, but remained in Britain, where he died in 1747.[34] His grandfather had, a century before, wished to pursue a scientific career in England, but had acquiesced to the stern conscience of a Puritan father. The John Winthrop of the eighteenth century, less conscience-bound, followed his scientific bent. The fortieth volume of the *Philosophical Transactions of the Royal Society* was dedicated to him. Winthrop had evidently found the atmosphere of Walpole's England more congenial than that of the more provincial, Puritan-influenced society of New England.

A third John Winthrop, great-grandnephew of the first colonial scientist, was elected to the Royal Society in 1766. He became, in 1738, at the age of twenty-four, Hollis Professor of Mathematics at Harvard. Winthrop was America's foremost astronomer; he made accurate observations on sun spots in 1739, and led the first American scientific expedition in 1761, when he went to Newfoundland to observe the transit of Venus. He was the first seismologist in America, and proposed the hypothesis that seismic disturbances are wave motions.

When New England was shaken by a severe earthquake in 1755, an intense theological controversy ensued. Puritan theologians held naturally that earthquakes were the expression of God's wrath. In Europe that same year, Voltaire was moved to a bitter pessimism by the earthquake at Lisbon, and wrote his memorable poem against the idea of God's goodness. John Winthrop, neither Calvinist nor Voltairean, refused to abase himself in awe before God's wrath, and also refused to call His Nature evil. Winthrop delivered a famous lecture on this subject at Harvard; it has been judged as "perhaps the earliest classic of American scientific literature."

> The world [said Winthrop] is governed by general laws; and general laws must, from the nature of them, be liable sometimes to do hurt. However, laws of this sort are sufficiently vindicated, not only as wise, but as good, if upon the whole they produce a maximum of good; (to borrow an expression from the Mathematicians;) and this, it is in the highest degree probable, all the laws of nature do.

A few years before, Winthrop had introduced the study of the calculus into the curriculum of Harvard College. Now he used its terminology to defend an essentially optimistic theory of the universe. "There is the most perfect coincidence," he wrote, "at all times, between God's government of the material and of the moral world" and "this ought to silence all the complaints of those who suffer either loss or terror by them. . . ." The world, said this colonial Leibnizian, is "a mix'd state"; nothing in it "is simply and absolutely evil"; rather, there is "an overbalanced good." [35] One could look for simple scientific laws in all phenomena in the conviction that they coincided finally with the highest good. Thus Winthrop dispelled Puritan fear and ignorance with the image of a benign scientific God.

When Winthrop was appointed professor at Harvard, its overseers deliberated as to whether they should raise questions concerning his theological conformity. There were fears that he might misguide the students. Fortunately, they decided not to put such questions, because they were afraid that Winthrop's answers would be unambiguously broad. Several years later, Winthrop was embattled in behalf of Benjamin Franklin with the orthodox Puritan clergy. Franklin's "iron points," attached to buildings for protection against lightning, would themselves, said the divines, be followed by earthquakes. Thus God would set at naught human efforts to interfere with His decrees. One Boston clergyman in 1770 said that it was impious "to prevent the execution of the wrath of heaven." Winthrop, guided by an ethics of enlightenment, replied with the known scientific facts of the matter. At his death, the memorial sermon said that "he was uniformly an advocate for the fullest liberty of conscience in all matters purely religious." [36]

☙ Physicians and Bureaucrats

In colonial America as in Britain, physicians, not clergymen, were the most numerous group among those elected to the Royal Society. Besides Zabdiel Boylston, there were Drs. John Mitchell, John Morgan, John Tennent, Arthur Lee, and Alexander Garden. Almost all these medical practitioners came from Southern colonies, whereas the clergymen were New Englanders. Furthermore, the doctors of divinity were men of the seventeenth century, whereas the doctors of medicine were of the eighteenth. Last, about half the physicians finally returned to England.

Indeed, physicians were among the most active experimenters and innovators of the colonial scientists. John Mitchell, for instance, served a parish in Virginia as physician to the poor, and introduced a method for treating yellow fever which was credited with having saved several thousand lives. He sent to the Royal Society "a very curious dissertation concerning the Colour of the skin in Negroes." He lived in America for more than twenty years, but was compelled by reasons of health to return to his native England, where he was shortly afterward elected to the Royal Society. John Morgan, founder of the medical school of the University of Pennsylvania, served the American Revolutionary Army as physician-in-chief and director-general of its hospitals. Dr. Alexander Garden, a Scottish physician, practiced in South Carolina, and studied its fauna and flora. He corresponded extensively with Linnaeus, and sent to Europe the first specimens of electric eels. Dr. Garden was, however, a Loyalist during the Revolution, and his properties were partially confiscated by the revolutionists. Thereupon, he left America permanently, and enjoyed English society, where he was fond "particularly of refined female society." He became vice-president of the Royal Society. Linnaeus commemorated him in the name of the flower "gardenia." Arthur Lee of Virginia, one of the Lees of Virginia, became, on the other hand, an important diplomat of the revolutionary government. Lee was trained as a doctor of medicine at Edinburgh, and elected to the Royal Society. Soon, however, he left medicine for law and politics. Most picturesque was Dr. John Tennent, an English-born physician, who believed in the Indian lore of the therapeutic use of rattlesnake root; it was a specific, he held, for pleurisy, gout, rheumatism, dropsy, and sundry nervous disorders. When Virginia proved not sufficiently grateful for his discovery, Dr. Tennent returned in 1739 to London. Perhaps he had imbibed, however, too much of Virginian freedom. In London, Dr. Tennent kept a Mrs. Carey under the name of Mrs. Tennent; he was tried for bigamy, but rescued from this predicament by an influential personage. He evidently then went to New York, and was elected to the Royal Society in 1765.

Among the Fellows of the Royal Society chosen from the colonies, there was, moreover, a group whom we might call "honorary scientific intellectuals." These were persons from the colonial officialdom who had achieved eminence and power, and who were elected to the Royal Society to add to their titles as well as to confer a vicarious prestige on the Society itself. These officials were usually Englishmen resident in America because of their appointments, and not part of the American scientific movement. They were men of the world who embellished their this-worldliness with a scientific association: Thomas Pownall, the able colonial governor of Massachusetts; Francis Nicholson, governor or lieutenant-governor in five colonies; William Burnet, governor of New York and New Jersey, godson of King William and Queen Mary, who had been expelled from Trinity College, Cambridge, for "idleness and disobedience" (Burnet was elected to the Royal Society, on Isaac Newton's motion, in 1705, when he was only seventeen years old); Francis Fauquier, later governor of Virginia; Peter Livius of New Hampshire, a royalist who became Chief Justice of Canada in 1777; Elihu Yale, who, though born in Massachusetts, became a rich colonial governor in Madras, and whose father, David Yale, refused to become a church member, and objected to theocracy in Massachusetts; James Edward Oglethorpe, the founder of the colony in Savannah, Georgia; Henry Ellis, who was elected to the Society several years before his appointment as governor of Georgia in 1757; and Robert Hunter Morris, born in New York, member of the Council of Proprietors in East Jersey and governor of Pennsylvania, who fought hard for the royal prerogatives and the class interests of the proprietors.

Morris never married, but had at least three natural children; he dropped dead at a dance.[37]

Benjamin Franklin

THE GREATEST SCIENTIST OF COLONIAL AMERICA was forthrightly an hedonist in both the theory and the conduct of his life. As a young man, Benjamin Franklin had written down his philosophy in *A Dissertation on Liberty and Necessity, Pleasure and Pain.* Its propositions, simple and straightforward, won him an introduction to Bernard Mandeville, author of the celebrated masterpiece of social hedonism, *The Fable of the Bees.* Franklin stated the axioms for a system of hedonistic ethics:

> 1. A creature when endu'd with Life or Consciousness, is made capable of Uneasiness or Pain. 2. This Pain produces Desire to be freed from it, in exact proportion to itself. 3. The Accomplishment of this Desire produces an equal Pleasure.[38]

Then Franklin derived some bold theorems, such as the one which held the distinction between virtue and vice to be meaningless.

Franklin, in later years, deemed it more prudent to be less blunt. His views became milder. The hedonistic basis of his thinking was, however, constant all his life. He never wrote a projected book, *The Art of Virtue*, but he has told us what its basic standpoint would have been:

> . . . that vicious actions are not hurtful because they are forbidden, but forbidden because they are hurtful, the nature of man alone considered; that it was, therefore every one's interest to be as virtuous who wish'd to be happy even in this world. . . .

Man's happiness in this world, his own biological nature, was the ultimate standard in Franklin's ethics. The God whom Franklin came to envisage was a kindly one: ". . . He is pleased and delights in the happiness of those He has created. . . . I firmly believe He delights to see me virtuous, because He is pleased when He sees me happy." [39]

The German sociologist Max Weber maintained that Franklin's famous maxims were an expression of the Calvinist ethic of asceticism. What does Weber mean by "Calvinist ethic"? "The summum bonum of this ethic," he says,

> . . . the earning of more and more money, combined with the strict avoidance of all spontaneous enjoyment of life, is above all completely devoid of any . . . hedonistic admixture. It is thought of so purely as an end in itself, that from the point of view of the happiness of, or utility to, the single individual, it appears entirely transcendental and absolutely irrational.[40]

Franklin's writings on ethics, however, make it abundantly clear that he was completely opposed to the Calvinist standpoint. To be sure, Franklin, as a boy, had read Cotton Mather's *Essays to Do Good*, and, like the Puritan divine, he advocated the virtues of frugality, temperance, and hard work. But for Franklin the basis for virtue was in the concrete requirements of living, not in Calvinist theology. To survive under the pioneer's conditions in colonial America, the virtues of thrift and industry were necessary. The metaphysics of election and predestination was quite beside the point. Franklin always had in view the ends he sought; they were not thrift for thrift's sake, or work for God's sake. Virtues for Franklin were means, not ends in themselves.

At the young age of forty-two, Franklin retired from active business affairs. He explained why in a letter written in 1748:

> I am in a fair way of having no other tasks than such as I shall like to give myself, and of enjoying what I look upon as a great happiness, leisure to read, study, make experiments, and converse at large with such ingenious and worthy men as are pleased to honor me with their friendship or acquaintance, on such points as may produce something for the common benefit of mankind, uninterrupted by the little cares and fatigues of business.

This was no ethics of ascetic accumulation of capital; it was the philosophy of a hedonistic utilitarian. Benjamin Franklin, businessman, was also the convivial man of pleasure, composing and singing songs in the tavern:

> Fair Venus calls; her voice obey;
> In beauty's arms spend night and day.
> The joys of love all joys excel,
> And loving's certainly doing well.[41]

In an Epicurean spirit, Franklin pondered organizing a "Society for the Free and Easy." He and his friends were skeptics as to metaphysical ultimates. Their club, the Junto, made a heroic effort to promote the language of skepticism. It forbade the use of such expressions as "certainly" and "undoubtedly." The idiom of dogmatism was under interdict, so that the member in good standing prefaced his utterances with "I conceive," or "so it appears to me at present." Franklin had long since abandoned the Presbyterian doctrines upon which he had been raised as either "unintelligible" or "doubtful." He wondered why people were so irrational as to demand such doctrines; he wondered why they enjoyed being reviled as half-devils, and with amused detachment he observed the powerful impact on Philadelphians of Whitefield's Methodist mission. The wise hedonist did not choose to war with his times on an unfavorable terrain.

By the middle of the eighteenth century, in Franklin's estimation, the arduous era of pioneer scarcity was over. The Puritan virtues of hard work had fulfilled their function, and the more pleasurable forms of art could come into their own. When he founded the American Philosophical Society in 1743, Franklin said that the time of "the first drudgery of settling new colonies . . . is now pretty well over," that persons could now "cultivate the finer arts," and by "philosophical experiments . . . multiply the conveniences or pleasures of life." Life in this uncertain world seemed to Franklin less a drama than a game, "a kind of chess, in which we have often points to gain, and competitors or adversaries to contend with." [42] In this world of unknowns and unknowables, the wise man, like a sagacious chess player, tries to maximize the joys of life.

The Quakers and the American Philosophical Society

PHILADELPHIA DURING THE AGE OF FRANKLIN was one of the world's scientific centers. In 1743, the first American Philosophical Society was founded by a circle of nine men, of whom Franklin was one. Of the nine, furthermore, five were or had been members of the Society of Friends. The original Philosophical Society languished into nonexistence, but later a revived Society numbered, by the year 1768, a hundred and forty-six resident members. Quaker merchants made up close to half of them. From such facts, it has been argued that there was an especial congruence between Quaker ethics and the spirit of experimental science. The empirical bent of the Quakers, it is said, tended to make the method of the "new philosophy" congenial to them, and their rational frame of mind found satisfaction in the search for scientific law. There was a basic identity, according to this view, between the appeal to experience of the new science and the Quaker appeal to immediate experience. "I came to know God experimentally," were the words of George Fox, founder of the Society of Friends.

Now, it is possible to take any system of ethics whatsoever and to argue on the basis of some vague verbal analogy that such and such a system of ethics is especially congruent with the scientific spirit. This could be done with the Mohammedan ethics, the Buddhist, and the Confucian. Such arguments substitute verbal dexterity for causal analysis. In the case of the Quaker philosophy, there were certainly strong components which might have been hostile to the scientific spirit. The first generation of Quakers, men like George Fox, had little of the rational temper. When they appealed to the mystical Inner Light, their appeal was to the individual's own absolute, unquestionable divine givenness—something quite different from the hesitant, groping, tentative verifications of the scientist. Why, asks Brooke Hindle justly, should Americans have used their leisure to study science when there was the more direct theological route to the knowledge of God? Rationalist tendencies began to appear only with the more earthly second generation of Quakers. They spoke of man's reason as a "secondary light" which can guide him, and they began to assimilate their individualistic outlook to the spirit of scientific study. With William Penn, they could say, "For a Man can never be certain of that, about which he has not the Liberty of Examining, Understanding, or Judging."

The fact is that, as prosperity and security came to the Quaker merchants in their new country, they became gentle hedonists. They gathered books "to read for delight and profit." The Prosperous James Logan treasured in his library such humanist classics as Erasmus's *Praise of Folly*, and even harbored such a heterodox work of hedonist political philosophy as Spinoza's *Tractatus Theologico-Politicus*.[43] Of the five men with Quaker background who joined with Franklin to found the American Philosophical Society, only one was to remain within the Quaker fold.

Dr. Thomas Bond, who with Franklin's help founded the Pennsylvania Hospital, was "disowned" by the Quaker meeting in 1742 for "disorderly conduct" involving the use of an oath. Phineas Bond was disowned in 1748 because he didn't come to meetings and took part in military activities. John Bartram, whom Linnaeus called the greatest living "natural botanist," was "read out of the meeting" because, evidently, as he "had learned more of the world and science he had found it difficult to remain as orthodox as his brethren." William Coleman, whom Franklin described as having "the coolest, clearest head, the best heart, and the exactest morals of almost any man I ever met with," was also ousted from the Quaker meeting. Coleman was among the five of the Society's first ten members who had been convivial cronies in Franklin's gay Junto.[44] The hedonism of the wine-drinking, merry song-singing fellowship of the Junto was more dominant among the founders of the Philosophical Society than the spirit of the Friends' meeting. The disowned Quaker scientists were akin to the hedonist Franklin rather than the mystic Fox. This first American Philosophical Society did not last three years. John Bartram said sadly that it could be revived "if we could but exchange the time that is spent in the Club, Chess and Coffee House for the Curious amusement of natural observations." [45]

The painstaking scholar Brooke Hindle, who argues that the Quaker ethic was especially conducive to the scientific standpoint, writes that "the internal nature of the Quaker way" involved a "positive attitude toward the study of nature" and a "rational and empirical approach to thought." However, the facts he adduces point to a contrary conclusion. The Quaker ethic, in its purity, was represented by a man such as John Woolman, with his "almost other-worldly concern with the religious teachings of the Society of Friends." But it was not among the otherworldly that science developed. Rather, it took roots in colonial Philadelphia among "a group of liberal Quakers, former Quakers, and near Quakers." In other words, when the Quaker ethic was leavened with liberal, hedonistic, this-worldly ideas, it became consonant with the scientific spirit. And this is true not only for the Quaker ethic, but also for the Calvinist, Catholic, Jewish, and Mohammedan ethics.

Thus, Charles Thomson, the leading person in Franklin's Junto of 1750, left the Presbyterian church in which he was raised, and was " 'attached to no system nor peculiar tenets of any sect or party.' " Of the seven Quakers in the Junto of 1766, all were "worldly Quakers," in disaccord with the Quaker pacifist decision. Before the revolution's end, the ties of four of them with the Friends were severed. The liberals led the American Society for Promoting and Propagating Useful Knowledge which was founded in 1766. Its vice-president, Samuel Powel, had, like many young well-to-do Quakers, transferred his allegiance to the more easygoing Anglican communion. The membership of the American Philosophical Society, founded in 1767, was distinctly non-Quaker in its temper. Both members and officers were predominantly Anglicans and Presbyterians.

Two scientific societies, as Brooke Hindle tells us, with different social compositions and political factions, were united in the formation of the revived American Philosophical Society—the American Society for Promoting and Propagating Useful Knowledge, and a reconstituted American Philosophical Society. Both of them by different routes had approximated to a hedonist-libertarian ethic. The nine members who founded the American Society in 1766 had a more "Quaker coloration"; "the Quaker mantle, however, was lightly worn by these young men," three of whom were within the next decade dissociated from orthodox Quakerism. "They were intellectually eager in a way that was not markedly true" of the pillars of Quaker society. When Charles Thomson read them a paper in 1768 on "the Sense of the Company," Quaker sense was transformed into hedonist-libertarian sense. "The Spirit of Enquiry is awake," said Thomson; the new Knowledge, however, would not be mere Speculation, but would be applied to the "common Purposes of life"; Society would see "the Arts of Living made more easy and comfortable, and, of Course, the Increase and Happiness of Mankind promoted."

The rival American Philosophical Society had a more patrician membership than the American Society. The latter was composed of tradesmen, artisans, and a teacher; the former included all the leaders of the Proprietary Party. The active scientists in the American Philosophical Society were a small nucleus of physicians, college teachers, and the astronomer David Rittenhouse; the Proprietary Party leaders brought it social prestige and political influence. Ease and wealth had led the Proprietary leaders away from the simplicities and austerities of Quaker life. Indeed, the wealthiest and leading citizens of Philadelphia, as Edward Ford notes, often rejected Christianity, although for reasons of expediency did not make public their rejection. The inclusion of many Quaker merchants in the unified American Philosophical Society led an Anglican priest to remark "that the Quakers had stepped forth and joined the votaries of Science." The remark is significant. It was a new departure which Quakers had taken under the influence of the liberal ideas which were affecting American thinkers of all religious persuasions during revolutionary times.[46]

David Rittenhouse, the most distinguished scientist apart from Franklin in the American Philosophical Society, showed in his career the union of the scientific spirit with the hedonist-libertarian ethic. This amazing son of a poor farmer possessed unusual mathematical and mechanical powers. Almost wholly self-taught, he had the good fortune to inherit a chest of tools which included an English translation of the first book of Newton's *Principia*. This opened a world to him. Like Newton, David could not be turned into a farmer. He was allowed to become an instrument- and clock-maker. Soon he was brought to the attention of scientific Philadelphia. He constructed the first telescope ever made in America, and the Philosophical Society co-operated with him in organizing for the observation of the transit of Venus in 1769. He became professor of astronomy at the University of Pennsylvania, and after Franklin's death was elected president of the American Philosophical Society, in 1791. Like Newton again, he was appointed in 1792 to serve as the first Director of the United States Mint. Rittenhouse was born the son of a Mennonite father and a Quaker mother. He himself however belonged to no church, and in no fashion acknowledged himself to be a Christian. William Cobbett openly called Rittenhouse an atheist; actually he was a deistic follower of the Newtonian philosophy. He believed that God intended the universal happiness of mankind, and that "every new happiness conferred upon us" was indeed an "advance towards the perfection of the divinity." Rittenhouse, moreover, joined in the successful fight against the Quakers in 1789 to bring theatre to Philadelphia. He himself translated a play, *Miss Sarah Lampson,* by the German cosmopolitan liberal Lessing.

Rittenhouse, moreover, was the president of the Democratic Society, which in 1794 not only passed resolutions of friendship for Revolutionary France but harbored a sympathy for the Whiskey Rebellion in Pennsylvania itself. No wonder that many years later in 1814, John Adams still nourished a grudge against Rittenhouse, as "a good, simple, ignorant, well-meaning, Franklinian democrat . . . an honest dupe of the French Revolution." [47]

The Charter of the American Philosophical Society stated the hedonistic-libertarian philosophy of the American scientific intellectuals: ". . . nations truly civilized (however unhappily at variance on other accounts) will never wage war with the Arts and Sciences and the common Interest of humanity. . . ." Its program was enunciated in its third *Transactions* in 1793:

> Philosophers are citizens of the world; the fruits of their labors are freely distributed among all nations. . . . Patriotic affections are in this, as in other instances, conducive to the general happiness of mankind. . . .[48]

This remained the philosophy of the American scientific intellectuals for a century and a half.

Conclusion

The scientific movement which flourished in eighteenth-century America had its roots in the liberal trends in religion and in the hedonist-libertarian ethic of the time. The ablest observers were struck by the liberal spirit which pervaded the Americans. George Berkeley, Irish-born Anglican divine, founder in philosophy of subjective idealism, and seeking to establish a college in the New World free from the corruption of the Old, noted in Rhode Island in 1729 that though there were many sects, there were also "many of no profession at all." He observed that "notwithstanding so many differences, here are fewer quarrels about religion than elsewhere, the people living peaceably with their neighbors, of whatever profession." Calvinism was evidently in such decline that when Berkeley gave a sermon, he is said to have remarked in generous recognition, "Give the devil his due, John Calvin was a great man." The well-to-do folk of Rhode Island lived a pleasant life to which the Calvinist sense of guilt was irrelevant. Fifty years later, St.-John de Crèvecoeur, wandering through various colonies and asking the question "What is an American?" found that "the fury of making Proselytes" was no part of him. Rather, "religious indifference is imperceptibly disseminated from one end of the continent to the other; which is at present one of the strongest characteristics of the Americans." The Protestant dogmas were recessive beliefs, ritualistic phrases, during the hedonistic-libertarian time of America's first authentic scientific movement.

Liberal hedonism was indeed the philosophy of the American Revolution and its scientific intellectuals. Thomas Jefferson, scientist and statesman, spoke for the scientific community when he affirmed, "I too am an Epicurean," and expressed his horror at the cruel God of Calvin:

> I can never join Calvin in addressing *his God*. . . . If ever man worshiped a false God, he did. The Being described in his five points is not . . . the Creator and benevolent Governor of the world; but a daemon of malignant spirit.

The joy in scientific activity was a primary impulse in Jefferson. Though Secretary of State in 1791, Jefferson wrote to a friend that while politics was his "duty," natural history was his "passion." While still a young law student, allocating his fifteen hours of daily study, he had written that mathematics and natural philosophy "are so useful . . . and are so peculiarly engaging and delightful as would induce every person to wish an acquaintance with them." When he retired from the presidency in 1809, he said that "nature intended me for the tranquil pursuits of science, by rendering them my supreme delight." Shortly before his death he wrote, "I revolt against metaphysical reading . . . the business of life is with matter that gives us tangible results." If Jefferson loved strategy and the turmoil of politics more than he avowed, it is noteworthy, however, that the three men whom he honored as the world's greatest were Bacon, Newton, and Locke. This was the Trinity of the deistic hedonist-libertarian. Jefferson called himself plainly a "Materialist," and said, "To talk of *immaterial* exist-ences, is to talk of *nothings*." The fantasy worlds of ancient and medieval metaphysics born of the self-hatred of human beings vanished in the Jeffersonian therapy of the prosperous, classless, egalitarian frontier:

> We must dismiss the Platonists and Plotinists, the Stagyrites, and Gamalielites, the Eclectics, the Gnostics, and Scholastics, their Logos and Demiurgos, Aeons and Daemons, male and female, with a long train of etc., etc., etc., or, shall I say at once, of nonsense.

The world according to Jefferson was not peopled with original sinners. With simple optimism he wrote that he did not believe "that fourteen out of fifteen men are rogues." [49]

Deism became widespread by the end of the eighteenth century; its followers even refused to call themselves Christians. Far north in Vermont, Ethan Allen wrote a treatise against Christianity, in which he declared that the Calvinist conception of God was evidence of "a diabolical temper of mind in the elect." Elihu Palmer in Newburgh ridiculed the Deity who was supposed to be "a fierce, revengeful tyrant, delighting in cruelty, punishing his creatures for the very sins which he causes them to commit. . . ." Tom Paine was read in every village, and his *The Age of Reason* became the handbook for homespun freethinkers, and was a welcome best-seller from the cultured towns of Massachusetts to frontier hamlets in Kentucky. This people's philosopher was the college hero at Yale, where in 1793 "most of the students were skeptical. . . ." At Dartmouth, only a single member of the class of 1799 was known as a professing Christian.[50]

But all this was soon to change. The nineteenth century opened with a great revival of religion from seaboard to frontier.

II

The Protestant Revival and the Decline of Science

WHY WAS IT THAT, AFTER SUCH PROMISING BEGINNINGS IN THE eighteenth century, American science was so retarded in its development during the first half of the nineteenth century? The tree planted by such men as Franklin "not only bore no fruit, but absolutely withered away. For half a century there was nothing worthy of the name of national science. . . . Two or three men of genius arose, but they received no stimulus to exertion from the public. . . ." In these words, the astronomer Simon Newcomb sadly summed up in 1876 the history of American science. "Two generations," he said, "have passed without America having produced any one to continue the philosophical researches of Franklin." [51]

The usual explanation for the decline of American science is that practical interests dominated the American people, that they had a virgin continent to conquer, and that all their energies were absorbed in this task. But this argument is scarcely tenable. Along the Eastern seaboard, the states had long enjoyed comfort, prosperity, and peace. The American population grew so rapidly that by the year 1840 it was greater by more than a million than that of England and Wales. There were numerous colleges and universities, and a considerable class of well-to-do persons existed. Franklin's judgment that "the first drudgery of settling new colonies" was "pretty well over" and that there was now the leisure "to improve the common stock of knowledge" was certainly no less true in the nineteenth century than it was in 1743.[52]

"Every American has twice as much leisure in the day as an European," observed the Marquis de Chastellux in 1783. "You are strangers to necessity," he told Americans. The academies and universities of America, he said, already rivaled those of the old world, and its "men of distinguished genius" marked an epoch in the history of the human mind.[53] Why then did the scientific inspiration of Franklin, Jefferson, and the American Philosophical Society fail to bring to fruition in the United States a great scientific movement?

Once again, our general theory of the roles of the hedonist-libertarian ethic as encouraging the scientific spirit, and the ethic of asceticism (including the Protestant form) as discouraging the growth of science, provides us with an answer to the problem, and finds considerable verification in the facts.

A scientific movement failed to arise in the United States at the outset of the nineteenth century because toward the year 1800 there began in America a strong revival of ascetic Protestantism. That was the year which marked the beginning of the Great Revival. Throughout different parts of the country, there was a stirring of religious interest and feeling. In frontier camp-meetings and more staid, respectable Eastern churches, the question of personal salvation became the dominant concern. Ministers admonished their congregations for their worldly concerns; conversions were frequent, and the occasion for deep emotional crises; and among the impoverished, emotionally starved people on the frontier, the advent of the preaching circuit rider was the occasion for a torrent of emotional release. The more ascetic Protestant sects came to be more numerous than the liberal ones. At the end of the colonial period, the Congregationalists and Presbyterians were the two leading denominations, whereas the Methodists were only ninth. By the year 1850, however, the Methodists and Baptists were the two largest denominations. The Baptists especially were conspicuous in the West for their anti-intellectualism; they felt that education impaired the vocation of a minister. There had been a similar upsurge of the Baptists and Methodists in an earlier Great Awakening in 1734, when George Whitefield went on his preaching mission through the colonies, but now the revival undid the republican deism of the revolutionaries. Vermonters, for instance, who had once chased ministers from their towns, began to build churches for themselves. The Methodist hegemony did not augur well for the cultivation of the sciences. John Wesley, the progenitor of Methodism, had said that "from many experiments" he found himself unable to study "to any degree of perfection, either mathematics, arithmetic, or algebra, without being a deist, if not an atheist." [54] The Methodist outlook was spontaneously hostile to science.

Now the educated classes of the seaboard did not, of course, participate in camp meetings. But among them too there was the phenomenon of revivalism. At Dartmouth College, where there had been in 1799 among the students only one professing Christian, they now wrestled in agony with their souls' guilt and salvation. The years 1804, 1815, 1819, 1821, and 1826 were times at Dartmouth for the "most extensive and powerful work of grace." Roswell Shurtleff, the professor of divinity, measured his success as a teacher by the number of conversions he achieved. In 1815, within four weeks, one hundred and twenty persons were converted among the students and village folk, to the great joy of the professor and his wife. When in 1829, there was a slackening in religious conversions in the colleges, a Congregationalist weekly complained, "Why so few conversions? Why, of the 3,000 students, have all but about 600 been left to remain still with unconverted hearts?"

What the causes of the religious revival may have been, we cannot inquire. Among the prosperous Easterners, there was a reaction against the French Revolution, with its bloodshed, threat to the social order, and ideological extremes; John Locke's philosophy, advocating the right to revolution, fell into disrepute, and a turn toward Coleridge's transcendentalism began.[55] Perhaps, too, some underlying cyclical movement of the emotions was taking place; the optimistic deism of Jefferson and Franklin was now something from which a new generation had to declare its independence. In his old age, Jefferson lamented in 1822 "the growth of Presbyterianism," Calvin's absurd doctrines, and the "threatening cloud of fanaticism." Especially did he deplore the new religiosity among women, pouring forth "the effusions of their love to Jesus, in terms as amatory and carnal, as their modesty would permit them to use to a mere earthly lover. . . ." [56]

Perhaps a post-revolutionary generation, with no enemy to war against, may have been tempted to war religiously against their own bodies' temptations. The upshot, however, was that during the first part of the nineteenth century the ablest intelligence of the universities was diverted into the problems of divinity and theology, not those of science. "At Cambridge," wrote Richard Henry Dana, Jr., author of *Two Years before the Mast* and a distinguished authority on international law, "when I was in college, we had very inferior men in every department of the natural sciences," which were presented as arts "detached from all those moral and intellectual relations" which awaken the feelings of the young. "All the best men took an unfortunate but, you will admit, a natural pride in neglecting them, and they were not necessary to collegiate rank." [57]

Science had little standing in the American universities during the first half of the nineteenth century. "The leading men of a college class," wrote Thomas Wentworth Higginson of the Harvard Class of 1841, "gravitated then as naturally to the Divinity School as now to the Law School." [58] Higginson was a noble example of the transcendentalist fervor which later placed its highest efforts and zeal in the anti-slavery cause. His impression of the flow of the highest intelligence toward divinity rather than law (or, still later, science) is fully confirmed by the available statistical facts. During the Revolutionary Era, from 1776 to 1800, the larger number of the graduates in thirty-seven leading colleges and universities went into the law; 1,022 graduates became lawyers as compared to 838 who entered the ministry. But during the two decades from 1821 to 1840, coinciding with the culmination of the religious revival, the positions were reversed; 2,863 graduates became ministers, whereas 2,517 chose legal careers. During this same period, only 87 graduates became engineers. At Harvard, from 1830 to 1850, the classes in the divinity school were at their maximum; at Yale, from the Revolutionary Era to 1840, the ministry contended with the law for the first place among its graduates; at Columbia, divinity and commerce vied for second place until the middle of the nineteenth century; at Brown, from 1811 to 1851, the ministry continously drew the highest percentage of its graduates; at Dartmouth, during the years from 1816 through 1825, when Roswell Shurtleff's saving powers were in full exercise, divinity displaced the law, which had long been the first choice of graduates. Throughout the nineteenth century, American philanthropic efforts were devoted to the support of theology rather than science. Theological seminaries in 1891 were assisted with an endowment of eighteen million dollars, while medical schools had only half a million.[59]

A measure of scientific work persisted in the American colleges during the two generations of anti-scientific reaction, but it was that minimum compatible with the clerical philosophy, and it lived off the residual hedonistic-libertarian energy of the eighteenth century. Benjamin Silliman, for instance, pursued a distinguished career in which he became, in 1802, the first professor of chemistry at Yale College, then went on to establish its first science laboratory, teach the first course ever given in geology in the United States, and also founded in 1818 the first successful scientific periodical, *The American Journal of Science*. But Silliman, when appointed to his chair, was quite ignorant of chemistry. He was a young lawyer of fine family. Therefore, directly after his appointment he went to Philadelphia, "which presented more advantages in science than any other place in our country." The ethic of Philadelphia, the scientific center, was very different from that of New Haven. Philadelphia "had largely thrown off the heavy hand of the Puritan tradition." Here for two years Silliman was inducted into a cheerful life where healths were drunk freely with wine, and where there were "fine ladies . . . sufficiently homogenous to possess in great degree the attraction of affinity." Here, too, he met the eminent Joseph Priestley, who, as Silliman wrote, "had become obnoxious in his native country on account of political and religious opinions, as he was a friend of civil liberty and his religious creed was Arian." Priestley's house had been destroyed in England by a mob which resented his sympathy for the French Revolution; he fled to Pennsylvania. Silliman himself only partially entered into the scientific standpoint; although as a young man he had confessed that he was little moved by "the awful truths of Christianity," in later years, as Huxley said, he "wrote with one eye on fact and the other on Genesis." He represented the minimal acquiescence of America to the scientific ethic during the religious revival.[60]

On the whole, during the first half of the nineteenth century, ministers and churches viewed science with suspicion, and were, indeed, "alarmed by its teaching and afraid of its destructive influences." The religious revival among the people at large, and the high status for divinity studies among the intellectuals, signified a return to the ascetic ethic. Franklin's benign attitude toward sexuality seemed heathen and irrelegious to the young theologically minded students. James Marsh, who introduced Coleridge's transcendentalism into the United States, brooded upon his original sinfulness and was troubled by the fact that he enjoyed the living intensity of Byron's poetry. He went to visit a friend "whom I knew to be, like myself, in great darkness and depression in order to join with him in lamenting our wretched state."[61] In Boston, Dr. Oliver Wendell Holmes, scientist and skeptic, considered his transcendentalist friends, despite their intellectual rebellion, to be sickly. "They throw away the healthy ruddy-hearted book because they crave something for their 'inner life,'" said Dr. Holmes; "their inner lives are perpetual mendicants." He looked back with pleasure on his life as a medical student in Paris, and was proud that he had been a leader in promoting the use of anaesthetics in America. But as a scientist and alleviator of human pain, he had encountered the force of Calvinist masochist asceticism even in Boston good society. When he secured the use of anaesthetics in childbirth, hc said:

> I was denounced as a blasphemous infidel defying Almighty God, who had imposed on the female descendants of Eve the pains of childbirth. Even some fairly intelligent women preferred to suffer without such relief. It was a battle of years, and I had to give many lectures at our Cambridge Medical School to induce young physicians to deal resolutely with the matter.

Holmes was indeed regarded as a "satanic materialist." The Calvinist doctrine of original sin especially evoked his lifelong criticism; Holmes protested against its crippling influence on children's minds and feelings, and wrote in his autobiographcal notes:

> No child can overcome these early impressions without doing violence to the whole mental and moral machinery of his being. He may conquer them in after years, but the wrenches and strains which his victory has cost him leave him a cripple as compared with a child trained in sound and reasonable beliefs.

Thus he recorded his own struggle to emerge as a scientist from the Calvinist gloom. "The machinery of modern Jesuitism" was his withering characterization of the orthodox Calvinist party in Massachusetts.[62]

The control of American colleges and universities by staunchly Protestant bodies, which usually appointed ministers as the presidents, further inhibited the development of scientific inquiry. "Such control," writes Shryock,

> . . . continued longer in American institutions than it did in outstanding Continental universities. And it was only after about 1875, when the direct influence of the Protestant churches upon universities was declining, that there was a marked increase in the latter's scientific activities.[63]

Three Scientific Deviants: Bowditch, Henry, and Gray

THOSE COURAGEOUS ISOLATED INDIVIDUALS who in the first half of the nineteenth century undertook to devote themselves to science were invariably persons who, in one way or another, assisted by chance and their own strength of character, had effected the transition from the Calvinist ethic to some mode of the hedonist-libertarian standpoint. Nathaniel Bowditch, Joseph Henry, and Asa Gray, American pioneers in mathematical astronomy, electricity, and botany, derived their energies in a psychological liberation from the Calvinist ethic.

Nathaniel Bowditch, the Herman Melville of American science, son of a poor, drunken cooper, was put to work at the age of ten to help support his family. Encouraged by a liberal Unitarian minister, William Bentley, to persist in his studies, educating himself by reading the whole of *Chambers' Encyclopedia*, studying mathematics as he sailed on voyages to Portugal, Africa, the Philippines, and the East Indies, Bowditch became the admired translator and expositor of Laplace's *Mécanique Céleste*. "His translation of *Mécanique Céleste*," wrote Newcomb, "made an epoch in American science by bringing the great work of Laplace down to the reach of the best American students of his time." To American seamen, Bowditch, author of *The New American Practical Navigator* (1801), was the "Great Pilot" who had made the seas safer by means of his labors. The biography of Bowditch, written by his son in 1839, tried in keeping with the spirit of that time to portray him in his formative years as "an insufferable little prig." That effort, notes the most recent biographer, Robert Elton Berry, was not altogether successful. The port of Salem, thronged with seafarers, was a "gay place" during the years in which Bowditch was growing up. The boys' club of which he was a member mixed music and drink. Bowditch loved their songs, but felt finally his comrades were leading him to neglect his studies. His companions indeed had become "infected with Tom Paine's infidelity," and Bowditch was not inclined to such extreme religious radicalism.[64]

"He was a live man!" they said of Bowditch. His nine years of sea voyages affected him somewhat the way they did Melville, who found a Fayaway in the South Seas and came to doubt whether the civilization which the Christian missionaries brought was happiness-giving. On his first voyage Bowditch was shocked by the amorous ways of the French colonists on the island of Reunion; he blushed and was mortified as their free-speaking women teased him for his virginity at the age of twenty-three. Gradually, during his five months there, however, he became tolerant of the islanders' mores, and toward the end of his stay reported more frequently to his journal, "Spent night ashore." To his journal, the young seaman Bowditch later confided too his more sophisticated impressions of the girls of Manila:

> You can live with them in their houses like man and wife and they are looked upon with respect. They are said to be the handsomest women in the world. Their dress is chiefly in white with a small skirt which reaches no lower than their knees, so that a small puff of wind would discover their nakedness, but the more modest ones wear a pair of white drawers underneath.

He deleted this paragraph when he gave a copy of his journal to the East India Marine Society in Salem.

The deck of his ship was Bowditch's dormitory, the seas and distant lands were his campus, as during all those years as a sailor, "with only the sea around him, and the sky above him," he devoted his hours to navigation, mathematics, and astronomy. He retained the rest of his life a childlike quality, as if he never had been schooled, said his pastor, into the conventions of artificial life, or "accustomed to conceal or stifle any of the innocent impulses of his nature." He retained too his dislike for religious fanaticism all his days. "He had no taste for the polemics or peculiarities of any sect, and did not love to dwell on the distinctive and dividing points of Christian doctrine." When Protestant mobs stormed a Roman Catholic convent in Charleston, Bowditch called on the Catholic bishop to express his abhorrence of their act. It "has awakened me from a pleasant dream of security," he said, "and shown to me that the fanaticism of one class of this our orderly community, if it had the power, would not want the will, to attack with fire and sword," those whose faith they hated. In later years, Bowditch saddened his pastor, the Reverend Alexander Young, by refusing to make a "public profession" of his religion, and thereby throw the weight of his influence into "the scale of Christianity." As he lay dying, he could not bring himself to assure a loved relative of a conviction on his part in personal immortality, while his suffering made him recall a word he had seen forty years before, "euthanasia," easy death, which he said is "the kindest wish of my friends." [65]

Joseph Henry (1797-1878), born of a Scottish Calvinist immigrant laborer, became in 1826 professor of mathematics at the Albany Academy, and co-discovered with Faraday the phenomenon of electromagnetic induction. In 1846, Henry became the first director of the Smithsonian Institution. Joseph Henry's break with the Calvinist ethic took place under the most dramatic circumstances when he was an adolescent. Apprenticed to a watchmaker, young Henry found that calling dull. Fortunately, however, in nearby Albany itself, there was an excellent theater, under the management of John Bernard, an English comedian, which Henry began to frequent. Soon it absorbed all his leisure, and fired him with the desire to make a career on the stage. He wrote, acted in, and produced plays for a society called the Rostrum, which elected him, at the age of sixteen, their president. Henry's biographer wonders and finds inexplicable "how Joseph Henry came to make these excursions from an austere home into the pagan world of the theatre." "It is difficult to reconcile," he says, "Henry's frequenting of the theatre with the somber Calvinism of his home." At this time, however, to while away an illness, Henry chanced to read a book of popular science, Gregory's *Lectures on Experimental Philosophy, Astronomy, and Chemistry*, published in London in 1808. A new drama unfolded itself before him. It was, he later recalled, "the first book I ever read with attention. It opened to me a new world of thought and enjoyment; fixed my attention upon the study of nature, and caused me to resolve at the time of reading it that I would immediately devote myself to the acquisition of knowledge." Joseph Henry remained a member in his later years of the Presbyterian Church, but his career in science was a corollary of the emotional liberation he experienced at John Bernard's theater with the Rostrum. He found in science a still more dramatic "enjoyment." [66]

Asa Gray, dean of American botanists, the stalwart defender of Darwin's theory of natural selection in the debate with Louis Agassiz, joined a Presbyterian church when he was twenty-five years old. He reconciled his theism with Darwinism, writing that he was

> in his own fashion, a Darwinian, philosophically a convinced theist, and religiously an acceptor of the "creed commonly called the Nicene" as the exponent of the Christian faith.

But Gray, too, had known the quickening winds of hedonist-libertarian feeling in the formative years which made him a seeker of science. Born in the village of Sauquoit, in New York's Mohawk Valley, the son of a tanner, Gray, like Bowditch and Henry, was not miseducated in the colleges of the time. He went to the Fairfield Academy and, when eighteen years old, to the Fairfield Medical School.

Encyclopedias brought men the word of science in those days; these volumes of collected learning fired Gray's imagination as they had Bowditch's, and as a book of popular science had opened a new world to Henry. The American man of science was as self-made as the American businessman, and an encyclopedia was working intellectual capital. Young Asa, working at the age of sixteen in a doctor's office, read the article on botany in the *Edinburgh Encyclopaedia*, which, says Hunter Dupree, was "very nearly the fount of all knowledge and inspiration in upstate New York." It cast a spell of joy over him; he determined to make botany his work. Then he began, aged seventeen, to serve a medical apprenticeship at Bridgewater under Dr. John Foote Trowbridge, nine miles away. Bridgewater, as chance would have it, was an isolated "outpost of eighteenth-century deism," a center of materialist ideas, with "its small circle of *philosophes*, the leader of whom was Dr. Trowbridge." Gray now imbibed the freedom of the empiricist mode of thought. When he read Sir William Lawrence's *Lectures on Physiology* at this time, he commented enthusiastically, "That Lawrence is a grand fellow,—a strong and agreeable writer. . . . He is a materialist—after my own fashion precisely. . . ."

The growing trend of religious orthodoxy brought Asa Gray into the Presbyterian Church, where he found a "renewed bond" with his parents, who had joined the Sauquoit church in 1826, during a time of religious excitement. But Gray's optimist philosophy and empiricist emotion remained an enduring part of character; "eighteenth-century rationalism stayed on as an essential part of his mental equipment." He could still speak sentimentally of Bridgewater as "the wickedest place I know," and admire his beloved Dr. Trowbridge, who in the midst of the religious revival, "still holds out and says they are all crazy." The God that Gray accepted was a benign one, not the awesome Calvinist potentate of predestination. He joined a church which adhered to what was called the New School theology; it was Presbyterianism minus Calvinism, or at least Presbyterianism minus predestination, and its adherents were waging a struggle for the control of the denomination. Gray's conversion had one terminological consequence. He had been led into science from his youth by the simple force of a "passion"; now he would speak of it as his "duty." Withal, he wrote:

> I have no more fondness for high Calvinist theology than for German neology . . . I have no penchant for melancholy, sober as I sometimes look, but turn always, like the leaves, my face to the sun.

Asa Gray's core of libertarian empiricism kept him apart from the transcendentalist current which became strong at this time among New England intellectuals. It rendered him immune to the ideas of *Naturphilosophie* and medieval realism which Agassiz brought with him from Europe. Gray remained a nominalist. He refused to regard a species as an ideal type which God had then copied in creation; a species for him simply expressed a fact of genetic kinship among individuals. "In resisting the idealism prevalent in American thought," says Professor Dupree, "Gray was starting on a lonely road which would set him off from the community more clearly than did his penchant for religious orthodoxy," and, indeed, he became "detached from his co-religionists." Agassiz saw in Darwin a menace to his Platonic metaphysics; Gray, the offspring of the Bridgewater Jeffersonian infidels, welcomed the triumph of empirical science and causal investigation.[67] Agassiz's theory, said Gray, was "theistic to excess," the work of an "idealizing philosopher."

Thus, the courageous, isolated scientific spirits of the America of the first half of the nineteenth century were surviving inheritors of the eighteenth-century hedonist-libertarian ethic of Jefferson and Franklin. They bore the imprint of the revival of Protestant asceticism, but in larger measure they withstood it.

Science and Democracy

A DEMOCRATIC SOCIETY, its proponents have often said, is one which is uniquely favorable to the scientific spirit; scientific method, with its openness to all data and observers, is said to be intrinsically democratic. Apart from such analogies, however, the sociological facts do not sustain the proposition that a democratic society is necessarily favorable to the sciences. The Congressmen who came to Washington from a Midwest which had experienced the intensity of the Great Awakening had pronounced traits of anti-intellectualism. The resourceful Dr. William Beaumont, the most remarkable medical scientist in America during the first half of the nineteenth century, experienced, for instance, this democratic anti-intellectualism. The story of Dr. Beaumont is part of American medical folklore. Called in 1822 to help a young Canadian fur trapper whose abdomen had been torn open by a gunshot wound, Beaumont saved the man's life, and began a series of experiments on the visible behavior of the stomach, thus opening an era of research on the physiology of digestion. In 1834, Dr. Beaumont, having long served his country as a military surgeon, sought an appropriation from Congress of ten thousand dollars to compensate him for his own financial sacrifices in his research. Respected persons supported his petition, but Congress refused to make the grant because it objected on principle to any appropriation of public funds for scientific purposes. As Edward Everett wrote to Beaumont: "The great difficulty lies in the theoretical objection to the Appropriation by Congress of money for any scientific or philanthropic purpose whatever." Beaumont, who took his Jeffersonian principles as "the legitimate sentiment of every real American," learned to his chagrin that democracy at its zenith in the Jacksonian era was suspicious of the scientific intellectual. John Quincy Adams, a past president of the United States, scion of a family which in the Revolutionary era had united political with intellectual interests, pleaded during those same years for the foundation of an astronomical observatory, "a light-house of the skies." Europe, he told Congress, had one hundred thirty of them, but America had none. His fellow-legislators ridiculed and rejected his proposal; when they authorized the more practically necessary coast survey, they were careful to stipulate in their Act that nothing in it was to be taken as approval for the construction of an observatory. The correspondent for the London *Athenaeum* in 1840 observed that a sovereign democratic people was unwilling to provide funds for the advancement of science.[68]

A democratic society, however, is multi-potential with respect to its attitude toward science. It can under certain conditions be anti-intellectual and under other conditions philo-intellectual. Most of the scientific men in America at the beginning of the nineteenth century were evidently democrats, the members of the American Philosophical Society in 1802 were actually attacked for their Jeffersonian leanings. Egalitarian democracy seemed the firmest social foundation for science. The situation, however, changed. "The very middle class," writes Shryock, "which did much for science during the early modern centuries, neglected in the United States to aid fundamental studies throughout most of the 19th Century." Various explanations have been offered to account for this change. It is said that "American society underwent a transformation between 1780 and 1830 from a relatively aristocratic to a relatively democratic one." [62] Tocqueville, observer of Jacksonian democracy, first advanced the thesis that an egalitarian democracy would inevitably be unfriendly to theoretical science. A democracy, in his view, would be receptive only to applied science, to technology. "Hardly anyone in the United States," wrote Tocqueville, "devotes himself to the essentially theoretical and abstract portion of human knowledge. In this respect the Americans carry to excess a tendency that is, I think, discernible, though in a lesser degree, among all democratic nations." "In aristocratic ages," he said, "science is more particularly called upon to furnish gratification to the mind; in democracies to the body." All classes, however, in American society turned away from the sciences during the Jacksonian period.

Tocqueville thought that economic expansion was absorbing all men's energies and leaving no surplus for the arts and sciences; he wrote in his notes, "Nature here offers a sustenance so immense to human industry that the class of theoretical speculators is absolutely unknown." But certainly economic expansion had equally characterized the America of the eighteenth century; Philadelphia, as we have seen, was before the American Revolution one of the world's scientific and intellectual centers. Economic growth can provide a tremendous stimulus to science provided that the intellectual class has scientific values. During the Jacksonian era, however, the movement from scientific to religious values was well advanced; the eighteenth-century hedonist-libertarian ethic was superseded by the neo-Protestant ethic. When Tocqueville asked John Quincy Adams whether the religious principle was decaying in America, Adams replied that, as compared to forty years ago, religion had gained.

> Forty years ago the Philosophy of Voltaire in France, the school of Hume in England, had unsettled all the beliefs of Europe. The repercussions made themselves strongly felt in America. Since then the crimes of the French Revolution have made a strong impression on us; there has been a reaction of feeling. . . .[70]

Adams's explanation of the religious revival no doubt omitted deep sources of the Great Revival in the frontier West. Tocqueville tended to give Federalist conservative interpretations of American civilization because the greater number of the persons he interviewed were Federalists, disaffected by the decline of their party's fortunes.

The quickening spirit of a democratic Socialist philosophy was able to make the little frontier town of New Harmony, Indiana, into a scientific capital.[71] If anti-intellectualism in the Midwest arose under the aegis of theological doctrine, the Utopian Socialists brought to Indiana a respect for and the desire to encourage science. Robert Dale Owen, son of the celebrated Robert Owen, took an active part from 1826 to 1828 in the New Harmony Colony. Later, as a congressman from Indiana, Owen introduced the bill that created the Smithsonian Institution and managed its passage, although vitiated by amendments, into law. Owen became a member of the Institution's first board of regents. New Harmony on the banks of the Wabash River, meanwhile, had become the home of a vigorous scientific movement. William Maclure, called by Silliman "the father of American geology"; Thomas Say, "the father of American zoology"; Constantine Rafinesque, pioneer ichthyologist of the West; and Charles Albert Lesueur, first classifier of the fishes of the Great Lakes, were part of its community. It became, in 1837, under David Dale Owen, a brother of Robert Dale Owen, headquarters of the United States Geological Center. Not without basis was the claim that New Harmony, if not the "greatest scientific center in America," was "the first important scientific outpost in the West." Certainly distinguished foreign scientists made it a point to visit New Harmony. Sir Charles Lyell, on his second visit to the United States, spent several days there, and found a good geological museum, where scientific lectures were given in the winter, and which the Legislature, "with a view of encouraging science," had exempted from taxes. Both Robert Owen and William Maclure were atheists, and many citizens of Indiana reproached New Harmony for its lack of a church or any form of religious instruction; it was said that the Owenites had converted the local church into a dance hall. Maclure and Owen did devote themselves to establishing the first schools for infants and manual training in the United States; Maclure especially desired to apply Pestalozzi's ideas on the education of children.

The democracy of Indiana was thus multipotential in its attitude toward science. Under the guidance of a Maclure, it saw the founding in 1838 of the New Harmony Working Men's Institute. But the same community would become indifferent to science when the activating presence of the scientific intellectuals was gone, and theological clerics filled their places. Maclure was indeed America's first Socialist scientific intellectual, seeking an alliance between science and the working class. His scientific distinction was uncontestable; he had made the first extensive geological survey of the United States, published in 1817 in the *Transactions of the American Philosophical Society*, and from that year on, for the next twenty-two years, was elected annually president of the Academy of Natural Sciences of Philadelphia. The Socialism of New Harmony and the vision of educating the working class led him into the last phase of his life. He died in 1840, in the seventy-seventh year of his life, in an obscure hamlet in Mexico, still following to the end, unyieldingly, his mission of Socialistic and scientific education. The scientific intellectuals could evidently give their philosophy to a democratic society, but only if they were ready to do battle with all the forces of anti-intellectualism. The upper classes, wrote Maclure in the *New Harmony Disseminator*, had the monopoly of property, knowledge, and power. To break this trinity, scientific education had to be brought to the people: "The nearly equal division of knowledge, will equalize both property and power." This, said Maclure, was the "moral revolution" which was taking place, the coming of the scientific revolution to the people.

The democratic principle as such does not make inevitably for anti-intellectualism, but the democratic principle molded by Protestant asceticism does. William Jennings Bryan in 1925 was the last powerful voice in this tradition of Protestant democratic anti-intellectualism.[72] He expressed eloquently the fear that the scientific intellectuals would control education in the public schools:

> Some have suggested that the scientists should decide what shall be taught. How many scientists are there? . . . If the number is put at eleven thousand, it makes about one scientist for every ten thousand people—a pretty little oligarchy to put in control of the education of all the children, especially when Professor Leuba declares that over half of the scientists agree with him in the belief that there is no personal God and no personal immortality.

Bryan's anti-intellectualism, however, was not part of the necessary workings of democracy, though a contemporary of his, H. L. Mencken, argued that such was precisely the case. The philosopher of democracy, John Dewey, more accurately saw in Bryan the voice of the middle classes in the Midwest who "are for the most part the church-going classes, those who have come under the influence of evangelical Christianity. . . ." The frontier democracy, Dewey noted, was imbued with the Protestant ethic of the Great Revival; these later Americans would never have elected a Jefferson, Adams, or Franklin even as a town selectman.

Whether the potential for anti-intellectualism is more pronounced in a democratic society than in an aristocratic one depends on specific historical circumstances. The envy of the less intellectually endowed for those more gifted, the desire of majorities to see differences obliterated and the unusual made to be like themselves, are well-known psychological agencies. But these psychological tendencies themselves do not make the development of anti-intellectualism a historical necessity. The democracy in Pericles' time was linked to such currents as the scientific philosophy of Anaxagoras; in the nineteenth century, workingmen in London and Glasgow flocked by the hundreds to attend courses of lectures by such scientists as T. H. Huxley.[73] And similar forces were at work in the American democracy despite the emotional attraction of religious revivalism and the absence of intellectual institutions in the new Midwestern communities.

During the generation before the Civil War, the lyceum movement spread throughout the United States, following close on the frontier's settlements. Almost every village in New England, reported an English visitor in 1853, had its lecture hall for scientific and cultural subjects. "It is a matter of wonderment . . . to witness the youthful workman, the over-tired artisan, the worn-out factory girl . . . rushing . . . after the toil of the day is over, into the hot atmosphere of a crowded lecture room." In the Midwest, the local tradesmen, farmers, and more learned folk hitched their horses outside the lyceums; they listened to the weekly lecturers who brought intellectual provender to a culture-seeking citizenry. Even in the midst and aftermath of the Great Awakening, there were many young men on the frontier like Abraham Lincoln who drew sustenance from the writings of Paine, Volney, and Voltaire.[74]

Boston, too, the intellectual center of the East, was beginning to become restive in the eighteen-forties with a purely theological diet. Charles Lyell, most distinguished of the English geologists then alive, came there in the autumn of 1841 to deliver a course of lectures on geology.[75] Upward of three thousand persons attended each of his lectures so that he was compelled to repeat them on the next afternoon.

> Among my hearers [wrote Lyell], were persons of both sexes, of every station in society, from the most affluent and eminent in the various learned professions to the humblest mechanics, all well dressed and observing the utmost decorum.

It was the responsibility of the patrons of physical science, said Lyell, to bring oral instruction to the middle and lower classes, just as the clergy brought theological dogma; otherwise they would "have no right to complain of the apathy or indifference of the public." Four years later, in 1845-46, Lyell was repeatedly struck by the spontaneous interest in science which arose in the egalitarian democratic settlements of the frontier. In newly settled villages of Alabama, where "ultra-democratic notions of equality" were so vigorous that rich people were ostracized and persecuted, Lyell found a sympathetic welcome for the scientific intellectual.

> Instead of the ignorant wonder, very commonly expressed in out-of-the-way districts of England, France, or Italy, at travellers who devote money and time to a search for fossil bones and shells, each planter seemed to vie with another in his anxiety to give me information in regard to the precise spots where organic remains

> had been discovered. Many were curious to learn my opinion as to the kind of animal to which the huge vertebrae against which their ploughs sometimes strike, may have belonged.

Evidently Tocqueville far overshot the evidence when he claimed to have perceived the incompatibility of egalitarian democracy with the scientific spirit. The young Frenchman evidently "saw" much too readily what his teacher Guizot had already taught him to "see," the incapacity of the masses to encourage the work of scientific intellectuals. But then New Harmony, Indiana, as Lyell noted, was remarkable for having neither church nor place of public worship; egalitarian democracy here was not tempered by Protestant asceticism.

In Pennsylvania, on the other hand, egalitarian democratic institutions did not preserve scientific intellectuals from persecution. The import of geological discoveries for the Book of Genesis was here debated in lecture halls and newspapers. The multitude, and a clergy which included Lutherans and Roman Catholics, censured those who advanced the new ideas of the earth's antiquity. "The social persecution was even carried so far," wrote Lyell, "as to injure professionally the practice of some medical men, who had given publicity to the obnoxious doctrines." An assault on physicians was very directly at this time one against science generally, because they were the principal social group from which the support for science emanated.[76] How then could intellectual liberty be safeguarded?

> The forms of government [Lyell answered], are not alone sufficient to secure freedom—they are but means to an end. Here we have in Pennsylvania a free press, a widely extended suffrage, and the most perfect religious toleration,—nay, more than toleration, all the various sects enjoying political equality, and, what is more rare, an equality of social rank; yet all this machinery is not capable, as we have seen, of securing so much of intellectual freedom as shall enable a student of nature to discuss freely the philosophical questions which the progress of science brings naturally before him.[77]

An egalitarian democracy, Lyell indeed perceived, was multipotential with respect to its attitude toward science. "It is as easy to teach a peasant or a child," he said, either the Biblical dogma or the Copernican hypothesis; the schools can inculcate either subservience to theological authority or independent confrontation of evidence.

⤙ The Revolution in Feeling

THERE WAS A MARKED GROWING INTEREST in science in the United States during the years immediately preceding 1848, the year of the European revolution of the intellectuals.[78] Louis Agassiz, fresh from Switzerland, found himself welcomed in America like the prophet of a new religion. Fifteen hundred listeners crowded into the Lowell Institute lecture hall in Boston to hear him in 1846; it was the largest audience Agassiz had ever seen, and he recalled that the famed Cuvier and eloquent Arago had spoken to audiences of only three or four hundred in Paris. In New York City, newsboys hawking the New York *Tribune* called out the special news of Professor Agassiz's lecture. Local scientific societies were springing up in many communities; their resources were rudimentary and their motives in part utilitarian, but the enthusiasm for Agassiz was a demonstration on behalf of science pursued for its own joy. The geologists were in the forefront of American science, because several states, prompted by a desire to know their own soils' resources, had established geological surveys. The geologists of the several states assembled in 1840 to found the first national scientific organization, the Association of American Geologists. Agassiz feared in 1847 that the geological emphasis would "tend to the detriment of science itself." "The geologists and mineralogists form the most numerous class among the savants of the country," he wrote, but he warned that "the utilitarian tendency thus impressed on the work of American geologists will retard their progress."

It required an empiricist revolution in the American philosophic climate to prepare the groundwork for a full-fledged American scientific movement.[79] In the summer of 1860, a young lad, John Fiske, who had already been reading with approbation Comte's positive philosophy, chanced on an announcement which he hurried to tell to his best friend:

> Oh, George, my soul is on fire! (to use a favorite expression of Horace), for Herbert Spencer is about to execute a gigantic series of Positive books on which he has been at work for years.

Shortly thereafter, young Fiske was almost expelled from Harvard College because of his positivist sympathies. In October, 1861, the young heretic was caught reading a volume of Comte in chapel. Students had been reading in chapel for years without censure, but communion with Comte could not be tolerated. The president and professor of philosophy of Harvard were both "very bitter" with the errant undergraduate whose misconduct in chapel was alleged to be the outcome of the positivist philosophy itself. Finally, they contented themselves with only a "Public Admonition" of Fiske, who was warned strictly not to try to spread his "mischievous opinions" or "to undermine the faith of his associates."

A host of young American thinkers shared experiences similar to that of John Fiske at this time. The Civil War delayed the full impact of the new empiricist philosophy; it was not a "scientific war," for little effort was expended to mobilize scientific abilities for the creation of new means of destruction.[80] The National Academy of Sciences, incorporated in 1863, was conceived of by the armed forces principally as a device for rejecting the numerous devices proposed by amateur inventors. As the smoke of the battlefields lifted, it was clear, however, that the transcendentalist and idealist hegemony was over. The new movement replaced Kant, Coleridge, and Hegel with Mill, Spencer, and Comte.[81] It returned to a standpoint akin to that of its revolutionary forebears, Jefferson and Franklin. Charles Francis Adams, back from his Army years, which he felt had educated him far more than Harvard, chanced in 1865,

> . . . upon a copy of John Stuart Mill's essay on Auguste Comte. My intellectual faculties had then been lying fallow for nearly four years, and I was in a most recipient condition, and that essay of Mill's revolutionized in a single morning my whole attitude. I emerged from the theological stage, in which I had been nurtured, and passed into the scientific. I had up to that time never ever heard of Darwin.

James Ford Rhodes, later a distinguished historian, studied Mill's book on Sir William Hamilton at the University of Chicago in 1866 and "thought Mill had the better argument." "Thus began," he said, "a profound respect for Mill that has always lasted." His roommate was reading Herbert Spencer's *Social Statics*, and from him Rhodes received his "first taste of the Spencerian philosophy." John W. Draper, who had once been a classmate of Mill at University College in London, a few years before the war moved under Comte's influence from the "speculative" to the "positive" stage; shortly thereafter he began to write his influential books espousing a religion of science. William Graham Sumner in 1866 was fascinated by the efforts of Buckle and Spencer to establish a science of society. Sumner had kept out of the Union Army when he graduated from Yale in 1863 because his father bought a substitute for him; he thus began his sociological thinking with an empirical bias that property is the "most basic interest of man." A few years later, young John Dewey, an undergraduate at the University of Vermont from 1875 to 1879, was finding a new world opened for him by Comte and Huxley with vistas more challenging then those he imbibed from his transcendentalist teacher, Torrey.

The representatives of the old intellectual order were appalled by the contagious spread of empiricist ideas. The Plummer Professor of Christian Morals, and Preacher to Harvard University, A. K. Peabody, lamented in 1867 that the "pendulum of opinion," vibrating with "amazing rapidity," had now brought about "an inrush of positivism."

> This philosophy [he said], is our besetting danger at the present moment. It has made large and rapid inroads. It is but a little while since Comte seemed a harmless dreamer, almost without disciples. Now not a few of the leading minds of the age must be numbered among his followers. Herbert Spencer is, probably, more read and admired than any other writer in the department of pure philosophy. . . .

and he was leading his followers to "dreary negation," to "a philosophy which has made an open covenant with death." "Mill," likewise, said Professor Peabody, "is perverting his unrivalled genius and acumen in the same direction." He concluded with melancholy reportage, "In all the natural sciences, an alarmingly large proportion of the younger adepts . . . are already pronounced positivists."

Within a generation, there was thus a leap from the theological to the scientific mode of thought. The elder Josiah Willard Gibbs was Professor of Sacred Literature at Yale. But his son, Josiah

Willard Gibbs the younger, felt the incipient materialistic trend strongly enough on the eve of the Civil War to enter Yale in 1858 as a student of engineering. He helped found a Mathematical Club at Yale in 1877 and a Physics Club in 1899. Theological concerns dropped away with little comment. A friend noticed that Gibbs listened to hymns but "did not regard the statements as to cosmogony and history, or the theories as to the future, set forth in those hymns, as either accurate or important." His ethic was a simple one—the consistent pursuit of the "greater happiness"—and his pleasure in science helped make him "the happiest man" that friends of his knew.[82]

Chauncey Wright, the precursor of pragmatism, was the leading spirit in Cambridge among the young scientists and philosophers who were working their way from transcendentalism to empiricism.[83] Wright had once been a follower of the Kantian Sir William Hamilton, but gradually Mill supplanted the Kantian "as Chauncey's constant, cherished philosophical companion; and the tie grew stronger and stronger to the end of Chauncey's life." A psychological revolution was evidently taking place among the new young generation of thinkers. Wright never wrote an autobiography, but he did once sit, in 1874, for a "mental photograph" in which "the patient" is "seated at a number of written questions, and writes his answers." Wright took pleasure in answering thirty-one questions, among which were the following:

> 30. What is your aim in life?
> *Ans.* To secure the most trustworthy happiness.
>
> 23. What is your idea of happiness?
> *Ans.* Undisturbed, easy occupation.
>
> 18. What is your favorite occupation?
> *Ans.* Mathematical problems.
>
> 19. What are the saddest words in the world?
> *Ans.* Those beginning with D.,—as death, debt, dishonor, and all the d— dises.
>
> 20. Your favorite prose authors?
> *Ans.* Stuart Mill and Charles Darwin.

The bachelor Wright curiously reported that "his only recurring form of dream was that of flying, or rather floating in the air, a little distance above the ground." The classical symbolism of sexual intercourse evidently prevailed in the unconscious of Cambridge's leading young empiricist.

Wright felt too that the scientific standpoint required a straightforward nominalist approach. He had pondered Max Müller's dictum that "myths are a disease of language," and he definitely believed that "realism" was "a most pernicious disease" with its transformation of general names into the names of metaphysical realities. Wright regarded the nominalist attitude as essential for safeguarding the freedom of human individuals. The realists, he said, make of their "society" an entity with claims which the persons who compose it do not have; realism was a handy tool for personifying (in current terminology) the social superego. Therefore, said Wright, "a reform in logic becomes necessary for the overthrow of many social and religious superstitions." He perceived that the basis of the scientific standpoint reached down into a social-emotional perspective which sought the happiness and freedom of individuals. The ultimate divergence between the scientific and anti-scientific philosophies was that between the hedonist-libertarian and ascetic-authoritarian ethics. Therefore, wrote Chauncey Wright:

> In fact, the two warfares, the philosophical and the social, or the theoretical and the practical, have been carried on side by side from the days of the schoolmen; and it is not an accident, but an historical consequence, that Mr. Mill is the modern champion at once of nominalism in logic and of individualism in sociology.

When he read Mill's *Subjection of Women*, Wright "rebelled," however, against the genetic analysis of some of his own a-priori prejudices. Finally, "cold logic" and psychological analysis persuaded him that Mill was substantially right.

> I had considered what little heaps of traditions and customs they [boys and girls] really are; how constantly, though unwittingly, parents and nurses, friends and teachers, are impressing them with artificialities of feeling and manner, thought and expression. . . .

Chauncey Wright helped his friend and co-worker on the *Nautical Almanac*, the astronomer Simon Newcomb, to make a similar transition from what the latter called "the world of cold and darkness" of his native Nova Scotia into "the world of sweetness and light" of science. Newcomb recalled the gloom of his life as a boy, the people working "from sun to sun," and his own "supposed mental breakdown" as a child. The vague rumor of a different kind of world—"where dwelt men who wrote books and people who knew the men who wrote books"—guided him from a Calvinist to a libertarian society.

The renaissance of American empiricism was formally recognized in the academic world when Charles W. Eliot, a young chemist newly appointed as President of Harvard, invited John Fiske to give a course of lectures in 1869-70 on a subject hitherto taboo, "The Positive Philosophy," [84] Fiske wrote his mother:

> . . . only 8 years ago I was threatened with dismissal from college if caught talking Comtism to any one. Now, without any solicitation on my part, I am asked to expound Comtism to the college, and defend or attack it as I like. This shows how vast is the revolution in feeling which has come over Harvard in 8 years. . . .

The empiricist "revolution in feeling" was helped to victory at Harvard by the radical change in its government in 1865. For many years, its controlling Board of Overseers had been composed mainly of the Governor and other officers of the State of Massachusetts, plus thirty persons elected by the state legislature. Local religious interests were thus enabled to thwart the liberal development of the university. In 1865, some bold spirits succeeded in breaking "this archaic ministerial and political alliance." A legislative act dissociated the state authority completely from Harvard University, and provided that all future overseers would be elected by the college's alumni. The new electorate at once broke with the notion that the president of Harvard had to be a clergyman. Education at Harvard began its transition from the metaphysical to the scientific stage. The clerical opposition remained strong; it was, for instance, able to prevent the appointment of Fiske as a permanent professor. But the libertarian trend was clear.

Above all, it was the opening of the Johns Hopkins University in Baltimore in 1876 which signified that American thought was entering upon its scientific stage. Here at last was a university dedicated frankly to scientific research, and with no theological commitment whatsoever. Harvard and Yale had to struggle to evolve from the theological to the scientific stage, and this difficult evolution left its mark. Johns Hopkins, on the other hand, was newborn with a scientific mission and with no theological heritage to surmount. Its enterprising president, Daniel Coit Gilman, was a veritable St. Paul of the scientific method, ardent for the new conception of "research." [85] This new word "research" had only just appeared in the English language in 1875, but its significance, as Gilman wrote,

> . . . had a very strong influence upon the organisation of one American university in the year 1876, and since that time the conception of "research" has spread throughout our land from peak to peak like the signal fires described by Greek dramatists.

Around him, Gilman gathered a group of professors and associates remarkable at once for their youth and scientific enthusiasm. Ira Remsen, Henry A. Rowland, and H. Newell Martin, the professors of chemistry, physics, and biology, were not yet thirty years of age. Rowland, who later ruled the first diffraction grating and made basic contributions to spectrum analysis, was an obscure assistant professor at the Rensselaer Polytechnic Institute, in Troy, New York; his work had been rejected for publication by the *American Journal of Science* at New Haven because he was regarded, at the age of twenty-four, as too young to publish. Fortunately, James Clerk Maxwell had recognized Rowland's powers and secured him publication in Great Britain. The one elderly man on the Johns Hopkins faculty was the British Jewish mathematician James Joseph Sylvester, a man of immense mathematical genius who, because he was a Jew, had never received his proper recognition in the academic world.[86] Gilman appointed Sylvester as a professor despite the many letters and intimations he received that Sylvester would be "hard to get on with." Sylvester gave the Johns Hopkins University seven years of inspiring teaching, and with Gilman's encouragement founded in 1878 the *American Journal of Mathematics*. Any suggestion of religious sectarianism was excluded from the university. In its early years, an announcement was posted on the bulletin board: "A brief religious service will be held every morning at 8:45 in Hopkins Hall. No notice will be taken of the presence or absence of anybody." Four of the first seven professors came from the families of ministers, but they welcomed the new libertarian spirit. Appropriately enough, the keynote address upon the opening of the University on September 12,1876, was given by the brilliant English zoologist Thomas Henry Huxley, Darwin's "bulldog," the agnostic empiricist who waged a mighty warfare all his life against ecclesiasticism. A torrent of criticism descended upon the university for its choice of a speaker. Moreover, there had been no introductory prayer at the inaugural lecture. "This was the storm-signal. . . . Huxley was bad enough; Huxley without a prayer was intolerable." [87] But the university held its own.

To its students, John Hopkins was a scientific paradise, the New Atlantis realized. The University established twenty fellowships to attract within its walls the most promising scientific talent in America. Josiah Royce, a young philosopher who heard Johns Hopkins' call in California, fifteen years later described the feelings of the pioneer band of graduate students:

> The beginning of the Johns Hopkins University was a dawn wherein " 'twas bliss to be alive." Freedom and wise counsel one enjoyed together. The air was full of noteworthy work done by the older men of the place, and of hopes that one might find a way to get a little working-power one's self. . . . One longed to be a doer of the word, and not a hearer only, a creator of his own infinitesimal fraction of a product, bound in God's name to produce it when the time came.

In the mathematical classes of Sylvester, said Fabian Franklin, the sequence of theorems was like a sequence of naked Asian brides:

> We were set aglow by the delight and admiration which, with perfect naïveté and with that luxuriance of language peculiar to him, Sylvester lavished upon these results . . . the Esther that supplanted this Vashti was quite certain to be found still more supremely beautiful.[88]

During the post-Civil War era, two new journals were founded whose respective fates were an indication of the underlying historical trend.[89] William T. Harris, the "American Hegel," as he was called, was from his idealist enclave in St. Louis much perturbed by the "immense editions" of Mill, Spencer, and Comte which the American people were buying. "If this is is American Philosophy," he wrote in the preface to the first number of *The Journal of Speculative Philosophy* in 1867, "it may be very much elevated by absorbing and digesting more refined aliment. . . . Let the spirit of inquiry once extend to thinkers like Plato and Aristotle, Schelling and Hegel . . . and what a phalanx of American thinkers we may have to boast of!" "The day of simple empiricism is past," Harris concluded. In fact, however, its sun was only rising. Harris' efforts to make idealism the national American philosophy went afoul of the deep-seated material temper. His journal's pages were increasingly filled with ponderous translations from German poets and metaphysicians until its quiet demise in 1893. Meanwhile, the *Popular Science Monthly*, founded by Edward Livingston Youmans, in 1872, became the spokesman for the scientific renaissance. Youmans, a gifted, self-educated man whose near-blindness did not stifle his determination to work for science, "did more than anyone else," in Fiske's opinion, "to prepare the way in America for the great scientific awakening which first became visible after the publication of *The Origin of Species*." The new journal had an unexpected success. Youmans wrote proudly to Spencer that they had to print two thousand copies more than their originally intended five thousand, and within a year their printings had gone up to twelve thousand. Among many people there was "a very deep feeling of hostility" to the magazine, and there were constant reports of "people who 'won't have it in the house.' " But the monthly grew and prospered in its purpose of combatting, as it said in its opening number, "the thralldom of ignorance." It naturally had its trial of freedom. The *Evening Post* attacked the publishers, D. Appleton & Co., for sponsoring a journal which printed the writings of such "pronounced atheists" as Herbert Spencer. Appleton had already discontinued publishing the *North American Review* because it carried articles by the celebrated atheist Demosthenes, Colonel Robert G. Ingersoll. Youmans decided it best to undertake a strategic terminological retreat. He weathered the storm with an essay, "The Charges Against the *Popular Science Monthly*," in which he portrayed Spencer as a guardian of "the Eternal and Infinite Spirit."

There were other empiricists who were encountering the resistance of the rear-guard idealists. Noah Porter, President of Yale, who had drunk deeply of transcendentalism in his youth, tried in 1879 to forbid William G. Sumner from using Spencer's

Study of Sociology in his senior social-science class; "it attacks every Theistic Philosophy of society," said Porter, "with cool and yet sarcastic effrontery." [90] Eleven members of the Yale Corporation were clergymen. The matter attracted considerable attention in the press. Sumner learned at first hand "the horror of Spencer's name" in the minds of some people. Sumner nonetheless defended himself energetically, and with considerable faculty support; he won the ruling that the university president had no veto power over the choice of textbooks. Sumner's rebellion against the mores was strictly limited; his own conservatism on political and economic questions was of the most immovable variety, and his attitude toward sexuality repressive. Nevertheless, he had broken with his heritage on a decisive point. He had moved the locus of human concern from theological salvation to earthly happiness. A pupil of his, such as Thorstein Veblen, could begin from their common scientific-ethical premise, and emerge with a wholly different political and economic theory.

Such, then, was the character of the "revolution in feeling" which made possible the emergence of a widespread scientific movement in the latter part of the nineteenth century. Darwinism provided largely the vocabulary for the articulation of this emotional revolution. As Professor Bert J. Loewenberg writes, "The old quarrel between medieval realists and scholastic nominalists reappeared in Darwinian guise. . . . Nominalism blended with a science which tended increasingly to emphasize the particular. . . ." [91] The senses were no longer to be deprecated, for they were the avenues to the varieties of things.

Probably the scientific awakening was impeded because so many of the young men who would have been its first bearers were killed in the Civil War. The percentage of casualties among the young intellectuals was in all likelihood even higher than the already extremely high rate among the nation's soldiers generally. The annals of the time tell of one such death after another; if T. W. Higginson, editing the *Harvard Memorial Biographies*, was able to say proudly that those memoirs had proved "that there is no class of men in this republic from whom the response of patriotism comes more promptly and surely than from its most highly educated class," and that to have demonstrated "incontestably this one point, is worth the costly sacrifice," still we can surmise that the finest of the scientific talent may well have been lost.[92] Oliver Wendell Holmes, Jr., and Lester Ward fortunately survived their military service and severe wounds to make their outstanding contributions to law and sociology; William James, Henry Adams, and Charles Peirce may have lived to do their work because they were not soldiers. The younger Josiah Willard Gibbs, later the pioneer in thermodynamics and statistical mechanics, and America's most gifted theoretical scientist, was evidently kept from the Union Army by ill health. Probably, however, a great part of the generation who would have been their co-workers died in battle.

Alone among the young men of the post-Civil War generation, Charles Peirce did not share fully in its empiricist hopes and revolution. But this was what indeed isolated him from the philosophical movement and rendered him, despite his logical and scientific work, uninfluential.[93] Youmans wrote from London in 1877, "Charles Peirce isn't read much on this side. Clifford, however, says he is the greatest living logician. . . ." Peirce became even more intellectually isolated in the United States. The transcendentalist motive in his philosophy grew stronger as he grew older. At the outset of his philosophical work, he wrote the later famous papers in which he set forth the principle of pragmatism; in those studies, Peirce still avowed himself a determinist, a believer in mechanical explanation, one prepared to take part "in a movement having a possible atheistical issue." His so-called realism at that time was in all except terminological preference so much like nominalism that Chauncey Wright was able to accept it. But Peirce still harbored the view that on the belief in General Ideas rested "the question whether there is anything of any more dignity, worth, and importance than individual happiness, individual aspirations, and individual life." In his earlier years Peirce had rejected "the tendency to personify every thing and to attribute human characters to it." In his middle age, however, he gave way to this very tendency, and criticized his youthful, scientific self as having been "too nominalistic to enable me to see that every general idea has the unified living thought of a person." The more isolated he became and the more disaffected with the entire drift of American institutions, the more he fell back upon a philosophy which in all its essentials was that of his transcendentalist father before him. Benjamin Peirce in his last years at Harvard was a relic of transcendentalism's great days; he was the only member of its faculty who helped William T. Harris plan the Concord School of Philosophy, a gallant, unsuccessful last stand of the transcendentalists to stem the empiricist wave. And his son, the propounder of pragmatism, grew incomprehensible to a generation which he tried to address in his father's terms.

The Puritan tradition in the United States, as Morris R. Cohen noted, bolstered up a hostility to idle speculation.[94] It would be wrong, however, to ascribe the source of this hostility to an all-absorbing devotion on the Puritans' part to business practicalities. For the Puritan leaders and divines were often at odds with the economic aims of their parishioners.[95] The Puritan ethic was not committed to capitalism, nor was it an apologia for the pursuit of profit. What it most clearly was was an ethic of asceticism and devotion to an austere God. Puritan asceticism denigrated an interest and pleasure in science, not because the latter was not profitable economically, but because any pleasure in physical objects was a suspect substitute for theological absorption. The scientific philosophers of the post-Civil War era proposed what was indeed an alternative religion of science to the Puritan creed. Although they were themselves models of proper behavior, they were exponents of a hedonist-libertarian ethic, for such indeed was the underlying philosophy in Comte, Mill, and Spencer. This was the "revolution in feeling" which set Americans' eyes and minds free to see and dwell upon the world of nature. This psychological revolution was, in Simon Newcomb's judgment, most evident among the American middle class. They became the eager readers of popular scientific literature and the science supplements of the New York *Tribune*. "The sentiment of wonder" was awakened in them, and they found that the discoveries of science, "when stated in untechnical language, read something like a fairy-tale." [96]

The American scientist, as he emerged in the first third of the twentieth century, tended in proportion to his achievement to have those qualities of intellectual and emotional independence which Galton had found characteristic of the English scientists of the nineteenth century. He tended to heterodox religious views.[97] According to the results of a questionnaire distributed among a representative sample of American scientists in 1914, as many as 58.2 per cent of them either disbelieved in or doubted the existence of God. A generation later, in 1933, that same questionnaire circulated among a similar sample by Professor Leuba showed that the percentage of disbelievers and doubters had risen to seventy. Even more striking was the difference in philosophy between the greater scientists and the lesser ones. As many as 68.4 per cent of the greater scientists in 1914 were disbelievers or doubters, while among their less eminent colleagues 51.8 per cent thus classified themselves. "There are fewer believers among the greater men, whether physicists or biologists," wrote Professor Leuba. "The smallest percentage of believers is found among the greater biologists; they count only 16.9 per cent of believers in God. . . ." The unorthodoxy of all classes of scientists was even more pronounced in 1933, when 87 per cent of the greater scientists and 65 per cent of the lesser ones ranged themselves among the disbelievers or doubters. Among the greater physicists, biologists, and psychologists, the percentages were 83, 88, and 98, respectively. The psychological traits which made for original achievement in science were those which also made for freedom from traditional religious beliefs.

Indeed, the great majority of American scientists three decades ago in 1926 evidently had no religious affiliation. A study at that time showed that about 70 per cent of distinguished American scientists (886 out of 1,189 names) gave no information as to church membership in their autobiographical answers for *Who's Who in America*. Of the 26 per cent (303 names) who did provide information concerning their religious preferences, liberal Protestants were preponderant in relative terms. The Unitarians, for instance, who constituted only .15 per cent of American church members, provided 12.21 per cent of the religious scientists; the Congregationalists, although but 2.34 per cent of the church folk, composed 21.78 per cent of this group. By contrast, the Methodists, a less liberal Protestant denomination, with the allegiance of 23.03 per cent of the church people, provided only 10.23 per cent of the religious men of science. The liberal ingredient added to the Protestant ethic was clearly the vital one for the scientific spirit —not the guilt, asceticism, or sin, but the hedonistic standpoint of the free individual. It was because Protestantism evolved closer to the liberal, secular standpoint that it had a greater part in the scientific movement than Roman Catholicism. But what Weber called the "Protestant ethic" was intrinsically—that is, psychologically—as hostile as the mediaeval ethic was to the spirit of scientific study.

NOTES

1. Samuel Eliot Morison, *The Puritan Pronaos* (New York, 1936), p. 234.

2. Irving A. Leonard, "Don Carlos de Sigüenza y Gongora: A Mexican Savant of the Seventeenth Century," *University of California Publications in History* (Berkeley, 1929), pp. ix, 9, 11-12, 59. Irving A. Leonard, "Hispanic Science and America," *University of Miami Hispanic-American Studies*, No. 8 (Coral Gables, 1949), p. 20.

3. Irving A. Leonard, "Don Carlos de Sigüenza y Gongora," p. 23.

4. Henry Bamford Parkes, *A History of Mexico* (rev. ed., New York, 1950), p. 110.

5. John Tate Lanning, *The University in the Kingdom of Guatemala* (Ithaca, 1955), pp. 1, 160-1, 16, 35, 202, 49, John Tate Lanning, *Academic Culture in the Spanish Colonies* (New York, 1940), pp. 18, 21-2, 43, 89.

6. John Tate Lanning, *The University in the Kingdom of Guatemala*, pp. 199, 176, 181, 179, 293-9.

7. *Ibid.*, pp. 154-7. Leopoldo Zea, *El Positivismo en Mexico* (2nd ed., México, 1953), pp. 59-63. Leopoldo Zea, "Positivism and Porfirism in Latin America," trans. Helene Weyl, in F. S. C. Northrop, ed., *Ideological Differences and World Order* (New Haven, 1949), pp. 169-91. Patrick Romanell, *Making of the Mexican Mind* (Lincoln, 1952), pp. 47-8. Theodore Apstein, *The Universities of Mexico* (Washington, 1946), p. 5. Irma Wilson, *Mexico: A Century of Educational Thought* (New York, 1941), p. 38.

8. Thomas Jefferson Wertenbaker, *The Puritan Oligarchy* (New York, 1947), p. viii.

9. *Ibid.*, pp. 189, 190, 201, 176, 203, 195, 202, 207, 258, 268-9, 271, 279.

10. Raymond P. Stearns, "Assessing the New England Mind," *Church History*, (1941), 258.

11. Perry Miller, *The New England Mind: The Seventeenth Century* (New York, 1939), pp. 223, 147, 22.

12. *Ibid.*, pp. 147, 22.

13. Theodore Hornberger, "Puritanism and Science: The Relationship Revealed in the Writings of John Cotton," *New England Quarterly*, X (1937), 504, 507, 508, 514.

14. S. E. Morison, "The Harvard School of Astronomy in the Seventeenth Century," *New England Quarterly*, VII (1934), 13-16.

15. Hornberger, *op. cit.*, p. 511.

16. Wertenbaker, *op. cit.*, p. 278. S. E. Morison, *Three Centuries of Harvard* (Cambridge, 1936), p. 83.

17. S. E. Morison, "The Harvard School of Astronomy in the Seventeenth Century," pp. 20-1. T. J. Wertenbaker, *op. cit.*, pp. 155-6, 263, 276. "Letter of Thomas Brattle, F. R. S., 1692," in *Narratives of the Witchcraft Cases, 1648-1706*, ed. George Lincoln Burr (New York, 1914), pp. 171-2, 182. Edward Doubleday Harris, *An Account of Some of the Descendants of Capt. Thomas Brattle* (Boston, 1867), pp. 6-7.

18. Frederick E. Brasch, "The Royal Society of London and its Influence upon Scientific Thought in the American Colonies," *Scientific Monthly*, XXXIII (1921), 346. Raymond P. Stearns, "Colonial Fellows of the Royal Society of London, 1661-1788," *William and Mary Quarterly*, III, 3rd Series (1946), 230. E. D. Harris, *op. cit.*, p. 14. Perry Miller, *op. cit.*, p. 121. S. E. Morison, *Three Centuries of Harvard*, p. 46.

19. W. Brattle, *An Ephemeris of Caelestial Motions, Aspects, Eclipses, etc. For the Year of the Christian Era, 1682* (Cambridge, 1682), *University Microfilms, American Culture Series, No. 80* (*Roll 8*), Ann Arbor.

20. Charles Edward Leverett, *The Leverett Memorial* (Boston, 1856), pp. 115, 123, 124. Barrett Wendell, *Cotton Mather: Puritan Priest* (Cambridge, 1926), p. 268.

21. Winthrop was elected to the Royal Society on May 20, 1663, among the original Fellows; Williams was elected on February 3, 1664. Cf. *The Record of the Royal Society of London* (4th ed., London, 1940), App. V, p. 378.

22. Roger Williams, "A Key into the Language of America," *Collections of the Rhode Island Historical Society* (Providence, 1827), Vol. I, pp. 121-122. For the Puritan position with regard to the Indians, cf. Roy H. Pearce, "The 'Ruines of Mankind': The Indian and the Puritan Mind," *Journal of the History of Ideas*, XIII (1953), 201. Also, Daniel Clarke Sanders, *A Lost Chapter from A History of the Indian Wars*, ed. Betty Bandel (Burlington, 1953), pp. iv-v. Edmund J. Carpenter, *Roger Williams* (New York, 1909), pp. 121-3. Also, T. J. Wertenbaker, *op. cit.*, p. 216. Cf. Barrett Wendell, *op. cit.*, p. 91.

23. James D. Knowles, *Memoir of Roger Williams* (Boston, 1834), pp. 310-11. T. J. Wertenbaker, *op. cit.*, pp. 27, 91, 220-1. S. E. Morison, "The Harvard School of Astronomy in the Seventeenth Century," pp. 17-18. Thomas Franklin Waters, *A Sketch of the Life of John Winthrop the Younger* (Cambridge, 1899), pp. 54-5.

24. S. E. Morison, *The Puritan Pronaos*, p. 14.

25. In arriving at this count, I have excluded those who were elected to the Royal Society primarily because of their holding such official posts as the governorships of a colony. In this group were William Penn, James Edward Oglethorpe, Henry Ellis, Francis Fauquier, Robert Hunter Morris, Thomas Pownall, William Burnet, and Francis Nicholson. I have included the name of Dr. John Mitchell though he was elected to the Royal Society two years after he had left Virginia for England. I have not included the names of Benjamin Thompson and James Bowdoin because their election to the Royal Society came after the colonial period, which I regard as terminating with the Declaration of Independence in 1776. Professor Stearns's list omits the names of Roger Williams and Thomas Brattle, but I have followed Frederick E. Brasch in including them. The eight Fellows from Massachusetts were: Thomas Brattle, William Brattle, Cotton Mather, John Leverett, Paul Dudley, Thomas Robie, Zabdiel Boylston and Professor John Winthrop. The two from Connecticut were the first two John Winthrops, the two from Pennsylvania were Benjamin Franklin and John Morgan. The three from Virginia were William Byrd, John Mitchell, and Arthur Lee. From Rhode Island, New Hampshire, South Carolina, and New York came Roger Williams, Peter Livius, Alexander Garden, and John Tennent respectively.

26. Robert K. Merton, for instance, infers that the high proportion of Massachusetts men indicates a preponderance of Puritans. Cf. R. K. Merton, "Science, Technology and Society in Seventeenth Century England," *Osiris*, IV (1938), 481.

27. S. E. Morison, *The Puritan Pronaos*, p. 16.

28. *The Writings of Colonel William Byrd of Westover in Virginia, Esq.*, ed. John Spencer Bassett (New York, 1901), p. xiv. *The Secret Diary of William Byrd of Westover (1709-1712)*, ed. Louis B. Wright and Marion Tinling (Richmond, 1941), pp. ix, xv, xix, xxi, xxiii.

29. Theodore Hornberger, *Scientific Thought in the American Colleges, 1638-1800* (Austin, 1945), pp. 25, 27.

30. George Lyman Kittredge, "Cotton Mather's Scientific Communications to the Royal Society," *Proceedings of the American Antiquarian Society*, XXVI (1916), 18. Kenneth Ballard Murdock, *Increase*

Mather (Cambridge, 1925), pp. 169-73. T. J. Wertenbaker, *op. cit.*, pp. 253, 267. *Dictionary of American Biography* (New York, 1929), Vol. II, p. 535.

31. Barrett Wendell, *op. cit.*, pp. 276-7. F. E. Brasch, *op. cit.*, pp. 352-3. *Dictionary of American Biography*, Vol. II, pp. 535-6.

32. Frederick G. Kilgour, "Thomas Robie (1689-1729), Colonial Scientist and Physician," *Isis*, XXX (1939), 473-90.

33. Dean Dudley, *The History of the Dudley Family* (Montrose, 1894), pp. 327, 313-18. *Dictionary of American Biography*, Vol. V, p. 483. Paul Dudley, *An Essay on the Merchandize of Slaves and Souls of Men* (Boston, 1731), pp. i, 32, 34.

34. John Winthrop, "Selections from an Ancient Catalogue of Objects of Natural History," *American Journal of Science*, XLVII (1844), 3.

35. F. E. Brasch, "John Winthrop (1717-1779), America's First Astronomer, and the Science of his Period," *Publications of the Astronomical Society of the Pacific* (1916), p. 9. Frederick G. Kilgour, "Professor John Winthrop's Notes on Sun Spot Observations," *Isis*, XXIX (1938), 355. *Dictionary of American Biography*, Vol. XX, p. 414. John Winthrop, "A Lecture on Earthquakes," reprinted in Frederick E. Brasch, "An Earthquake in New England During the Colonial Period," *Bulletin of the Seismological Society of America*, VI (1916), 39, 40-2.

36. Edward Wigglesworth, *A Discourse Occasioned by the Death of the Honourable John Winthrop* (Boston, 1779), p. 24. *The Dictionary of American Biography*, Vol. XX, p. 415. F. E. Brasch, "John Winthrop," p. 4. Brooke Hindle, *The Pursuit of Science in Revolutionary America, 1735-1789* (Chapel Hill, 1956), p. 88. Richard Anderson, *Lightning Conductors: Their History, Nature, and Mode of Application* (London, 1880), pp. 26-27.

37. R. P. Stearns, *op. cit.*, pp. 208-68. Brooke Hindle, *op. cit.*, pp. 50-8, 340. Lawrence Martin, "John Mitchell," *Dictionary of American Biography*, Vol. XIII, pp. 50-1; John A. Krout, "Robert Hunter Morris," *D.A.B.*, Vol. XIII, pp. 225-6; James H. Peeling, "John Morgan," *D.A.B.*, Vol. XIII, pp. 172-4; Wyndham B. Blanton, "John Tennent," *D.A.B.*, Vol. XVIII, p. 369; Donald Culross Peattie, "Alexander Garden," *D.A.B.*, Vol. VII, pp. 132-3; Percy S. Flippin, "Francis Fauquier," *D.A.B.*, Vol. VI, p. 301; James Truslow Adams, "William Burnet," *D.A.B.*, Vol. III, p. 295; Leonard W. Labaree, "Francis Nicholson," *D.A.B.*, Vol. XIII, pp. 499-502; Stanley M. Pargellis, "Elihu Yale," *D.A.B.*, Vol. XX, pp. 590-1; Leonard W. Labaree, "Thomas Pownall," *D.A.B.*, Vol. XV, pp.

161-3; Robert Greenhalgh Albion, "Arthur Lee," *D.A.B.*, Vol. XI, pp. 96-101; Amos A. Ettinger, "James Edward Oglethorpe," *D.A.B.*, Vol. XIV, pp. 1-3.

38. Benjamin Franklin, *A Dissertation on Liberty and Necessity, Pleasure and Pain*, ed. Lawrence C. Wrock (New York, 1930), pp. 30-1.

39. *The Autobiography of Benjamin Franklin*, ed. John Bigelow (New York, 1916), p. 201. Carl Van Doren, *Benjamin Franklin* (New York, 1938), p. 81.

40. Max Weber, *The Protestant Ethic and the Spirit of Capitalism*, trans. Talcott Parsons (New York, 1948), p. 53. Also, I. Bernard Cohen, *Benjamin Franklin: His Contribution to the American Tradition* (Indianapolis, 1953), pp. 112-14.

41. Cf. Herbert W. Schneider, "The Significance of Benjamin Franklin's Moral Philosophy," *Studies in the History of Ideas* (New York, 1925), p. 305. Carl Van Doren, *op. cit.*, p. 145.

42. *The Autobiography of Benjamin Franklin*, p. 202. For the details of Whitefield's revivalism and hysteria, the people crushed to death at his meetings, and his attacks on the colleges, cf. Eugene E. White, "The Protasis of the Great Awakening in New England," *Speech Monographs*, XXI (1954), 10-20. Carl Van Doren, *op. cit.*, pp. 136, 139. Ralph S. Bates, *Scientific Societies in the United States* (New York, 1945), p. 6. Dr. Benjamin Franklin, *The Morals of Chess* (Philadelphia, 1802), p. 25.

43. Frederick B. Tolles, *Meeting House and Counting House: The Quaker Merchants of Colonial Philadelphia, 1682-1763* (Chapel Hill, 1948), pp. 175, 193, 195, 206, 210, 213. J. Bell Whitefield, "The Scientific Environment of Philadelphia, 1775-1790," *Proceedings of the American Philosophical Society*, 92 (1948), 10-11. Carl and Jessica Bridenbaugh, *Rebels and Gentlemen: Philadelphia in the Age of Franklin* (New York, 1942), pp. 305-6, 356-7. H. McLachlan, *Essays and Addresses* (Manchester, 1950), p. 60.

44. Frederick B. Tolles, *op. cit.*, p. 231. *Dictionary of American Biography*, II, 26. Carl Van Doren, *op. cit.*, p. 139.

45. Brooke Hindle, *op. cit.*, p. 72.

46. *Ibid.*, pp. 122-33. Brooke Hindle, "The Quaker Background and Science in Colonial Philadelphia," *Isis*, XLVI (1955), 243 ff.

47. Edward Ford, *David Rittenhouse: Astronomer Patriot, 1732-1796* (Philadelphia, 1946), pp. 9, 144, 158-9, 182, 197. William Barton, *Memoirs of the Life of David Rittenhouse* (Philadelphia, 1813), pp. 141, 412, 532, 576, 592. Brooke Hindle, *The Pursuit of Science in Revolutionary America*, p. 269.

48. Gilbert Chinard, "The American Philosophical Society and the

World of Science," *Proceedings of the American Philosophical Society*, 87 (1943), 3-10. Edwin G. Conklin, "The American Philosophical Society and International Relations," *Proceedings of the American Philosophical Society*, 91 (1947), 1-9.

49. *The Works of George Berkeley*, ed. Alexander Campbell Fraser (Oxford, 1871), Vol. IV, pp. 158-60. J. Hector St. John de Crèvecoeur, *Letters from an American Farmer* (reprinted New York, 1957), pp. 46-7. *The Life and Selected Writings of Thomas Jefferson*, ed. Adrienne Koch and William Peden (New York, 1944), pp. 534, 632, 693, 701, 705-6. Edwin T. Martin, *Thomas Jefferson: Scientist* (New York, 1952), pp. 3-4, 26, 17, 36.

50. G. Adolf Koch, *Republican Religion: The American Revolution and the Cult of Reason* (New York, 1933), pp. 32, 61, 242, 280. Herbert M. Morais, *Deism in Eighteenth Century America* (New York, 1934), pp. 121, 154, 162-3. Cf. Albert Post, *Popular Freethought in America, 1825-1850* (New York, 1943), pp. 18-23.

51. Simon Newcomb, "Abstract Science in America, 1776-1876," *North American Review*, CXXII (1876), 96, 100.

52. Albert H. Smyth, ed., *The Writings of Benjamin Franklin* (New York, 1905-07), Vol. II, p. 228. Quoted in Brooke Hindle, *The Pursuit of Science in Revolutionary America*, p. 1. Abbott Payson Usher, *An Introduction to the Industrial History of England* (Boston, 1920), p. 270.

53. Marquis de Chastellux, "Letter I to Mr. Madison, Professor of Philosophy, in the University of Williamsburgh," *Travels in North-America in the Years 1780-81-82*, trans. by an English Gentleman (New York, 1828), pp. 381-6.

54. W. W. Sweet, "The Protestant Churches," *Annals of the American Academy of Political and Social Science*, LVI (1948), 45. Catharine C. Cleveland, *The Great Revival in the West: 1797-1805* (Chicago, 1916), p. 120. H. Richard Niebuhr, *The Social Sources of Denominationalism* (Meridian ed., New York, 1957), p. 167. Robert E. Schofield, "John Wesley and Science in 18th Century England," *Isis*, XLIV (1953), 338. Elizabeth K. Nottingham, *Methodism and the Frontier* (New York, 1941), pp. 26, 177.

55. Baxter Perry Smith, *The History of Dartmouth College* (Boston, 1878), pp. 134, 233-5. Lewis S. Feuer, "James Marsh and the Conservative Transcendentalist Philosophy," *New England Quarterly*, XXXI (1958), 8-9. Sandford Fleming, *Children and Puritanism* (New Haven, 1933), p. 194. K. L., "Prayer for Colleges," *Vermont Chronicle*, February 12, 1830, V, 25. Merle Curti, "The Great Mr. Locke: America's Philosopher, 1873-1861," *Huntington Library Bulletin* (1937), 11, 130.

56. *The Writings of Thomas Jefferson*, ed. Paul L. Ford (New York, 1899), Vol. X, pp. 242-244.

57. Daniel C. Gilman, *The Life of James Dwight Dana* (New York, 1899), p. 187.

58. Thomas Wentworth Higginson, *Cheerful Yesterdays* (Boston, 1899), p. 105. Cf. Richard Harrison Shryock, "American Indifference to Basic Science during the Nineteenth Century," *Archives Internationales d'Histoire des Sciences*, XXVIII (1948), 54.

59. Bailey B. Burrett, *Professional Distribution of College and University Graduates, United States Bureau of Education Bulletin*, 1912: No. 19, Whole No. 491 (Washington, 1912), pp. 20, 25, 38, 42, 45, 62, 76, 78, 95, 143. Richard Harrison Shryock, *op. cit.*, p. 55.

60. John F. Fulton and Elizabeth H. Thomson, *Benjamin Silliman, 1779-1867: Pathfinder in American Science* (New York, 1947), pp. 21, 26, 27, 30, 31, 137, 172.

61. Daniel C. Gilman, *op. cit.*, pp. 181-2. *The Remains of the Rev. James Marsh, D.D., with a Memoir of His Life*, ed. Joseph Torrey (Burlington, 1852), pp. 18-20. Also Lewis S. Feuer, *op. cit.*, p. 11.

62. Moncure Daniel Conway, *Autobiography* (Boston, 1904), Vol. I, pp. 384-5. The word "anaesthetic" was invented by Holmes. Cf. Eleanor M. Tilton, *Amiable Autocrat: A Biography of Dr. Wendell Holmes* (New York, 1947), pp. 148, 187-8, 252, 344-5, 324-5.

63. Richard Harrison Shryock, *op. cit.*, p. 54.

64. Alexander Young, *A Discourse on the Life and Character of the Hon. Nathaniel Bowditch* (Boston, 1838), p. 100. Robert Elton Berry, *Yankee Stargazer: The Life of Nathaniel Bowditch* (New York, 1941), p. 35. Nathaniel Ingersoll Bowditch, *Memoir of the Translator*, in Marquis de La Place, *Mécanique Céleste*, trans. Nathaniel Bowditch (Boston, 1839), Vol. IV, p. 151.

65. Robert Elton Berry, *op. cit.*, pp. 60-71. N. I. Bowditch, *op. cit.*, pp. 115, 121, 131, 147, 154. Alexander Young, *op. cit.*, pp. 79, 85, 91-2.

66. Thomas Coulson, *Joseph Henry: His Life and Work* (Princeton, 1950), pp. 6-7, 12-15, 292. William F. Magie, "Joseph Henry," *Dictionary of American Biography*, Vol. VIII, pp. 550-3.

67. Asa Gray, *Darwiniana* (New York, 1876), pp. vi, 141, 142, 176. A. Hunter Dupree, *Asa Gray: 1810-1888* (Cambridge, 1959), pp. 14, 21, 45, 20, 47, 135, 152-3, 220-2, 231-2, 260. *Letters of Asa Gray*, ed. Jane Loring Gray (Boston, 1893), Vol. I, pp. 13, 322. Edward Lurie, "Louis Agassiz and the Races of Man," *Isis*, XLV (1954), 238-9. Bert James Loewenberg, "The Reaction of American Scientists to Darwinism," *American Historical Review*, XXXVIII (1933), 690-1.

68. Jesse S. Myer, *Life and Letters of Dr. William Beaumont* (St. Louis, 1912), pp. 29, 218, 220. G. Brown Goode, "The Origin of the National Scientific and Educational Institutions of the United States," *Papers of the American Historical Association*, IV (1890), 55-8. A. Hunter Dupree, *Science in the Federal Government: A History of Policies and Activities to 1940* (Harvard, 1957), p. 44.

69. Dumas Malone, *The Public Life of Thomas Cooper, 1783-1839* (New Haven, 1926), p. 171. R. H. Shryock, *op. cit.*, p. 63. Cf. Simon Newcomb "Abstract Science in America, 1776-1876", *op. cit.*, p. 115.

70. Alexis de Tocqueville, *Democracy in America*, trans. Henry Reeve and Francis Bowen, ed. Phillips Bradley (New York, 1953), Vol. II, p. 42. However, an undercurrent of scientific interest evidently persisted in the first third of the nineteenth century. An English traveler reported: "Science is rather generally diffused in the United States." I. Finch, *Travels in the United States of America and Canada* (London, 1833), pp. 26, 82-4. George William Pierson, *Tocqueville in America* (New York, 1959), pp. 75, 284-5, 443.

71. George B. Lockwood, *The New Harmony Movement* (New York, 1907), pp. 3-5, 82, 257, 338-9. Robert Dale Owen, *Threading My Way* (New York, 1874), pp. 284-5. Richard William Leopold, *Robert Dale Owen: A Biography* (Cambridge, 1940), pp. 27-8, 228. Samuel G. Morton, "A Memoir of Alexander Maclure," *American Journal of Science*, XLVII (April-June, 1844), 1-17. Frank Podmore, *Robert Owen* (London, 1906), p. 298 ff. Sir Charles Lyell, *A Second Visit to North America* (3rd ed., London, 1855), Vol. II, p. 271. William Maclure, *Opinions on Various Subjects Dedicated to the Industrious Producers* (New Harmony, 1831), Vol. I, pp. 149, 199; Vol. II (1837), pp. 437-41; Vol. III (1838), pp. 105, 224-5.

72. *The Memoirs of William Jennings Bryan*, by Himself and Mary Baird Bryan (Chicago, 1925), pp. 526-7. M. R. Werner, *Bryan* (New York, 1929), p. 307. John Dewey, "The American Intellectual Frontier," *New Republic*, XXX (1922), 303-4, reprinted in John Dewey, *Characters and Events*, ed. Joseph Ratner (New York, 1929), Vol. II, pp. 447-52.

73. Bernard H. Becker, *Scientific London* (New York, 1875), pp. 186-7, 202-3.

74. Max Berger, *The British Traveller in America, 1836-1860* (New York, 1943), p. 158. Quoted from Alfred Bunn, *Old England and New England* (London, 1853), p. 30. David Mead, *Yankee Eloquence in the Middle West: The Ohio Lyceum 1850-1870* (East Lansing, 1951), pp. 1, 21. Carl Bode, *The American Lyceum* (New York, 1956), pp. 177-9.

Carl Schurz, *Reminiscences* (New York, 1907), Vol. II, pp. 158-9. William H. Herndon and Jesse W. Weik, *Life of Lincoln*, ed. Paul A. Angle (Cleveland, 1949), pp. 102, 354-60.

75. Sir Charles Lyell, *Travels in North America, Canada, and Nova Scotia* (2nd ed., London, 1855), Vol. I, pp. 108, 111. Sir Charles Lyell, *A Second Visit to North America* (3rd ed., London, 1855), Vol. II, pp. 73-4, 271-2, 294. Cf. Joseph Le Conte, *Autobiography* (ed. William Dallam Armes, New York, 1903), pp. 174-6.

76. "A majority of the professional scientists in the old South were M.D.'s." Thomas Cary Johnson, Jr., *Scientific Interests in the Old South* (New York, 1936), p. 80.

77. Sir Charles Lyell, *A Second Visit to North America*, Vol. II, pp. 314-6, 291, 282. Cf. Dumas Malone, *The Public Life of Thomas Cooper, 1783-1839*, pp. 209-10.

78. John Fiske, *Edward Livingston Youmans: Interpreter of Science for the People* (New York, 1894), p. 443. Jules Marcou, *Life, Letters, and Works of Louis Agassiz* (New York, 1896), Vol. I, pp. 281-2, 289; Vol. II, p. 2. *Louis Agassiz: His Life and Correspondence*, ed. Elizabeth Cary Agassiz (Boston, 1886), Vol. II, p. 437.

79. Cf. Simon Newcomb, *op. cit.*, p. 112. John Spencer Clark, *The Life and Letters of John Fiske* (Boston, 1917), Vol. I, pp. 139, 233-4.

80. Nathan Reingold, "Science in the Civil War," *Isis*, XLIX (1958), 307, 309, 317. Simon Newcomb, *The Reminiscences of an Astronomer* (Boston, 1903), p. 87.

81. Charles Francis Adams, *An Autobiography, 1835-1915* (Boston, 1916), p. 179. M. A. De Wolfe Howe, *James Ford Rhodes: American Historian* (New York, 1929), p. 23. Donald Fleming, *John William Draper and the Religion of Science* (Philadelphia, 1950), pp. 6-7, 49, 78, 140, 163. Harris E. Starr, *William Graham Sumner* (New York, 1925), pp. 48, 72, 257, 394. John Dewey, "From Absolutism to Experimentalism," in *Contemporary American Philosophy*, ed. G. P. Adams and W. P. Montague (New York, 1930), Vol. II, pp. 13, 20. A. P. Peabody, *The Positive Philosophy* (Boston, 1867), pp. 3-4.

82. Lynde Phelps Wheeler, *Josiah Willard Gibbs: The History of a Great Mind* (New Haven, 1951), pp. 8, 26, 52, 176. Cf. *The Scientific Papers of J. Willard Gibbs* (New York, 1906), Vol. II, p. 282.

83. *Letters of Chauncey Wright*, ed. James Bradley Thayer (Cambridge, 1878), pp. 152-3, 162-3, 299-300, 370, 372. Chauncey Wright, *Philosophical Discussions* (New York, 1877), pp. 400, 403-4. Simon Newcomb, *op. cit.*, pp. 11, 21, 71-2.

84. John Spencer Clark, *The Life and Letters of John Fiske*, pp. 320-1, 327, 349, 376.

85. Daniel Coit Gilman, *The Launching of a University* (New York, 1906), pp. 14-15, 242-3. Abraham Flexner, *Daniel Coit Gilman: Creator of the American Type of University* (New York, 1946), pp. 65-6. Fabian Franklin, *The Life of Daniel Coit Gilman* (New York, 1910), pp. 197-8. J. S. Ames, "Henry Augustus Rowland," *Dictionary of American Biography*, Vol. XVI, pp. 198-9.

86. D. C. Gilman, *op. cit.*, p. 66. F. Franklin, *op. cit.*, pp. 212-15. A. Flexner, *op. cit.*, p. 69. David Eugene Smith, "James Joseph Sylvester," *Dictionary of American Biography*, Vol. XVIII, pp. 256-7. Alexander Macfarlane, *Lectures on Ten British Mathematicians of the Nineteenth Century* (New York, 1916), p. 121. Macfarlane's account of Sylvester's unhappy few months as a professor at the University of Virginia in 1841-42 is evidently highly inaccurate. He describes Sylvester as having used a sword-cane to defend himself against a student's physical violence. The actual story is one in which the anti-Semitism of both the Richmond community and the University of Virginia condoned insulting behavior on the part of a student toward Sylvester. The events are narrated in Philip Alexander Bruce, *History of the University of Virginia: 1819-1919* (New York, 1921), Vol. III, pp. 73-7. Sylvester was probably the first Jew appointed as a university professor in the United States.

87. F. Franklin, *op. cit.*, pp. 220-1. D. C. Gilman, *op. cit.*, pp. 20-3, 61.

88. Josiah Royce, "Present Ideals of American University Life," *Scribner's Magazine* (1891), 383. Alexander Macfarlane, *op. cit.*, pp. 116-17. F. Franklin, *op. cit.*, p. 229. For the character of Henry A. Rowland, in revolt against classical culture, cf. D. C. Gilman, *op. cit.*, pp. 70-2. Thomas C. Mendenhall, "Henry A. Rowland: Commemorative Address," in *The Physical Papers of Henry Augustus Rowland* (Baltimore, 1902), pp. 1-17.

89. William T. Harris, "Preface," *Journal of Speculative Philosophy*, I (1867), 1. John Fiske, *op. cit.*, pp. 4, 302, 313, 552-4. Also, John Fiske, "Edward Livingston Youmans," in *A Century of Science* (Boston, 1902), pp. 62-3, 78-9, 82. Bert James Loewenberg, "Darwinism Comes to America, 1859-1900," *Mississippi Valley Historical Review*, XXVIII (1941), 346.

90. Harris E. Starr, *William Graham Sumner*, pp. 346, 359, 362. A. G. Keller, *Reminiscences of William Graham Sumner* (New Haven, 1933), pp. 52-8.

91. Bert James Loewenberg, "Darwinism Comes to America, 1859-1900," p. 364.

92. *Harvard Memorial Biographies*, ed. Thomas Wentworth Higginson (Cambridge, 1866), Vol. I, pp. iv-v. *Letters of Chauncey Wright*,

pp. 47-9. Lynche Phelps Wheeler, *Josiah Willard Gibbs: The History of a Great Mind* (New Haven, 1951), p. 30.

93. John Fiske, *op. cit.*, p. 340. Charles S. Peirce, *Chance, Love and Logic*, ed. Morris R. Cohen (New York, 1923), pp. 121-2, 128-219. Chauncey Wright, "Two Notes on Mr. C. S. Peirce's Review of Berkeley," *The Nation*, XIII (Nov. 30, 1871), 355-6. Charles S. Peirce, *op. cit.*, pp. 124, 265. *Collected Papers of Charles Sanders Peirce*, ed. Arthur W. Burks (Cambridge, 1958), Vol. VIII, p. 38. Cf. Frederic I. Carpenter, "Charles Sanders Peirce: Pragmatic Transcendentalist," *New England Quarterly*, XIV (1941), 34-48. *Benjamin Peirce*, ed. Moses King (Cambridge, 1881), pp. 27, 40, 58-9. Benjamin Peirce, *Ideality in the Physical Sciences* (Boston, 1881), pp. 31-3, 43-56. Also cf. *Sketches and Reminiscences of the Radical Club*, ed. Mrs. John T. Sargent (Boston, 1880), pp. 379-80.

94. Morris R. Cohen, *American Thought: A Critical Sketch* (Glencoe, 1954), p. 67.

95. E. A. J. Johnson, *American Economic Thought in the Seventeenth Century* (London, 1932), pp. 62, 63, 86, 92. *Bradford's History of the Plymouth Plantation, 1606-1646*, ed. William T. Davis (New York, 1908), pp. 293-4.

96. Simon Newcomb, "Abstract Science in America, 1776-1876," *North American Review*, CXXII (1876), 115.

97. James H. Leuba, *The Belief in God and Immortality: A Psychological, Anthropological and Statistical Study* (Boston, 1916), pp. 250, 254. James H. Leuba, "Religious Beliefs of American Scientists," *Harper's*, CXIX (1934), 294-6. Harvey C. Lehman and Paul A. Witty, "Scientific Eminence and Church Membership," *Scientific Monthly*, XXXIII (1931), 546-8. Also cf. R. H. Knapp and H. B. Goodrich, *Origins of American Scientists* (Chicago, 1952), p. 275. In the most recent study, Anne Roe reports, "None of my subjects spontaneously mentioned church activities as important to him." The overwhelming majority "have long since dismissed religion as any guide to them. . . ." Anne Roe, *The Making of a Scientist* (New York, 1952), pp. 61-2.

Epilogue

THE ETHIC OF THE SCIENTIFIC REVOLUTION, AS WE HAVE SEEN, was that of an optimistic, expansive view of human life. It was filled with the conviction that science would enhance human happiness. It had confidence in the human estate and in the aims and possibilities of human knowledge. It proposed to alleviate drudgery, and to transform work from an eternal curse to a human joy. It aspired, in its reading of the book of nature, to abrogate the tired dictum of Ecclesiastes, "Knowledge increaseth sorrow." Above all, the scientific revolutionists felt themselves part of an international community of scientific intellectuals who were pointing a way beyond the religious and national creeds which divided mankind.[1] Thus, the American Philosophical Society in 1780 assumed that its members could, despite their country's war with England, communicate freely with English scientists. Its charter declared "that it shall and may be lawful for the said Society by their proper officers, at all times, whether in peace or war, to correspond with learned Societies, as well as individual learned men, of any nation or country. . . ."

The scientific revolutionists had a firm faith in the triumph of human rationality. They knew that scientific advances made possible new modes of destructive warfare, but they believed that the advent of peace would thereby be hastened—for certainly, they thought, people would prefer peace rather than mutual self-destruction. Shortly after the first balloons were flown in 1783, Benjamin Franklin wrote optimistically that now that "five thousand balloons, capable of raising two men each" could be constructed as cheaply as five warships, the age of wars was over. For what princes would wish to undertake the huge expenditure for defense against such an attack? Scientific advance would thus convince "Sovereigns of the Folly of wars." When Franklin was asked what use this new invention would be, he replied, "What good is a new-born baby?" [2] The image of birth was a familiar metaphor among the scientific revolutionists.

During our generation, however, science has become the bearer of a death wish. A scientific counterrevolution has been taking place. When J. Robert Oppenheimer, on July 16, 1945, saw at Almagordo, New Mexico, the first explosion of an atomic bomb, he recalled the lines of the Bhagavad-Gita, "I am become death—the shatterer of worlds." Two years later, Oppenheimer said, "The physicists have known sin; and this is a knowledge which they cannot lose."

No scientist in the seventeenth century would have dreamed of saying "I am become death." For the scientific revolutionists regarded themselves as harbingers of life. They came to undo the age-old damage to men's minds, to liberate them with the light of knowledge from the dark mythology of original sin. Today a thanatistic conception of knowledge is operative in the scientific unconscious; to know an object is to destroy it. The "new philosophy" of the seventeenth-century scientists was virtually done to death by the committee of scientists which recommended the use of the atomic bomb on the Japanese mainland in 1945. Since then, an ethic of original sin, translated into the languages of decision-making, power-seeking, and electronic computation, has pervaded scientific circles. The scientist is no longer the scientific revolutionist but the laboratory managerialist. The scientists are becoming just one more of society's interest groups, lobbying for their greater share in the national income, and for the perquisites of power and prestige. Scientists, enlisted in nuclear warfare, have become hostile to the hedonist-libertarian ethic, and have nearly severed the cosmopolitan bond of the scientific community.

Among the various groups which had a voice in the decision to use the atomic bomb, the official leaders of science were the least humane. The military chiefs, oddly enough, showed the greatest human compassion. Admiral Leahy declared that to drop the atomic bomb on the Japanese was to adopt "an ethical standard common to the barbarians of the Dark Ages. . . . I was not taught to make war in that fashion. . . ." General Eisenhower hoped we would not "take the lead in introducing into war something as horrible and destructive." General Marshall had compunctions about the bomb's use. On the other hand, the statesmen from left to right, without exception, were singularly oblivious of the moral issues involved. President Truman, in some ways the most Lincolnesque figure to have occupied the White House in the last century, the unsuccessful storekeeper with a common man's touch, read the memorandum of April 25, 1945, from his Secretary of War, Henry L. Stimson: "Within four months we shall in all probability have completed the most terrible weapon ever known in human history. . . . The world in its present state of moral advancement compared with its technical development would be eventually at the mercy of such a weapon. In other words, modern civilization might be completely destroyed." The President, relying on the counsel of his Secretary and the Scientific Advisory Panel, disregarded the moral issues, and looked upon the question solely as a "military decision." He never coped with the fact that a novel type of warfare was being declared ethically admissible, never thought of the fact that he was contributing to a collapse of the already fractured moral standards of the world. He scarcely pondered the new guilt and anxiety that he was bequeathing to the next generation. His fellow-statesmen were of the same mind. Prime Minister Churchill of Great Britain made similar calculations leading to an identical conclusion, and the leader of the Labour Opposition, Clement Attlee, concurred. Joseph Stalin, on behalf of the Soviet Union, wished the Americans "good use" of the bomb against the Japanese. The patrician Secretary of War, Stimson, sensitive to the arts, decided to spare the city of Kyoto, renowned for its shrines. People were more expendable; the bomb was to be used against Hiroshima, a dual target, a "military installation" surrounded by civilian houses, "most susceptible to damage." "The face of war is the face of death," he later said.[3] As for the Scientific Advisory Panel, composed of four most eminent scientists—Enrico Fermi, Ernest O. Lawrence, J. Robert Oppenheimer, and Arthur H. Compton—it advised and agreed on this final decision. A grotesque compulsion seemed to preside over the deliberations as to the use of the bomb. Japanese arms were beaten, the first peace overtures from the enemy had been received, their navy was destroyed, their economy shattered. The experiment, however, had to be made. Einstein, the godfather of the atomic project, a man with the classical ethics of the scientific revolution, was "completely powerless," as he later said, "to prevent the fateful decision." [4]

Civilization swung a full hundred and eighty degrees from the century of Galileo, Descartes, and the Royal Society to the era of our own Scientific Advisory Panel. For once, the scientists could say they had the accord of public opinion; a poll in the United States, Canada, Britain, and France showed that overwhelming majorities in 1945 approved the atomic bombing of Hiroshima. But herein was the tragedy of the scientific intellectuals. They were no longer the guardians of the "new philosophy," the prophets of a new hope. They were technicians with the prejudices of ordinary men carried away with pride by their new technological accomplishment. A process of what Norbert Wiener has called "the increasing entropy" of the scientific intellect and ethic was under way.

The four great men of the Scientific Advisory Panel believed that there could have been no other decision. Arthur Compton felt that a "firm negative stand" on his part "might still prevent an atomic attack on Japan," but that military considerations made the attack essential. Enrico Fermi had no faith in political progress, and was for the full use of scientific resources: "Whatever Nature has in store for mankind, unpleasant as it may be, men must accept, for ignorance is never better than knowledge." Some of his colleagues at Los Alamos, conscience-stricken, tried to organize on behalf of some scheme of world peace. Fermi would have no part in such activities.[5] What would Bishop Sprat have written, in a new *History of the Scientific Society*, of the virtuosi who felt humanity must press on with nuclear experiment even if it destroyed itself in the process?

During those last fateful weeks, some scientists tried somehow to prevent the use of the atomic bomb. James Franck tried to persuade the administration that the bomb's use was morally reprehensible and that a test demonstration on a barren island before Japanese observers would be effective in bringing about the Japanese surrender. The powerful Scientific Advisory Panel, however, argued that such a test was not practicable; they were for nothing short of the bomb's full military use against a Japanese city. Leo Szilard in desperation prepared a petition, signed by sixty-seven scientists, which said plainly that the bomb's use would be an international crime which would set the precedent for an era of destruction. "Almost without exception," says Szilard in retrospect, "all the creative physicists had misgivings about the use of the bomb." [6] Yet his petition in 1945 elicited a counter-petition among scientists advocating atomic warfare against Japan: "If we can save even a handful of American lives, then let us use this weapon—now!" [7]

According to Norbert Wiener, the managerial scientists were influenced by two types of motives in advocating the bomb's use. In the first place, they had spent billions of dollars, and wished to be able to justify these huge expenditures before any later Congressional interrogation. In this eventuality, "the position of the high administrators of nuclear research would be much stronger if they could make a legitimate or plausible claim that this research had served a major purpose in terminating the war." Second, writes Wiener, there were

> . . . the desires of the gadgeteer to see the wheels go round. Moreover, the whole idea of push-button warfare has an enormous temptation for those who are confident of their power of invention and have a deep distrust of human beings. . . . It is unfortunate in more than one way that the war and the subsequent uneasy peace have brought them to the front. [Although the] working scientists felt very little personal power and had very little desire for it, there was a group of administrative gadget workers who were quite sensible of the fact that they now had a new ace in the hole in the struggle for power.[8]

In Nazi Germany, of course, the bureaucratization and sadistification of science had meanwhile proceeded to the most advanced levels. Werner Heisenberg, a genius in theoretical physics with the political philosophy of a Nazi storm trooper, "considered the Nazis' efforts to make Germany powerful of more importance than their excesses." Toward the end of the war, he said, "How fine would it have been if we had won this war." He opposed Nazi stupidities only when they hurt German science, and he talked with Himmler to persuade him that Einstein's theory of relativity, essential in practical work, should not be proscribed because of Einstein's Jewishness. But he also appreciated the Nazis for their presumable readiness to give money "if the plans one has are large enough." Fortunately, Heisenberg never thought of using plutonium for a bomb, and his design for a uranium pile was inferior. When the American bomb was exploded at Hiroshima, the deepest dejection and chagrin came over the interned German physicists, not from humanitarian motives, but because they had failed to invent the bomb for Adolf Hitler. Walther Gerlach, the distinguished physicist, "was the most violently upset of all. He acted like a defeated general. He, the 'Reichsmarshal' for nuclear physics, had not succeeded in his assignment." [9] A hysteria came over the Nazi scientists from which they later emerged with suitable rationalizations. They remained assertive "Aryans." They complained that American Negro troops were among their guards. They were the genteel scientific wing of the moral degeneracy which performed lethal experiments on prisoners and annihilated several million human beings.

The new idol, Experiment, seemed to demand the largest possible magnitude of destruction. An American physicist winced when a Japanese radiologist congratulated him during the first week of the occupation: "I did the experiments years ago, but only on a few rats. But you Americans—you are wonderful. You have made the human experiment!" The benefactors of humanity were transmuted into its malefactors.

The career of the brilliant physicist Edward Teller was perhaps symbolic of the erosion of the classical ethic of science. Brooding in 1940 whether it was right or wrong for science to serve war, convinced in 1945 that the bombing of Hiroshima was a mistake, opposed in 1946 to secrecy in scientific research, he still declared in 1947 that atomic war might "endanger the survival of man," and held to the hope that "a successful, powerful, and patient world government" would secure the co-operation of the Soviet Union in the long run.[10] As the gloom, however, of the so-called Cold War deepened between the United States and the Soviet Union, as the paranoid Stalin put his impress of suspicion and mistrust on the nations' dealings, scientific intellectuals shed their residues of political idealism and became technicians of massive destruction. Edward Teller became the spokesman for the development of magno-destructive hydrogen bombs as well as for their continued testing. When Bertrand Russell proposed to Einstein in 1955 that they bring together an international group of scholars and scientists who would warn all nations of the perils created by atomic weapons, Einstein wrote ruefully that, in America, "the most renowned scientists, who occupy official positions of influence, will hardly be inclined to commit themselves to such an 'adventure.' " [11]

A new species of young scientist is said to be arising in America. He has no use for the hopes of the "new philosophy" of the seventeenth century. He has no philosophy; a few scraps of managerial ideology suffice for him.

> We are raising a generation of young men [writes Norbert Wiener], "who will not look at any scientific project which does not have millions of dollars invested in it. . . . We are for the first time finding a scientific career well paid and attractive to a large number of our best young go-getters. The trouble is that scientific work of the first quality is seldom done by the go-getters, and that the dilution of the intellectual milieu makes it progressively harder for the individual worker with any ideas to get a hearing. . . . The degradation of the position of the scientist as an independent worker and thinker to that of a morally irresponsible stooge in a science-factory has proceeded even more rapidly and devastatingly than I had expected.[12]

The new scientists entering into the positions of national influence, writes the editor of the *Bulletin of the Atomic Scientists*, will be "less intellectual, less different in their interests, social habits and attitudes from people in other walks of life." [13]

When Hitlerism came upon Germany, Einstein said, "The representatives of the scientific world have failed in their duty to defend intellectual values because they have completely lost their passionate love of them. . . . This is the only reason why vicious individuals of inferior intellect have been able to seize power. . . ." [14] The social forces of the atomic age tended similarly to corrupt the ethics of the scientific revolution.

The youth of the United States is now full of admiration for science; scientific careers have become highly desired. But, as the sociologists and pollsters say, the "image" of the scientist has been profoundly transformed. Once he was conceived very much as Sinclair Lewis conceived Arrowsmith—a selfless, disinterested seeker after truth, a benefactor of humanity. Now the sociologists find a new ingredient in the way American youth pictures the scientist; there is an admixture of brutality and sadism in his character. High-school students in the United States feel that the goals of science are not only humanitarian but also "destructive (dissecting, destroying enemies, making explosives that threaten the home, the country, or all mankind)." The scientist is also regarded as very likely engaged in pursuit of his individual gain ("making money, gaining fame and glory").[15] He is no longer, however, the embodiment of the free spirit: "If he works for a big company . . . he is just a cog in a wheel"; if for the government, he is bound to keep secrets, and is under constant surveillance. Einstein, a surviving voice from the classical revolution of 1905, warned at this time that the independence of the scientist was being threatened from within; "the shrewd methods of intellectual and psychic influence brought to bear upon the scientist will prevent the development of genuinely independent personalities. Intellectual individualism and the thirst for scientific knowledge," continued Einstein, "emerged simultaneously in history and have remained inseparable." Now, however, "the man of science has retrogressed to such an extent that he accepts as inevitable the slavery inflicted upon him by national states. He even degrades himself to such an extent that he obediently lends his talents to help perfect the means destined for the general destruction of mankind." Four years later, in 1954, Einstein amazed his fellow-Americans by saying that if he were a young man, deciding again how to make his living, "I would not try to become a scientist or scholar or teacher. I would rather choose to be a plumber or a peddler. . . ."[16]

Science fiction is, from one standpoint, a reflection of the fears and anxieties with which the imaginative reading public regards science and scientists. The tone of science fiction has tended to become increasingly "finimundialist." What is finimundialism? It is a frame of mind which is obsessed with the thought that the world is coming to an end, that atomic radiation, the collapse of the solar system, interplanetary war, the advent of a comet, heat death, or uncontrollable epidemic will soon terminate all human existence. The scientists of the seventeenth century, by contrast, transmitted to literary intellectuals their own attitude of "natiomundialism." Their new world in birth was to be not only braver but—more important—freer and happier. Cyrano de Bergerac wrote his *Voyage to the Moon* in a vein of Epicurean cheerfulness. Cyrano, the empiricist follower of Gassendi, the libertine student of Campanella and Descartes, took pleasure in ridiculing through the eyes of the Moon's inhabitants the wars of earthly princes. With impish Cartesian doubt, he turned things topsy-turvy to awaken his fellow-planetarians from the torpor of their customs. There, where the Moon was not a Moon but a World, he depicted a realm which practiced free love, where "a woman may bring her action against a man for refusing her," and where parents gave obedience to their children. During the nineteenth century, Jules Verne, its most famous synthesizer of science and romance, remained all his life a confirmed optimist, secure in his Catholic faith yet firm in his belief in the triumph of human sanity. The science-fiction writer of today, however, tells of the end of the world—the final chapter written by the sinfulness of man raised to its highest power by the available tools of science. H. G. Wells, greatest of the science-fiction writers, began life as a pupil of Thomas Henry Huxley, strong in his teacher's faith of evolutionary progress. When he died a few months after Hiroshima, he was a total finimundialist: "This world is at the end of its tether. The end of everything we call life is close at hand and cannot be evaded. . . . The writer is convinced that there is no way out or round or through the impasse. It is the end." [17] Contemporary philosophy meanwhile has likewise become filled with this theme of self-destruction. Bertrand Russell, foremost of philosophers, wrote with prescience three decades ago of the new standpoint which would prevail among scientists; power-knowledge would supersede the science which was once born of love of things and persons; underlying emotions of hatred and aggression would come to pervade science, which would be eaten away by its own self-corrosive skepticism.[18]

There is a vitality, however, in the tradition of the scientific intellectuals of the seventeenth century that will survive the hegemony of the managerial technician. For their aspiration coincided with the universal nature of man in his deepest consciousness, and as such still partakes of a deathless quality. The anxieties that irrationalize men are not rooted in the nature of things; they are phenomena of time and place. The rule of the managerial technicians is not itself a technological necessity; it depends largely on the condition of unstable equilibrium in which the perpetual fear of atomic war prevails. The human spirit itself remains discontent with the perversion of its noblest aims to the service of destruction. With only a modicum of good fortune, the "new philosophy" may once more be renewed, and in altered circumstances be able to assert itself once again.

NOTES

1. The Charter of the Royal Society in 1662 granted it the privilege "to enjoy mutual intelligence and knowledge with all and all manner of strangers and foreigners." *The Record of the Royal Society of London* (3rd ed., London, 1912), pp. 67-8. Thomas Birch, *The History of the Royal Society of London* (London, 1756-1757), Vol. I, pp. 406-7.

2. I. Bernard Cohen, "Benjamin Franklin and Aeronautics," *Journal of the Franklin Institute*, 232 (1941), 103-4, 112.

3. Henry L. Stimson, "The Decision to Use the Atomic Bomb," *Harper's*, 194 (February, 1947), 100.

4. *Einstein on Peace*, ed. Otto Nathan and Heinz Norden (New York, 1960), p. 589.

5. Laura Fermi, *Atoms in the Family* (Chicago, 1945), pp. 244-6. Arthur Compton, *Atomic Quest: A Personal Narrative* (New York, 1956), p. 247.

6. *U.S. News and World Report*, XLIX (August 15, 1960), 68, 64. Cf. Farrington Daniels and Arthur H. Compton, "A Poll of Scientists at Chicago," *Bulletin of the Atomic Scientists*, IV (February, 1948), 44. Michael Amrine, *The Great Decision: The Secret History of the Atomic Bomb* (New York, 1951), pp. 146-7.

7. Arthur H. Compton, *Atomic Quest*, pp. 241-2.

8. Norbert Wiener, *I Am a Mathematician* (New York, 1956), pp. 304-7.

9. Samuel A. Goudsmit, *Alsos* (New York, 1947), pp. 114-18, 120, 135, 168.

10. Philip Morrison, "The Laboratory Demobilizes," *Bulletin of the Atomic Scientists*, II (November, 1946), 5. Laura Fermi, *op. cit.*, p. 220. *U.S. News and World Report*, XLIX (August 15, 1960), 75. Edward Teller, "A Suggested Amendment to the Acheson Report," *Bulletin of*

the Atomic Scientists, I (June 1, 1946), 5; "Atomic Scientists Have Two Responsibilities," III (December, 1947), 356; "How Dangerous Are Atomic Weapons?," III (February, 1947), 36.

11. *Einstein on Peace,* p. 631.

12. Norbert Wiener, "A Rebellious Scientist After Two Years," *Bulletin of the Atomic Scientists,* IV (November, 1948), 338-9. Earl W. Lindveit, *Scientists in Government* (Washington, 1960), p. 1.

13. Eugene Rabinowitch, "History's Challenge to Scientists," *Bulletin of the Atomic Scientists,* XII (1956), 239.

14. *Einstein on Peace,* p. 220. Cf. Max Born, "Physics and Politics," *Bulletin of the Atomic Scientists,* XVI (1960), 199.

15. Margaret Mead and Rhoda Metraux, "Images of the Scientist Among High-School Students," *Science,* 126 (August 30, 1957), 386-7.

16. *Einstein on Peace,* pp. 535-6, 613.

17. Cyrano de Bergerac, *A Voyage to the Moon,* trans. A. Lovell (New York, ed. of 1899), pp. xv, 137, 143, 152. Marguerite Allotte de la Füye, *Jules Verne,* trans. Erik de Mauny (New York, 1956), pp. 49-50, 213. H. G. Wells, *Mind at End of Its Tether* (New York, 1946), pp. 1-4.

18. Bertrand Russell, *The Scientific Outlook* (New York, 1931), pp. 94, 100.

APPENDIX A

Harvey and Gilbert: Precursors of the Royal Society

THE SCIENTIFIC INTELLECTUALS OF THE ROYAL SOCIETY CONSTITUTED a movement; they had a sense of mission, a sense of unity, a sense that they were the bearers of the "new philosophy." They had roots in their own English past, in the work and standpoint especially of their two precursors, William Harvey, the discoverer of the circulation of the blood, and William Gilbert, pioneer in the science of magnetism.

Harvey was known in his time as an ardent Royalist. *The Journal of the House of Commons* in 1643 recorded that Dr. Harvey had withdrawn from St. Bartholomew's Hospital, "and is retired to the party in arms against the Parliament." Harvey had strong personal reasons for loyalty to the monarch Charles I. When he published his book on the circulation of the blood, in 1628, Harvey's medical practice fell greatly, "and 'twas believed," as Aubrey tells us, "by the vulgar that he was crack-brained, and all the physitians were against him." The king, however, showed a genuine interest in Harvey's researches, and appointed Harvey in 1630 to be his personal physician. Their association was both close and enduring. In 1643, at the battle of Edgehill, Harvey was entrusted with the care of the two boy princes, afterward Charles II and James II. When Harvey required animals for dissection and vivisection, "the great prince," as Harvey writes,

> . . . whose physician I was, besides taking much pleasure in such inquiries and not disdaining to bear witness to my discoveries, was pleased in his kindness and munificence to order me an abundant supply of these animals [deer], and repeated opportunities of examining their bodies.

Thus, in 1651, Harvey still testified to the greatness of his king, executed two years before by the rebels. Harvey himself experienced the fury of a revolutionary mob. In August, 1642, when it became known that the king had raised his standard at Nottingham, a mob of Parliamentary soldiers burst into Harvey's lodgings, stole all his furniture, and wantonly destroyed and scattered his notes and papers. "Hence it has come to pass," Harvey wrote, "that many observations, particularly on the generation of insects, have perished with detriment, I venture to say, to the republic of letters."

The republic of letters seemed to Harvey disrupted by Cromwell's Commonwealth and the Puritans. Harvey had already seen the havoc and misery which religious fanaticism had brought upon Europe. He wrote home, from his travels on the continent in 1631:

> . . . we could scarce see a dog, crow, kite, raven or any other bird, or any thing to anatomise, only some few miserable people, the relics of the war and the plague had made anatomies before I came. It is scarce credible in so rich, populous, and plentiful countries as these were that so much misery and desolation, poverty and famine should in so short a time be. . . . I interpret it well that it will be a great motive for all here to have and procure assurance of settled peace.

Harvey himself held to the most liberal views in religion; he was, in effect, a pantheistic deist. To the title page of his lectures at the College of Physicians in 1616, he attached the motto, "Everything is full of Jove." The finger of God, he said, was the same as nature, equally manifest throughout every detail of the world. And all the attributes of nature were to be referred to the Almighty, who was identical, said Harvey, with Aristotle's Divine Mind, Plato's Soul of the Universe, *natura naturans*, and the Gentiles' Saturn and Jove. When George Ent in 1650 visited Harvey in his old age, he "found him, Democritus-like, busy with the study of natural things, his countenance cheerful. . . ."

The image of the laughing materialist Democritus was far from the Puritan visage. Harvey lamented that "the Commonwealth is full of distractions" and himself adrift in his time "as in the open sea." The old Royalist was indeed at sea in the Puritan revolution. He took solace in his scientific studies, which he loved for their own sake—"the examination of the bodies of animals has always been my delight," "a balm for my spirit." With his liberal religion, he felt more kinship with the refined society of the Court than with the dour Calvinist theologians. In 1636, Harvey was sent to Italy to buy pictures for the king's collection. He transmitted his benign influence to the men who founded the Royal Society. For in 1645 Harvey was designated by the king to become Warden of Merton College at Oxford, to supplant a Presbyterian who had joined the rebels. Harvey held office for only a year; he retired when Oxford was captured by the Parliamentary army in 1646. That brief year, however, was enough for Harvey's scientific spirit to affect such men at Oxford as Scarbrough, Willis, and Wren. Scarbrough indeed, after being expelled from Cambridge for his Royalist sympathies, was drawn to Oxford by the luster of Harvey's name. William Harvey, the greatest of the English scientists of the first half of the seventeenth century, was alien to the spirit of the Puritan ethics; he was among the hedonist liberals.[1]

William Gilbert was the most distinguished man of science in the reign of Queen Elizabeth. His treatise *De Magnete*, published in 1600, opened the new century with an inquiry into a new science and with a use of the new experimental method. As Edgar Zilsel has written in a memorable essay, Gilbert's work was "the first printed book, written by an academically trained scholar and dealing with a topic of natural science, which is based almost entirely on actual observation and experiment."[2] What can be said of the motivation of this man who opens the great era of English science?

Gilbert was an Elizabethan figure, filled with the adventurous zest of an age which was unparalleled for its achievements in exploration, seacraft, poetry, and drama. Gilbert was Queen Elizabeth's physician; his manner and bearing had "the clearness of Venice glass," "ripe, and long lasting in his perfection." The Virgin Queen liked her physician, and "stamped on him many marks of her favor." Gilbert received an annual pension from Elizabeth to help him with his researches. He was a scientist who blended well with her court, for his "complexion" was "cheerful, an happiness not ordinary in so hard a student and retired a person." He was said to be "stoical, but not cynical . . . reserved, but not morose."[3]

The striking thing about Gilbert's *De Magnete* is that God is virtually absent from its pages. Later scientists would interlard their prefaces with acknowledgments to Divine Providence, but Gilbert fails to invoke the Deity in his preface, "To the Candid Reader, Studious of the Magnetic Philosophy." English science in the seventeenth century opens on a secular note. Gilbert, at the outset, declares his impatience with the traditional learning, the "ocean of books whereby the minds of the studious are bemuddled and vexed," and "whereby the common herd" are "made intoxicated, crazy, puffed up." He turned from the way of the "lettered clowns" and "wrong-headed rabble"; to "philosophize freely, as freely, as in the past" was the practice of "the Egyptians, Greeks, and Latins." Gilbert proposed to write plainly, use intelligible words, and avoid pedantic terminology.

Theological language can be described as one in which the proportion of words with concrete, empirical referents is low. In Gilbert's scientific language, the ratio of empirical words to the total number is high. The hedonistic court of Elizabeth, with its delight in the senses and its own fresh, vigorous, sensuous idiom, was yielding a by-product—a language of knowledge in which there would be the same striving for sensory meaning.

It was not a casual circumstance that the science in which the Elizabethan spirit of adventure manifested itself was that of magnetism. Much of Gilbert's work was centered around the compass needle, which was indeed a symbol of the Elizabethan age. "Nothing ever has been contrived," wrote Gilbert, "by the art of man nor anything been of greater advantage to the human race than the mariner's compass. . . ." The role of lodestone in creating England's empire had been unique. Within their memory, said Gilbert's friend Edward Wright, thanks to "the God-given favor of this stone," continents had been discovered and "the whole circle of the globe has been circumnavigated more than once by our own Drake and Cavendish." Gilbert's special hope was to devise a method whereby seamen could determine their latitudes by observing the dip of the magnetic needle. He had on hand the observations of many Englishmen who "on long sea voyages" had "observed the differences of magnetic variation"—Thomas Hariot, Robert Hues, Edward Wright, Abraham Kendall. Hariot had been tutor and surveyor in Virginia for Sir Walter Raleigh; Hues had been with Cavendish around the world and had dedicated a book to Raleigh; Edward Wright, a mathematician, had sailed with the Earl of Cumberland to the Azores; and Kendall had sailed with Drake. If Gilbert had succeeded in his design, it would have been a boon to English navigators.[4]

Gilbert's research has been linked to the stimulus of Elizabethan craftsmen, metallurgists, miners, and manual workers. Certainly Gilbert drew from such sources information and techniques. He wrote a veritable tribute to iron:

> Its use exceeds that of all other metals a hundredfold; it is smelted daily; and there are in every village iron forges. For iron is foremost among metals and supplies many human needs, and they the most pressing.

The association of his work, however, with the interests and spirit of the Elizabethan sea adventurers was even more impressive; the navigational enterprise was always in the background. Here was not the spirit of accumulation through abstinence, frugality, saving, and the

Protestant ethic. Raleigh and Drake were men of a hedonistic age, glorying in self-expression, engaging in pirate wars against the Spaniard. The English scientists partook of their spirit.

God appears toward the end of Gilbert's book, when the author is engaged in the pantheist animistic speculation that soul is found in all things. But the whole tenor of this speculation was alien to the Calvinist spirit. For Gilbert argues against the abject lot of the earth and all its objects. The lowliest objects "are themselves possessed of souls"; otherwise, "the earth were void and dead and without any use." And in the host of souls, "in their great and delightful diversity the Creator taketh pleasure." When Gilbert did essay theology, he conceived of God as a Sovereign Elizabeth, delighting in the variety of her empire. There were no somber hues in Gilbert's cosmos.

Such was the man who was as "addicted" to science as other Elizabethans were to exploration. He never married, "purposely," it is said, "to be more beneficial to his brethren." He ridiculed writers who treated their subjects "esoterically, miracle-mongeringly, abstrusely, reconditely, mystically." "Such philosophy," he wrote, "bears no fruit." They waste "oil and labor, because, not being practical in the research of objects in nature." [5] Before he went to Elizabeth's court, he used to gather, with friends in a society or college, at his residence in Colchester. The first germination of the scientific society was making its appearance.[6] Later, Gilbert served as President of the Royal College of Physicians. He corresponded with the bold Venetians Paoli Sarpi and Sagredo. Elizabethan science was filled with the spirit of pleasure in the human adventure which was to grow in the seventeenth century, counterposed to the harshness of theological ethics and controversy.

N O T E S

1. D'Arcy Power, *William Harvey* (London, 1897), pp. 54-5, 85, 88, 124-5, 133, 147-8, 186-7, 242. Geoffrey Keynes, *The Personality of William Harvey* (Cambridge, 1949), pp. 11, 15, 29, 31-6.

2. Edgar Zilsel, "The Origins of William Gilbert's Scientific Method," *Journal of the History of Ideas*, II (1941), 1.

3. Thomas Fuller, *The Worthies of England*, ed. John Freeman (London, 1952), pp. 178-9.

4. William Gilbert, *On the Loadstone and Magnetic Bodies, and on the Great Magnet the Earth*, trans. P. Fleury Mottelay (New York, 1893; reprinted, New York, 1958), pp. xxxvii, xlviii, xlix, 1, 6, 14. Edgar

Zilsel, *op. cit.*, p. 16. Silvanus P. Thompson, *William Gilbert, and Terrestial Magnetism in the Time of Queen Elizabeth* (London, 1903), p. 13.

5. William Gilbert, *op. cit.*, pp. 42, 310, 5, 77, x.

6. Sir William Hale-White, *Bacon, Gilbert and Harvey* (London, 1927), p. 47.

APPENDIX B

The Enigma of Newton

CAN WE INQUIRE SOMEWHAT INTO THE PSYCHOLOGICAL SOURCES OF Newton's godlike scientific genius? Newton's father died before the son was born; his mother remarried when Isaac was less than two, and left him in the care of his grandmother while she went to live with her second husband. Like Kepler, Newton was born prematurely, and like Kepler, too, he suffered a severe experience of maternal rejection on the part of a mother whom he loved dearly and to whom he always remained attached. The loneliness of the child who has suffered a traumatic emotional deprivation characterized his growing years; he "was never known scarce to play with the boys abroad at their silly amusements," said Miss Storey, to whom he was apparently later engaged to be married,

> but would rather choose to be at home, even among the girls, and would frequently make little tables, cupboards, and other utensils for her and her playfellows to set their babies and trinkets on.

The story bespeaks a child yearning for the mother's affection and security which he has lost, and finding it in games of imaginary households with girls. In maturity, he was almost never known to laugh. His early years had evidently imprinted on him a melancholy spirit. But he had one unending source of joy as a child; "his absorbing interest lay in the design and construction of mechanical toys and models." It was "a passion for making mechanical toys and models," says More. According to his schoolmates, Newton, instead of playing with the boys,

> busied himself in making knick-knacks and models of wood in many kinds. For which purpose he had got little saws, hatchets, hammers, and all sorts of tools, which he would use with great dexterity.

They remembered a wooden clock and windmill he fashioned, and especially recalled how Newton had placed a mouse in the windmill and that Newton joked as "the mouse made the mill turn round when he pleased." How far one might see in this curious experiment a frustrated, deep-seated Oedipal longing, with the mouse and mill as male and female symbols respectively, we can only speculate. His mother, when Newton was sixteen years old, tried to make a farmer out of him, but in a most un-Puritan indifference to industry he paid no attention to the straying cattle, and whittled away with his knife to make more mechanical toys. It was the same hedonistic "associative play" which Einstein regarded as the life spirit of science. No wonder that legend depicts an idle Newton under an apple tree as he conceived the law of gravitation.

Political circumstances could scarcely have favored the child's attachment to the Puritan ascetics. The neighborhood knew the depredations of civil war. Newton's grandmother, suspected of sympathy for the Royalist cause, was probably, in More's opinion, "frequently forced to evade embarrassing questions of the Commonwealth soldiers and of the local magistrates." Newton's own sympathies as a boy were also evidently Royalist. In his room at the Grantham school where he spent four years, Newton kept a picture of the Martyr King, Charles I, and under it he inscribed verses of tribute.[1]

Newton found in science an emotional absorption and unity which had been denied him in his familial relations. The episodes and metaphors of his work have the impress, as did Kepler's work, of this theme of longing for a restored unity. He first thought in 1665 of the system of gravity, it was said, "by observing an apple fall from a tree." Did the apple falling to the earth with the theme of the seed's return to the mother release a flood of emotional energy for a tremendous original insight? We can only speculate. It is noteworthy, however, that the "two golden years" of Newton's creativity came when, in 1665, the Great Plague closed Cambridge University, and Newton returned to live in seclusion with his mother at her farm at Woolsthorpe. The stepfather had died in 1656, when Isaac was sixteen years old, and the lad had tried for more than a year to farm his mother's new estate, but without success. From 1665 to 1667 came Newton's three great discoveries of the method of fluxions, the composition of light, and the law of universal gravitation. His mother's death in 1690 may very well have been a principal cause in the termination of his scientific career. For it was during the next years that Newton developed the symptoms of persecution and the fears that his friends were deserting him.[2] Did his mother's death reawaken all those feelings of rejection which had darkened his childhood? He came to dislike science whenever it awoke the trauma of rejection. The controversies with Hooke and Leibniz over priorities in discovery embittered him inordinately. These competitions for first place seemed to awaken the childhood trauma of seeing his mother leave him to live with another man and his children. He then personified science as an untrustworthy, fickle woman.

> Philosophy is such an impertinently litigious Lady, that a man had as good be engaged to lawsuits, as to have to do with her. I found it so formerly, and now I am no sooner come near her again, but she gives me warning.

Science at such times offered not security but insecurity, not trust but suspicion, and Newton would brood:

> I see I have made myself a slave to philosophy. . . . I will resolutely bid adieu to it eternally, excepting what I do for my private satisfaction, or I will leave it to come after me; for I see that a man must either resolve to put out nothing new, or to become a slave to defend it.

Scientific research was very much for Newton a matter "for my private satisfaction," a matter of immediate pleasure and private happiness. There was a strong flavor of narcissistic self-sufficiency in his reluctance to disclose his ideas, to risk giving something of his own to other persons. His famous *epistola posterior* to Oldenburg on October 24, 1676, which set forth his discovery of the calculus, was an indecipherable medley of letters and numbers. As a scientist, said Newton, he seemed to himself

> . . . to have been only like a boy playing on the sea-shore, and diverting myself in now and then finding a smoother pebble or prettier shell than ordinary, while the great ocean of truth lay all undiscovered before me.

Again, in his self-image, he harked back to his childhood, playing by himself, enjoying himself alone, finding for himself symbolic seed, while the ocean, the great maternal symbol, remains still unattained before him. A narcissistic hedonist in his underlying emotion toward his work, Newton's greatness, like Kepler's, may thus have been the product of a response to maternal rejection, not through ascetic self-immolation, but through seeking a kind of surrogate unity in the conquest of the world of nature. This shift from masochist asceticism to self-assertive mastery over nature is exactly part of the psychological revolution which differentiated modern from medieval man, and made science possible.

Personal happiness came to Newton only in his later years, when, after his recovery from his breakdown, he entered fully into the political and social world. The *Principia* had been published in 1687, and as illness receded in 1694, he seemed liberated from some torment. That year Charles Montague, later Lord Halifax, became Chancellor of the Exchequer. Montague had been one of Newton's favored "small band of students," but his gift for versifying had drawn him toward a political career. When Newton took his seat in the House of Commons on January 22, 1689, as a member from Cambridge University, he was reunited with his old student who was now one of the great Whig parliamentarians. Newton enjoyed attending the sessions of Parliament far more than he ever had the Royal Society. With Montague's accession to political power, Newton was glad to avail himself of political patronage. As More says, "When he became a gentleman, he abandoned science and scholarship without any apparent regret." [3] "His whole outlook on life seems to have changed . . . he mingled in society and lost all desire for the academic life and for scientific work." [4] The society of scientists, which had become contentious and traumatic, was something he would reject himself. The underlying hedonistic impulse remained, the drive which had taken him toward the "private satisfaction" of science, but now he found a fuller, non-narcissistic pleasure in public life and government service.

Newton was a hedonist in scientific research who rebelled against the first appearances of competitive rivalry and organizational politics among scientists. The scientific pleasure was sullied and defiled when competitive situations awoke anxiety. He turned from it to the political world, which at least awoke no narcissistic anxieties. He exchanged the pebbles on the shore for the mastery of all England's coins. He became very much a man of his times. He wrote letters to his nephew, a profligate clergyman, which, though reproachful in tone, were later destroyed because it was feared that Newton's reputation might suffer if people knew that he was familiar with such coarse language. It was the country clergy who defeated Newton when he tried to be elected to Parliament again in 1705.[5] Perhaps they saw deeper than Newton himself cared to avow into the hedonistic-libertarian basis of the new science.

All his life Newton was interested in questions of theology. His posthumously published *Observations upon the Prophecies of Daniel and the Apocalypse of St. John* have usually bewildered Newton's biographers with its tortuous interpretations of Daniel's vision of the "four great beasts" and the fourth beast with ten horns and an eleventh "which came up." During the years which followed his completion in 1687 of the *Mathematical Principles of Natural Philosophy*, and which preceded his mental illness of 1693, Newton turned increasingly to his theological studies. He wrote to John Locke in February, 1691, saying that when he would meet him again, "I should be glad to have your judgment upon some of my mystical fancies." [6] What light do Newton's "mystical fancies" shed upon his underlying character? Was there anything distinctive in Newton's interpretation of Daniel's vision which would enable us to draw some inferences from his "mystical fancies" to his underlying emotions? For we can compare the process of Biblical interpretation with that which takes place in story-completion and sentence-completion tests. The person who completes an unfinished story reveals to us something of his underlying emotions by the last incident which he projects. Newton, as the interpreter of Daniel, is almost a subject in a "projective test," providing us perhaps with some clues as to his deepest feelings and hopes.

Now, the apocalyptic visions of Daniel were evidently written very soon after the desecration of the Temple of Jerusalem in December, 167 B.C., when the Jews were under the oppression of the Syrian Greek king, Antiochus Epiphanes. The writer evidently intended to strengthen the will and courage of the Jews by reminding them of other empires which had oppressed them and which had vanished into history's oblivion. The Jews once more would be delivered from their oppressor, and the faithful would triumph. So the author of Daniel, an ancient Toynbee, reviewed the spectacle of the civilizations which rose and fell: "And four great beasts came up from the sea, diverse one from another." These were the four empires, the Babylonians, the Medes, the Persians, and the Greeks. But then came the forecast of the fifth kingdom, the fifth monarchy:

> And in the days of these kings shall the God of heaven set up a kingdom, which shall never be destroyed: and the kingdom shall not be left to other people, but it shall break in pieces and consume all these kingdoms, and it shall stand for ever.[7]

The meaning to be attached to this apocalyptic verse became a matter of import to England during the years of Newton's childhood and youth.

To John Calvin, it was clear that the fifth monarchy signified the coming of Christ. It was an empirical event which had already taken place; Christ's kingdom had destroyed all the earthly kingdoms such as Rome which stood in its way. True, there was the empirical difficulty of the subsequent advent of Mohammedanism, but Calvin waved this aside. He acknowledged there was a Turkish empire which "at this day, excels in wealth and power . . . but it was not God's purpose to explain future events after the appearance of Christ." [8] A century later, however, during Newton's boyhood, the Fifth Monarchy Men, the extreme left wing of the English revolutionaries of the Cromwellian era, began to interpret the vision of Daniel as a prediction of the social revolution which was at hand. As Louise Fargo Brown has described it, in the circles of soldiers and agitators of Cromwell's army, preachers began to seek the explanation of the crisis of their time in "those most obscure and mystical books, the prophecy of Daniel and the Revelation of John." There was little controversy in the seventeenth century concerning the identity of the four kingdoms. What, however, did the Fifth Monarchy portend? The end of the Thirty Years' War suggested the last days of the Roman monarchy, and the Fifth Monarchy Men now dared to hope that their civil war would usher in the new social order ruled by Jesus. They saw themselves, to use Blake's words, as the builders of Jerusalem in England's green and pleasant land.

Thus the Fifth Monarchy Men studied their Daniel as others later studied Marx and Lenin. The disruptive little horn which appeared on the head of the fourth beast and made war against the saints they interpreted variously as the papacy, William the Conqueror, and Charles I. They conjectured that 1666 would see their final triumph over all the world. As they came into conflict, however, with the more moderate and realistic Cromwell, they decided in disillusionment that Oliver was the Little Horn of Daniel's prophecy, and his rule that of the Beast.[9]

Newton's interpretation of the apocalyptic vision in Daniel was, on the one hand, secular-minded as compared to Calvin's, and, on the other, more one of steady, gradual progress than the millennial perspective of the Fifth Monarchy Men. Calvin had rendered a theological interpretation of history in which history really ended when Jesus accomplished his mission in Roman times. The Fifth Monarchy Men had given a social interpretation of history which terminated in social revolution, the kingdom of Jesus. Newton tried in a confused way to project the Baconian philosophy of progress into the prophetic imagery of Daniel. He tried to read the apocalyptic vision of Daniel as if it were an essay by an ancient Condorcet foreseeing the indefinite progress of man. Newton refused to end human history with a coming of Jesus. He wrote to John Locke denying that the triumph of the Ancient of Days signified the rule of Jesus over the nations. "But whence are you certain," wrote Newton, "that the Ancient of Days is Christ? Does Christ anywhere sit upon the throne?" With one variance from Calvin, Newton interpreted the four kingdoms as the four historical empires of Babylonia, Persia, Greece, and Rome. But where Calvin took the fifth monarchy as the rule of Jesus, Newton took it in a secular sense, as a forecast of indefinite secular progress. In the language of theology, he was trying to set forth the scientific intellectual's philosophy of history. It was not that of social revolution or God's entry into history, but that of indefinite progressive achievement.

Thus, guided by an embryonic philosophy of progress, Newton departed from Calvin's interpretation of Daniel on several subsidiary items. Where Calvin took the little horn as referring to the Caesars who warred against the Church, Newton took it as referring to the Church of Rome, which grew corrupt as it accumulated to itself "temporal dominion." Where Calvin interpreted the ten horns of the fourth beast as referring loosely to the several provinces of the Roman Empire, Newton gave them a more dynamic historical rendering as the various barbarian kingdoms which came into existence after the Goths overturned the "dreadful and terrible" Roman beast with its "great iron teeth." But the society which was to succeed the Roman church was not to be founded in sudden millenarian fashion; rather, said Newton, its dominion was to grow "by degrees." [10] The prophets, said Newton, spoke a figurative language drawn "from the analogy between the world natural, and an empire or kingdom considered as a world politic." "The whole world politic consisting of heaven and earth signifies the whole world politic consisting of thrones and people . . ." Newton tried to make these analogies convey the hopes of the English scientific intellectuals. The papal power would vanish, and a vague Unitarian benevolent creed would guide men.

For there is no doubt that Newton, who in physics said "*Hypotheses non fingo*," was prepared to assert most of the received theology to be nonsense. He sought to show that verses in the New Testament which were used to defend the doctrine of the Trinity were forgeries. He regarded Jesus as simply a human being who, when he called himself the Son of God, meant nothing more than that God had "sent him into the world." Newton wrote that the Trinitarian doctrine of Homoousian—that the essence of Father and Son is identical—"is unintelligible." The backward portion of humanity loved such doctrines, but they ill befitted the free-minded philosopher. "It is the temper of the hot and superstitious part of mankind, in matters of religion," Newton said, "ever to be fond of mysteries; and for that reason, to like best what they understand least." [11] Newton, as a scientific intellectual, had tried to formulate an optimist philosophy of history in which the benevolent God who perhaps made of space his sensorium would use time for the perfectibility of man.

In the midst of his Biblical exegesis, Newton stated emphatically his rejection of masochist asceticism. He traced how Roman Christianity had mistakenly come to identify "holiness" with "abstinence from marriage," how the ascetics actually pronounced "that matrimony was no purer than a rape," how the influential Encratites, the Continentes, had not only forbidden marriage, "that primitive ordinance of God," but had indirectly accused God, he wrote,

> for having created both male and female for the propagation of the human race. They also inculcated the necessity of abstaining from animal food, and thus proved themselves ungrateful to that God who also has created all things for our use. They also denied the primitive purity of man.

The Christian church, said Newton, came under the hegemony of these Encratites, thereby fulfilling Daniel's prophecy that a king would arise who would not regard "the desire of women." The "sincere Christians" were displaced by monks with their "profession of a single life." [12] Thus Newton linked the revival of true religion with the acknowledgment of "the desire of women" and the fulfillment of God's benevolent law of sexuality. Sexual satisfaction, not frustration, was more compatible with the path to holiness.

Curiously, the millenarian language of revolution came to Newton's pen as he set down his vision of the world to come. With the decline of Roman Christianity "by degrees," "the last age of the world" would be close at hand. "But if the last age," wrote Newton, "the age of opening these things [prophecies], be now approaching, as by the great successes of late Interpreters it seems to be, we have more encouragement than ever to look into these things." For "the main revolution" predicted by the prophets had not yet come to pass, "the signal revolutions" whose occurrence would finally make clear the significance of their predictions. God's providence in human history would then be manifest. What the character of "the main revolution" would be in detail, Newton never ventured to say. He only remarked that Christ's Second Coming was a metaphorical way of referring to the "things to be done" for "setting up a kingdom wherein dwells righteousness." [13] The Unitarian Master of the Mint, one has the feeling, conceived of the kingdom of righteousness as one ruled by enlightened scientific intellectuals.

NOTES

1. Louis T. More, *Isaac Newton* (New York, 1934), pp. 16, 252, 246, 7, 10, 12, 609, 15. Sir Isaac Newton, *Theological Manuscripts*, ed. H. McLachlan (Liverpool, 1950), p. 9.

2. Louis T. More, *op. cit.*, pp. 44, 41, 380-1, 390.

3. David Eugene Smith, "Newton in the Light of Modern Criticism," in *Sir Isaac Newton, 1727-1927*, ed. F. E. Brasch, papers prepared under the auspices of the History of Science Society (Baltimore, 1928), p. 10. Florian Cajori, "Newton's Twenty Years' Delay in Announcing the Law of Gravitation," *ibid.*, p. 176. Louis T. More, *op. cit.*, pp. 191-2, 394, 217-8, 345-6.

4. Louis T. More, *op. cit.*, p. 352. Newton wrote to Flamsteed that he did not love to be thought "to be trifling away my time [about mathematical things] when I should be about the King's business." Augustus De Morgan, *Newton: His Friend: and his Niece* (London, 1885), p. 105.

5. Louis T. More, *op. cit.*, p. 463. Sir John Craig, *Newton at the Mint* (Cambridge, 1946), p. 33.

6. Lord King, *The Life and Letters of John Locke* (London, 1884), p. 218.

7. The Book of Daniel, 2: 44.

8. John Calvin, *Commentaries on the Book of the Prophet Daniel*, trans. Thomas Myers (Grand Rapids, 1948), Vol. I, p. 187.

9. Louise Fargo Brown, *The Political Activities of the Baptists and Fifth Monarchy Men in England During the Interregnum* (Washington, 1912), pp. 12, 22, 25, 45, 49, 116.

10. Sir David Brewster, *Memoirs of the Life, Writings, and Discoveries of Sir Isaac Newton* (2nd ed., Edinburgh, 1860), Vol. II, p. 261. Louis T. More, *op. cit.*, p. 629.

11. Sir David Brewster, *op. cit.*, Vol. II, p. 259. Sir Isaac Newton, *Theological Manuscripts*, pp. 120-1. Louis T. More, *op. cit.*, pp. 642-3, 637.

12. Sir Isaac Newton, *Observations upon the Prophecies of Daniel*, trans. P. Borthwick (London, 1831), pp. 209-15, 128.

13. Sir Isaac Newton, *Observations upon the Prophecies of Daniel and the Apocalypse of St. John* (London, 1733), pp. 251-2.

APPENDIX C

The Membership of the Royal Society

ON JUNE 22, 1663, THERE WERE A HUNDRED AND NINETEEN PERSONS listed as members of the Royal Society.[1] What proportions of them were Puritan or hedonist, Parliamentarian or Royalist? *The Dictionary of National Biography* and biographical writings usually provide us with sufficient ground for a classification, but occasionally we are placed in the situation of the microscopist who gazes at his specimen for hours trying to make a decision. Sometimes the character of a Fellow's philosophy has to be judged not from his utterances or writings, which may not exist, but simply from the closeness of his participation in the activities of Charles II. An indeterminate margin of error remains in such qualitative evaluations. Where the final result, however, is so overwhelmingly in one direction, we may infer that our conclusion is reasonably secure. What, then, are our findings in detail concerning the hundred and nineteen members of the Royal Society?

Sixty-eight of them were, in varying degrees, predominantly Royalist in their political outlook or associations. They were: Annesley, Ashmole, Aubrey, Baines, Peter Balle, William Balle, Bate, Bathurst, Barrow, George Lord Berkeley, Sir John Birkenhead, Richard Boyle, Viscount Brouncker, David Bruce, Robert Lord Bruce, George Duke of Buckingham, William Lord Cavendish, later Duke of Devonshire, Charleton, Clarke, Croone, William Cavendish, Earl of Devonshire, Sir John Denham, Sir Kenelme Digby, Henry Pierrepont, first Marquis of Dorchester John Dryden, Erskine, Evelyn, Le Fevre, Sir John Finch, Graunt, Glisson, Christopher Lord Hatton, Thomas Henshaw, Nathaniel Henshaw, Holder, Hooke, Hoskyns, Jones, Alexander Bruce, Earl of Kincardin, Long, Lucas, Sir Robert Moray, Sir Anthony Morgan, Sir Paul Neile, William Neile, Sir Thomas Nott, Oldenburg, Sir Robert Paston afterwards Earl of Yarmouth, Pope, Sir Richard Powle,

Quatremaine, Rooke, Edward Montagu, Earl of Sandwich, Scarburgh, Sir Henry Slingesby, Sir Robert Southwell, Sprat, Stanhope, Sir Thomas Stanley, Sir Samuel Tuke, Waller, Ward, Sir Joseph Williamson, Christopher Wren, Matthew Wren, Thomas Wren, Sir Cyril Wyche, Sir Peter Wyche.

At least forty-three of the Royalist group, moreover, were, in different measure, linked with attitudes of the hedonist-libertarian ethics. They were: Annesley, Ashmole, Aubrey, Baines, Bathurst, Barrow, George Lord Berkeley, Sir John Birkenhead, Viscount Brouncker, George Duke of Buckingham, William Lord Cavendish, later Duke of Devonshire, Charleton, Clarke, William Cavendish, Earl of Devonshire, Sir John Denham, Sir Kenelme Digby, Henry Pierrepont, first Marquis of Dorchester, John Dryden, Evelyn, Le Fevre, Sir John Finch, Christopher Lord Hatton, Henshaw, Holder, Hooke, Hoskyns, Jones, Sir Thomas Nott, Oldenburg, Sir Robert Paston, afterwards Earl of Yarmouth, Pope, Quatremaine, Rooke, Edward Montagu, Earl of Sandwich, Sir Henry Slingesby, Sir Robert Southwell, Sprat, Sir Thomas Stanley, Sir Samuel Tuke, Waller, Ward, Sir Joseph Williamson, Christopher Wren.

In addition, there were seven Fellows who tended to be nonpartisan in their political standpoint but whose ethic was of a liberal variety, ranging from a moderate to a pronounced hedonism. They included Robert Boyle, Ent, Petty, Povey, Whistler, Wilkins, and Wylde.

Twelve of the Fellows may be characterized as having been partisans of the Parliamentary cause—Sir Edward Bysshe, Coxe, John Earl of Crawford and Lindsay, Goddard, Haake, Harley, Hill, Viscount Massarene, Packer, Peter Pett, Powle, and Vermuyden. Not all of these, however, were attachd to the Calvinist outlook. Goddard, for instance, was evidently hedonist in his ways. Among the Calvinists we can place five Fellows—the Earl of Crawford and Lindsay, Haake, perhaps Hill, Viscount Massarene, and Vermuyden.

Four of the members of the Royal Society are best described as vacillators; they shifted too basically and frequently from one side to another for them to be classified in a significant way. They were Charles Howard, Pell, Wallis, and Willoughby. The three foreign Fellows may be described as generally liberal-hedonist, or anti-Calvinist, in their philosophy. The information concerning the ethical and political philosophies of the twenty-five remaining Fellows is either nonexistent, unavailable, or too meager to provide for a reasonable characterization.

Thus, of the ninety-four Fellows concerning whom we have evidence, only five can be regarded as adherents to the Puritan ethics, while at least fifty-four were hedonist libertarians. Sixty-eight were

Royalists in their political attitudes or actions; only twelve were Parliamentarians.

The dominant ethic of the membership as a whole of the Royal Society on May 20, 1663, was not that of the Puritan virtues; it was hedonist-libertarian.

Such a typical Fellow as Sir Kenelme Digby perhaps exemplified the ethical philosophy of the Royal Society. Sir Kenelme was always at odds with Puritan morality. This member of the Council of the Royal Society was brought up in the Roman Catholic faith; his father had been executed for involvement in the Gunpowder Plot. Sir Kenelme's romance with the promiscuous beauty Venetia Stanley was celebrated. When he married her, against his mother's wishes, he said that " 'a wise man, and lusty, could make an honest woman out of a brothell-house.' "[2] Digby published a book in 1643, his *Observations* on Browne's *Religio Medici* from the Roman Catholic standpoint. In 1645, he went to Rome as envoy of the English Catholic committee to secure money from the Pope for the royalist cause. As a scientific intellectual, Digby held religious views which, says his biographer, "might more fitly hail from Athens than from Rome, or Geneva either, for that matter." "We are not likely to err," wrote Digby, "if we but look into our own hearts, which are the temples he delighteth most in, and then worship that Author of nature according as we find written there. . . ." His love for Venetia Stanley led him to write of sexual love in terms which philosophers had hitherto reserved for God:

> And this joy and content of lovers, beside that it is the highest and noblest we can possess, is also the securest, and placed, as it were, in sanctuary, out of the hands of fortune and change; for the ground of it is in ourselves, and we need the help of no exterior thing to make it complete, it dependeth upon our wills which we govern as we please: therefore, this is the true happiness that a wise man ought to aim at, since that himself is master of it and he can give it to himself when he list.

The expurgated passages of Kenelme Digby's *Private Memoirs* are an ode to the physical beauty of Venetia, and a lyric of the lover's joy in the discovery of his mistress's body. Havelock Ellis said they "embodied the final efflorescence of the pagan English Renaissance." He contrasted them with the depiction of woman by St. Odo of Cluny, who regarded beauty as "skin-deep, drowned in excretions which we should scarcely care to touch with the finger's tip." By contrast, Digby finds that in "that darkness did glisten a few drops of sweat like diamond sparks, and had a more fragrant odor than the violets or primroses. . . ." Digby, says Ellis, represented the logic of life, and St. Odo that of death.

Hedonistic libertarians, whether Catholic or Protestant, nonconformist or Anglican, atheist or believer, were the mainstay of the Royal Society in the seventeenth century. Roman Catholics, especially through the powerful Howard family, were intimately involved in the rise of English science. William Howard, Viscount Stafford, was in 1665 elected a Fellow of the Royal Society, and in 1672 served as a member of its council. Eight years later he was executed on the false charge that he was conspiring to raise a Papal army in England. Henry Howard, Duke of Norfolk, became a Fellow of the Royal Society in 1666. He was a close friend of John Evelyn, his fellow-Royalist, whom he visted in 1645 at Padua, where Evelyn was studying science. Howard served the Society well during the critical period after the great fire of London. He granted it the use of rooms at Arundel House for meetings, and on Evelyn's request gave it the greater part of his library. The Society sold most of it, and used the considerable proceeds to buy scientific books. Edward Somerset, Marquis of Worcester, a dedicated Roman Catholic, worked hard to organize an Irish army to invade England, and gave succor to Charles I. Apart from political intrigue, Worcester's chief activities were in the field of technology. For many years, he carried on experiments to construct what might have been a primitive model of a steam engine.[3] He planned also to establish a "college of artisans." Lastly, there was the monarch himself, Charles II, who inclined toward Catholicism as the religion most compatible with an easy morality. As Charles said, "he could not think God would make a man miserable only for taking a little pleasure out of the way." The same Charles had a laboratory at Whitehall, where he "was far more active and attentive than at the council board," and, on Pepys' advice, founded a Mathematical School for instruction in the science of navigation. If most of his nights were devoted to the pleasures of his ladies, it is still undeniable that in early May, 1661, he kept a vigil all through the night with a party of scientists to observe through his great telescope an eclipse of Saturn.

NOTES

1. Cf. *The Record of the Royal Society of London* (2nd ed., London, 1901), pp. 8-10. The Council of the Royal Society was named on April 22, 1663, and the original Fellows chosen on May 20th. Four

more Fellows were added on June 22nd. Cf. *The Record of the Royal Society of London* (4th ed., London, 1940), App. V, Chronological Register of Fellows, pp. 375 ff.

2. John Aubrey, *Brief Lives, chiefly of Contemporaries, set down by John Aubrey, between the years 1669 and 1696*, ed. Andrew Clark (Oxford, 1898), Vol. I, p. 230. E. W. Bligh, *Sir Kenelm Digby and his Venetia* (London, 1932), pp. 42, 48-9, 56, 295.

3. *Dictionary of National Biography*, ed. Sir Leslie Stephen and Sir Sidney Lee (London, 1921-22), Vol. X, pp. 32, 81; Vol. XVIII, p. 644. Arthur Bryant, *Samuel Pepys: The Years of Peril* (New York, 1935), p. 87.

Index